NUCLEAR THEORY

Frontiers in Physics

A Lecture Note and Reprint Series

DAVID PINES, ***Editor***

P. W. Anderson	**CONCEPTS IN SOLIDS:** *Lectures on the Theory of Solids*
N. Bloembergen	**NUCLEAR MAGNETIC RELAXATION:** *A Reprint Volume*
Geoffrey F. Chew	**S-MATRIX THEORY OF STRONG INTERACTIONS:** *A Lecture Note and Reprint Volume*
R. P. Feynman	**QUANTUM ELECTRODYNAMICS:** *A Lecture Note and Reprint Volume*
R. P. Feynman	**THE THEORY OF FUNDAMENTAL PROCESSES:** *A Lecture Note Volume*
Hans Frauenfelder	**THE MÖSSBAUER EFFECT:** *A Collection of Reprints with an Introduction*
Robert Hofstadter	**NUCLEAR AND NUCLEON STRUCTURE:** *A Reprint Volume*
Leo P. Kadanoff and Gordon Baym	**QUANTUM STATISTICAL MECHANICS:** *A Lecture Note Volume*
A. M. Lane	**RECENT DEVELOPMENTS IN NUCLEAR THEORY:** *A Lecture Note and Reprint Volume*
R. Omnès and M. Froissart	**MANDELSTAM THEORY AND REGGE POLES:** *An Introduction for Experimentalists*
George E. Pake	**PARAMAGNETIC RESONANCE:** *An Introductory Monograph*
David Pines	**THE MANY-BODY PROBLEM:** *A Lecture Note and Reprint Volume*
E. J. Squires	**COMPLEX ANGULAR MOMENTA AND PARTICLE PHYSICS:** *A Lecture Note and Reprint Volume*
L. Van Hove, N. M. Hugenholtz, and L. P. Howland	**PROBLEMS IN THE QUANTUM THEORY OF MANY-PARTICLE SYSTEMS:** *A Reprint Volume*

NUCLEAR THEORY

PAIRING FORCE CORRELATIONS AND COLLECTIVE MOTION

★

A. M. LANE
AERE, Harwell

W. A. BENJAMIN, INC.
1964 New York Amsterdam

NUCLEAR THEORY
Pairing Force Correlations and Collective Motions

Library of Congress Catalog Card Number 63-13759
Manufactured in the United States of America

The final manuscript was received June 25, 1963; this volume was published December 21, 1963

The publisher is pleased to acknowledge the assistance of Zeb Delaire, who composed the volume, and William Prokos, who designed the dust jacket

W. A. BENJAMIN, INC.
New York, New York

EDITOR'S FOREWORD

The problem of communicating in a coherent fashion the recent developments in the most exciting and active fields of physics seems particularly pressing today. The enormous growth in the number of physicists has tended to make the familiar channels of communication considerably less effective. It has become increasingly difficult for experts in a given field to keep up with the current literature; the novice can only be confused. What is needed is both a consistent account of a field and the presentation of a definite "point of view" concerning it. Formal monographs cannot meet such a need in a rapidly developing field, and, perhaps more important, the review article seems to have fallen into disfavor. Indeed, it would seem that the people most actively engaged in developing a given field are the people least likely to write at length about it.

"Frontiers in Physics" has been conceived in an effort to improve the situation in several ways. First, to take advantage of the fact that the leading physicists today frequently give a series of lectures, a graduate seminar, or a graduate course in their special fields of interest. Such lectures serve to summarize the present status of a rapidly developing field and may well constitute the only coherent account available at the time. Often, notes on lectures exist (prepared by the lecturer himself, by graduate students, or by postdoctoral fellows) and have been distributed in mimeographed form on a limited basis. One of the principal purposes of the "Frontiers in Physics" series is to make such notes available to a wider audience of physicists.

It should be emphasized that lecture notes are necessarily rough and informal, both in style and content, and those in the series will prove no exception. This is as it should be. The point of the series is to offer new, rapid, more informal, and, it is hoped, more effective ways for physicists to teach one another. The point is lost if only elegant notes qualify.

A second way to improve communication in very active fields of physics is by the publication of collections of reprints of recent articles. Such collections are themselves useful to people working in the field. The value of the reprints would, however, seem much enhanced if the collection would be accompanied by an introduction of moderate length, which would serve to tie the collection together and, necessarily, constitute a brief survey of the present status of the field. Again, it is appropriate that such an introduction be informal, in keeping with the active character of the field.

A third possibility for the series might be called an informal monograph, to connote the fact that it represents an intermediate step between lecture notes and formal monographs. It would offer the author an opportunity to present his views of a field that has developed to the point at which a summation might prove extraordinarily fruitful, but for which a formal monograph might not be feasible or desirable.

Fourth, there are the contemporary classics—papers or lectures which constitute a particularly valuable approach to the teaching and learning of physics today. Here one thinks of fields that lie at the heart of much of present-day research, but whose essentials are by now well understood, such as quantum electrodynamics or magnetic resonance. In such fields some of the best pedagogical material is not readily available, either because it consists of papers long out of print or lectures that have never been published.

"Frontiers in Physics" is designed to be flexible in editorial format. Authors are encouraged to use as many of the foregoing approaches as seem desirable for the project at hand. The publishing format for the series is in keeping with its intentions. Photo-offset printing is used throughout, and the books are paperbound, in order to speed publication and reduce costs. It is hoped that the books will thereby be within the financial reach of graduate students in this country and abroad.

Finally, because the series represents something of an experiment on the part of the editor and the publisher, suggestions from interested readers as to format, contributors, and contributions will be most welcome.

David Pines

Urbana, Illinois
August 1961

PREFACE

The contents of this book were prepared as a course of 30 lectures delivered at Harwell in 1962. The main object of the course was to bridge the gulf between the theorist and experimenter. This has suddenly widened in the last few years through the arrival of the theories of pairing and collective effects in nuclei. Experimenters have found such theories disconcerting because of their sharp break with traditional methods of nuclear theory. The break is made to appear more complete than it really is by the awesome jargon that has accumulated around the new theories: Cooper pairs, random phase approximation, linearization procedure, time-dependent Hartree-Fock theory, Bogoliubov-Valatin transformation, particle-hole interaction, etc. When the spurious mystery accompanying this terminology has been taken away, there remains an irreducible residue of unfamiliarity to one versed in traditional methods. This consists in the use of the formalism of second quantization with its operators of creation and destruction. *It is absolutely necessary to devote appropriate time and mental effort to the mastery of this formalism, if any detailed understanding of the new theories is to be achieved.* Actually, the formalism is not so terrible. Unfortunately, it is often first encountered in connection with meson field theory, where the formidable array of several unfamiliar methods can inspire a persistent aversion to any of them. If the method of second quantization is isolated from the rest, it is easy to learn it and how to use it. Since one can sometimes arrive at the same answers in nuclear theory by using the traditional methods, some students may well find that they can learn the method most easily in the context of nuclear theory.

A further difficulty encountered by the prospective student of the new theories is that they exist at present only in the form of a large number of research papers. Most of these use individual notation and techniques. This book will reduce the time and effort needed to pursue and understand all these papers, by combining them for the first time into a systematized comprehensive review. Relatively generous discussion of relevant experimental data is included.

The book will be most useful to:

1. Experimenters who wish to learn about the exciting new advances in nuclear theory, and who have a background of quantum mechanics and previous theories of nuclear structure, especially the shell model.

2. Theoretical students who intend to do research in nuclear theory. The book gives an up-to-date account of the frontiers that they have to cross.

3. Lecturers who give courses on nuclear structure and who wish to include accounts of the most recent discoveries and concepts.

A. M. LANE

Harwell, England
October 1963

ACKNOWLEDGMENTS

The publisher wishes to acknowledge the assistance of the following organizations in the preparation of this volume:

The Physical Review, for permission to reprint the articles from *The Physical Review*.

North-Holland Publishing Co., for permission to reprint the articles from *Nuclear Physics*.

CONTENTS

NUCLEAR THEORY

INTRODUCTION

Before 1953, the only detailed nuclear wave functions used in calculation were those of the shell model. Although surprisingly successful in some situations, it had always been clear that their neglect of the correlation effects of internucleon forces rendered them useless in a wide range of problems. Three major deficiencies of the shell model were:

1. Its failure to reproduce observed total energies of nuclei.
2. Its inability to give a simple prescription for configuration mixing in the considerable number of nuclei where such mixing is important. As a simple instance, (p,d) studies in O^{16} indicate that even this closed shell system has appreciable mixing of the type $(1p)^2 \to (1d)^2$.
3. Its failure to predict or describe the strong "collective" excitations that are observed in nuclei, especially those of the quadrupole type. In even-even nuclei, the relevant data are the (low) position of the first excited (2+) state and its (high) transition probability to the ground (0+) state.

Since 1953, there have been three major advances† in nuclear theory, each one tailored to correct one of these deficiencies:

---

† The second two theories are distinguished from the first by making use of methods developed in other fields of physics (superconductivity and plasma oscillations). Further, they are naturally stated in the representation of second quantization rather than the coordinate representation. The reason for this can be seen by considering the type of approximation made in these two theories. In all theories the essential problem is the evaluation of the expectation value $\langle \psi | V | \psi \rangle$, where ψ is the wave function and V the interaction. This interaction V is, in the above representations, $\frac{1}{2}\Sigma_{i,j}\, v_{i,j}$ (i,j = particles) and $\frac{1}{2}\Sigma_{\alpha\beta\gamma\delta} \langle \alpha\beta | v | \gamma\delta \rangle\, a_\alpha^+ a_\beta^+ a_\delta a_\gamma$ $(\alpha, \beta, \gamma, \delta \equiv$ states). In the shell

1. "Brueckner theory," 1953.
2. "Pairing force theory," 1959.
3. "Collective motion theory," 1960.

The Brueckner theory (1) starts from the shell model and extends it so that the force between each pair of nucleons is taken into account to all orders (instead of to first order in the ordinary shell model). In this sense, the new model is an "independent pair model" in place of the "independent particle model." At the same time, it follows the earlier model by ignoring situations in which three particles are close enough to interact simultaneously.

In the present lectures, we discuss only theories (2) and (3); these are concerned with the energy spectra of nuclei, i.e., relative nuclear energies rather than absolute ones. Of course, the introduction of the explicit effects of internucleon forces into a shell-model calculation affects both relative and absolute energies, so the two types of problem are not generally independent or separable. However, they can be separated roughly if the forces are such that they produce on the wave function two distinct kinds of effect which can be associated with the two problems. *This is the basic assumption that must be made,* the two effects being:

A. Strong short-range two-particle correlations which critically affect the absolute energy but are not essential for the prediction of relative energies. In terms of configuration mixing, the correlations imply a small amount of mixing from each of the vast number of distant orbitals.

B. Configuration mixing in which nucleons in occupied orbitals near the top of the Fermi sea are transferred to any low-lying empty orbitals. Such mixing affects mainly the highest energy fraction of the nucleons [unlike (A), which affects all nucleons]. Thus (B) is not

---

model, one approximates the wave function ψ by the shell-model form ψ_0, and uses the exact coordinate form of V. Also in the Brueckner theory, one approximates the wave function; in this case, one takes it to be ψ_0', the shell-model form with pair correlations. (Later one defines t by $\langle \psi_0' | v | \psi_0' \rangle \equiv \langle \psi_0 | t | \psi_0 \rangle$ and works with this "effective" interaction.) In contrast, in theories (2) and (3), one approximates V rather than ψ, and tries to find exact solutions ψ for the approximated form of V. There is no point in approximating the coordinate dependence of V, since the basic difficulty is that it is a two-body interaction, whatever its dependence. Rather one tries to approximate V by retaining its most important (largest) matrix elements, and discarding the rest, and then tries to get an exact wave function for the retained part. Clearly this is naturally stated in terms of the second quantization formalism: One simply drops or retains terms in the sum over particle states α, β, γ, δ.

important for the absolute energy but may be vital for relative energies of low-lying states which arise from rearrangement of the highest energy nucleons.

Brueckner theory shows how effects (A) can be taken into account by replacing the two-body potential of a pair of free nucleons by a modified two-body potential, whose strength is given by the theory and may differ considerably from that of free nucleons. It would appear most consistent to use this modified potential for considering effects (B) in the present lectures. However, since the strength will usually be treated as a parameter, this is not of direct practical importance.

The fact that the single-particle spectrum of spherical nuclei is strongly banded into groups of orbitals means that effects (B) will be more important in some nuclei than others. According to a recent paper by Wyatt, Wills, and Green [(*Phys. Rev.*, **119**, 1031 (1960)], a typical part of the spectrum is as shown in the figure below. One sees

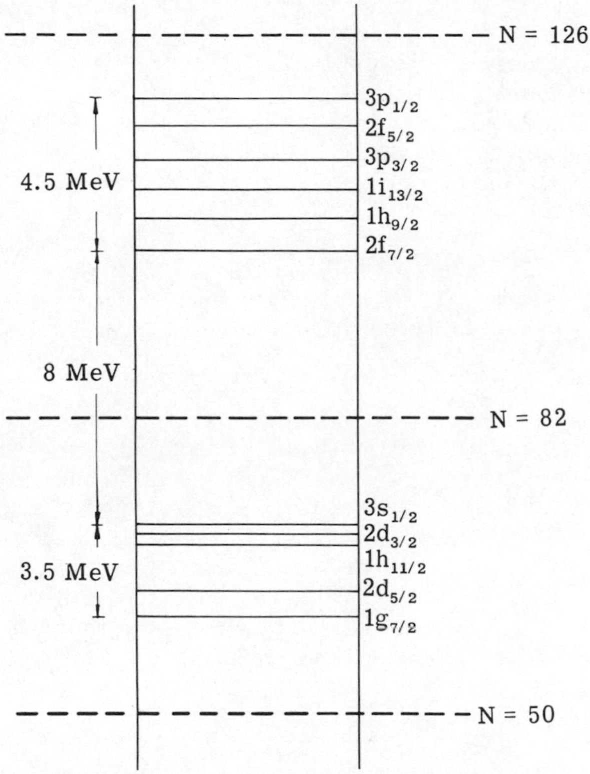

Part of the spectrum of particle levels available to nucleons in heavier nuclei.

that the magic number gaps in the particle spectrum are $\sim 7\frac{1}{2}$ MeV, whereas the spacing inside a band of levels is 10 times less (more like 100 times in the case of the $3s_{1/2}$, $2d_{3/2}$, $1h_{11/2}$ subband or if magnetic sublevels are counted separately). Thus if the matrix elements of internucleon forces are $\gtrsim$ mean spacing inside a band but $<$ magic number gaps, we shall find strong configuration mixing between levels of a band but little mixing between bands. This means strong mixing for nuclei between magic numbers but little for those with magic numbers like Pb^{208}.

When the nucleus is strongly deformed, as in the rare earth nuclei, the magic number gaps in the spectrum disappear and the bands are spread into each other. In this case, there may be no natural limit imposed on the energies of levels eligible for mixing.

In Parts I and II we shall discuss theories (2) and (3), respectively.

PART I

PAIRING FORCE THEORY

THE notion of "pairing" between particles in a system can be traced back to the seniority quantum number set up by Racah[1] in 1942 in atomic studies. The idea was derived independently in superconductivity studies in 1957. In 1959, following the suggestions of Bohr, Mottelson, and Pines,[2] and of Mottelson,[3] the first detailed application of pairing force theory to the nucleus was made by Belyaev.[4] An extensive jargon has grown up around this theory: "energy gap," "quasi-particles," "Cooper pairs," "Bogoliubov transformation," "occupation probabilities." The mathematics is almost identical to that used in the theory of the superconducting state. It enables one to treat mixing due to "pairing forces" in an essentially exact way, and is thus unique in the quantum mechanical treatment of the many-body problem. However, before this mathematical technique can be applied to nuclear physics, one must check that nuclear forces have sufficient in common with pairing forces to justify their being replaced by them. Mottelson[3] and Belyaev[4] have given convincing arguments on this point which we shall mention below. The "pairing forces" affect what may be called the "intrinsic spectra" and the "intrinsic structure" of nuclei, i.e., those features underlying any over-all collective motions.

The pairing force idea is also very useful in systematizing discussion of nuclei. Suppose that computing machine power were such that diagonalizations of configurations could be performed for actual nuclear forces (as has been done for F^{19} and other nuclei). Although this would enable detailed qualitative fits to nuclear data to be made, it would not facilitate any general qualitative discussion of the physics. To do this, one must extract from the problem the essential ingredients of the basic physical effects. This is precisely what the pairing force represents.

The chart below illustrates the progress of the pairing force theory in nuclear physics in terms of the basic publications.

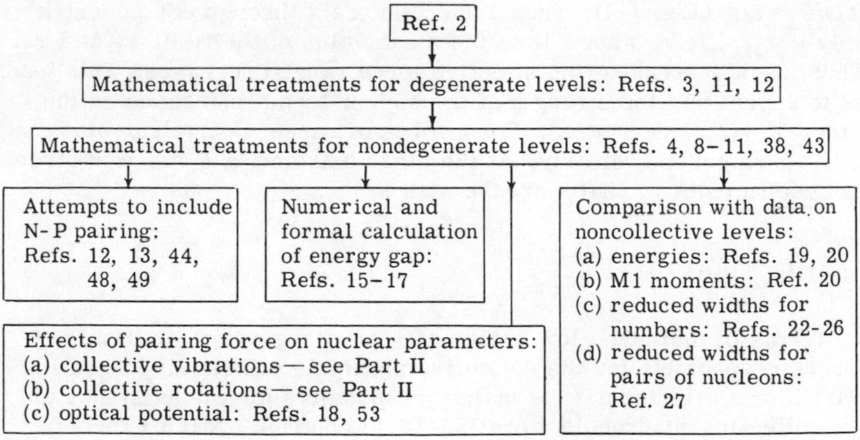

1

PAIRING FORCES AND THEIR EFFECTS IN SPECIAL SITUATIONS

In much of this and the next section we follow the excellent lecture course given by Mottelson[3] at Les Houches in 1958.

1-1 SOURCE OF PAIRING EFFECTS

Let us see how a force $v(r_{12})$ can be broken into parts which can be identified with pairing forces and multipole forces. Generally

$$v(r_{12}) = \sum_k f_k(r_1,r_2)P_k(\cos\theta_{12})$$

If particles 1 and 2 are in orbitals confined to a fairly restricted radial region, the dependence on r_1,r_2 may be ignored for a particular k. The function P_k drops from its maximum at $\theta_{12} = 0$ in angular distance $\sim 1/k$ (Fig. 1-1). Thus 1 and 2 interact through component k only if $r_{12} < R/k$, where R is the mean value of the radii r_1 and r_2. Thus, as k increases, the effective force range decreases. This leads us to expect that the strength of the high k terms increases as the range of $v(r_{12})$ decreases. For a force of range $\gg$ nuclear size, only $k = 0$ is important, clearly. At the other extreme, a δ-function force has coefficients f_k that increase with k:

$$f_k = \delta(r_1 - r_2)\frac{2k+1}{2\pi r_1^2}$$

Terms of individual low values of k are long-range multipole forces responsible for the collective multipole effects discussed in Part II (e.g., the term f_2 is mainly responsible for the existence of the collective quadrupole vibrations). In contrast, pairing force

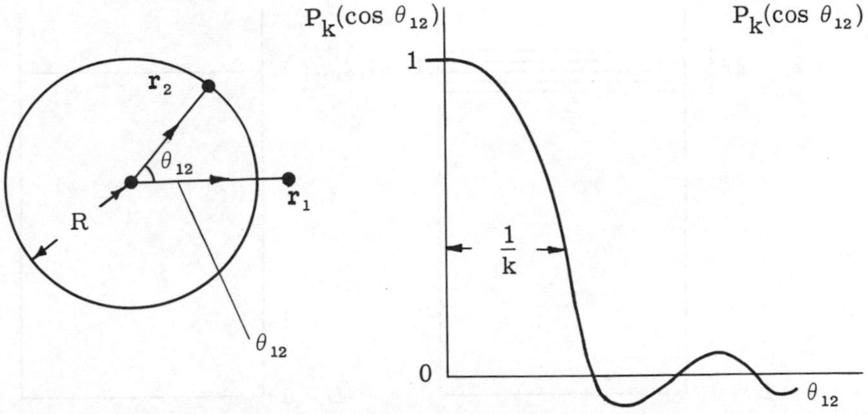

Figure 1-1 Dependence of kth term in $v(r_{12})$ on angular separation θ_{12} between the particles 1 and 2.

effects come from all the high k terms, representing the short-range effects of $v(r_{12})$. We have not yet shown that this is so, but do so by means of a simple example.

1-2 EFFECT OF SHORT-RANGE FORCES ON STATES OF ℓ^2

Consider two particles in the same ℓ orbit coupled to various states of total angular momentum (A.M.) $L = 0, 1, 2, \ldots, 2\ell$.

The state $L = 0$ is

$$u(r_1)\, u(r_2) \left\{ \sum_m Y_{\ell m}(1) \left(Y_{\ell m}(2) \right)_t \right\}$$

where t denotes time-reversed, which is the same as complex conjugation. The angular part of this is $P_\ell(\cos\theta_{12})$, so we see that the wave function has its maximum at separation $\theta_{12} = 0$, so short-range forces act strongly in the state of $L = 0$.

For general L, the maximum occurs at $\theta_{12} \sim L/\ell$, so only terms with $k < \ell/L$ contribute to the energy. Thus we expect that only the state of $L = 0$ is much affected in energy by short-range forces. (The same conclusion follows from a purely classical picture of the two particles. When they have zero total A.M. they are bound to come near from time to time, but this is not so for higher A.M.). A standard shell-model calculation with a δ-function force gives exactly this result (see Fig. 1-2). The actual depression of the ground state is proportional to $(2\ell + 1)$.

Exactly the same result follows from use of the pairing force,

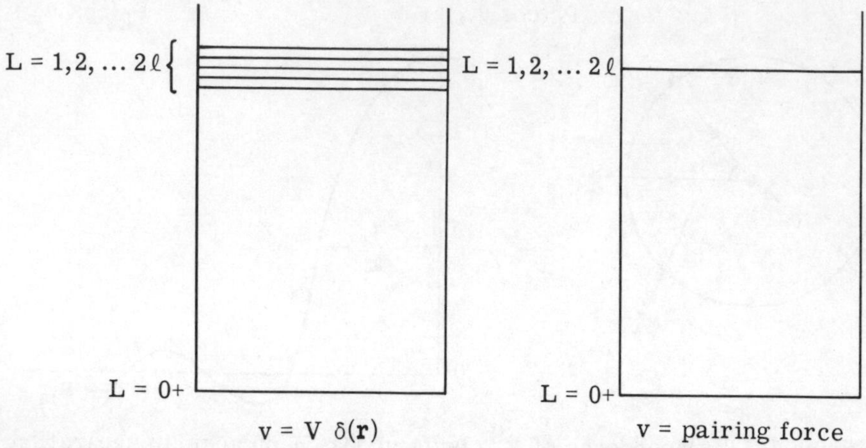

Figure 1-2 Spectrum of states of configuration ℓ^2 for δ-function and pairing forces (schematic).

except that the states of $L \neq 0$ are quite degenerate instead of approximately so. The force may be defined as

$$\left\langle \ell m_\ell, (\ell m'_\ell)_t \,|\, \tilde{\mathcal{G}} \,|\, (\ell \tilde{m}_\ell), (\ell \tilde{m}'_\ell)_t \right\rangle = -|G|\, \delta_{m_\ell m'_\ell}\, \delta_{\tilde{m}_\ell \tilde{m}'_\ell}$$

where the states are not antisymmetrized (A.S.). We see that the force acts only on pairs of particles, a pair being such that one particle is in the time-reversed state of the other. The usual sign convention for time-reversed states is

$$\left(\Psi_{JM}\right)_t = (-)^{J+M}\, \Psi_{J-M}$$

In the representation $|\ell m_\ell, (\ell m_\ell)_t\rangle$ this force has the matrix

$$\underline{\tilde{\mathcal{G}}} = -|G| \begin{pmatrix} 1 & 1 & 1 & 1 & \dots \\ 1 & 1 & 1 & \dots & \\ 1 & 1 & \dots & & \end{pmatrix}$$

the dimension being $(2\ell + 1)$. The eigenvectors (a_n) and values (E_n) satisfy

$$(\underline{\tilde{\mathcal{G}}} - E\underline{1})\,\underline{a} = 0$$

$$|\underline{\tilde{\mathcal{G}}} - E\underline{1}| = 0$$

It is easy to see that only one state has $E_n \neq 0$, viz., that with

$$\underline{a}_0 = \begin{pmatrix} 1 \\ 1 \\ 1 \\ \vdots \\ 1 \end{pmatrix} \qquad \text{and} \qquad E_0 = -(2\ell + 1)\,|G|$$

All other 2ℓ states are degenerate, with $E_n = 0$ and $\widetilde{\mathcal{G}}a_n = 0$.
These states may be labeled with L, and have

$$a_{Lm_\ell} = (\ell m_\ell \ell - m_\ell \mid L0)(-)^{\ell - m_\ell}$$

The even L (spatially symmetric) states are those of $S = 0$, $T = 1$. The odd L (spatially A.S.) states have $S = 1$, $T = 1$, and all matrix elements between these states vanish. If $T = 0$ is allowed, we have new states with opposite S to those above, but the same L's as before, and at the same energies. Thus the original depressed state of $L = 0$, $S = 0$, $T = 1$ is degenerate with the state $L = 0$, $S = 1$, $T = 0$. If a dependence of the force on S, T is introduced, then this degeneracy is removed. One naturally chooses the dependence so that the $S = 1$, $T = 0$ state comes below that of $S = 0$, $T = 1$ as in the deuteron. When many-particle wave functions are considered, this gives rise to a difficulty, the various $S = 1$ pairs can couple to give a number of different total spins J. This difficulty does not arise if all particles are of one kind so that only $S = 0$, $T = 1$ pairs occur, and the total spin can only be $J = 0$. This illustrates one of the difficulties met when one tries to extend the pairing force model of like particles to include both kinds. (See Sec. 5-1 for further discussion of this.)

1-3 EFFECT OF SHORT-RANGE FORCES ON STATES OF j^2

If we now transform to a $j - j$ coupling representation, the same pairing forces as above give pairing spectra, as in Fig. 1-3. The distances between degenerate groups are the spin-orbit splittings. The energy depressions of the $J = 0$ states are $\alpha_j^2(2\ell + 1)\,|G|$, where α_j is the amplitude of the $(L = 0, S = 0)$ state in the $(j^2)_{J=0}$ state. This is $[(2j + 1)/2(2\ell + 1)]^{1/2}$. Exactly the same spectrum occurs if the above pairing force is replaced by

$$\left\langle (jm)(jm')_t \mid \mathcal{G} \mid (j\widetilde{m})(j\widetilde{m}')_t \right\rangle = -|G|\,\delta_{mm'}\,\delta_{\widetilde{m}\widetilde{m}'}$$

where we now understand the two-particle states on either side of the matrix element to be antisymmetrized. Since states are A.S.,

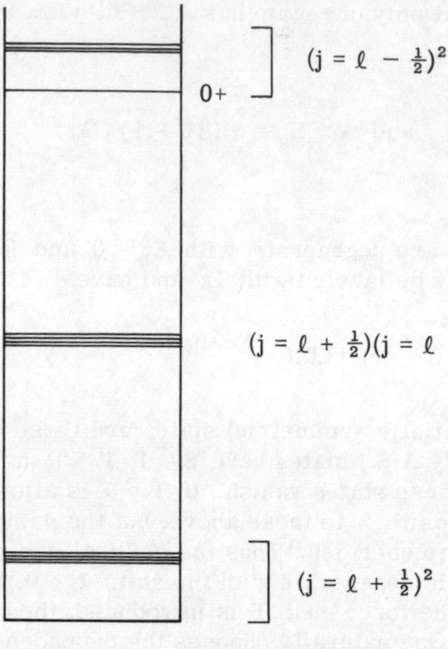

Figure 1-3 Spectrum of states of ℓ^2 in the presence of a strong spin-orbit force and weak pairing force.

the number of them is $\Omega \equiv \frac{1}{2}(2j+1)$; the lowering of the $J = 0$ states is $|G|\,\Omega$. Notice that we have not yet considered any matrix elements between pair states of different j's.

The extended definition of the pairing force is

$$\left\langle j_1 m_1 (j_2 m_2)_t \,|\, v \,|\, j_3 m_3 (j_4 m_4)_t \right\rangle_{A.S.}$$

$$= -|G|\, \delta_{j_1 m_1, j_2 m_2}\, \delta_{j_3 m_3, j_4 m_4}$$

This may be restated as

$$\langle (j_1 j_2) J \,|\, v \,|\, (j_3 j_4) J \rangle = -\tfrac{1}{2}\, \delta_{J0}\, |G|\, \hat{j}_1 \hat{j}_3$$

where $\hat{j} \equiv (2j+1)^{1/2}$. This will be a reasonable representation of an actual force only if matrix elements of the latter satisfy two requirements:

(a) $\overline{|\langle(j_1 j_2)J|v|(j_3 j_4)J\rangle|}_{J\neq 0} \ll \overline{\langle(j_1^2)0+|v|(j_3^2)0+\rangle}$, where the bar signifies the mean taken over all j-values considered.

(b) $\langle(j_1^2)0+|v|(j_3^2)0+\rangle/\hat{j}_1\hat{j}_3$ is essentially independent of j_1 and j_3.

A breakdown of requirement (b) can be catered for within the essential framework of the theory, as we shall see in Sec. 3-3, but requirement (a) is vital. We refer to a force to which this applies as a generalized pairing force:

$$\langle(j_1 j_2)J|v|(j_3 j_4)J\rangle_{A.S.} = \tfrac{1}{2}\,\delta_{J0}\,G_{j_1 j_3}\,\hat{j}_1\hat{j}_3$$

We shall now consider the δ-function force,

$$v = V\ \delta(r)$$

which has matrix elements (for antisymmetrized states):

$$\langle(j_1 j_2)J|v|(j_3 j_4)J\rangle_{A.S.}$$
$$= \frac{V}{8\pi}(-)^J X(j_1 j_2 J)\,X(j_3 j_4 J)\,I(\ell_1\ell_2\ell_3\ell_4)$$

where

$$X(j_1 j_2 J) = (-)^{j_1 - j_2 + \frac{1}{2}(\ell_1+\ell_2)}\sqrt{2-\delta_{\ell_1 j_1 \ell_2 j_2}}\ \frac{\hat{j}_1\hat{j}_2\hat{\ell}_1\hat{\ell}_2}{\hat{J}}$$
$$\times\,(\ell_1 0 \ell_2 0|J0)\,W(\ell_1 \tfrac{1}{2} J j_2, j_1 \ell_2)$$

and the $I(\ell_1\ell_2\ell_3\ell_4)$ is the radial integral:

$$I(\ell_1\ell_2\ell_3\ell_4) = \int_0^\infty u_{\ell_1}u_{\ell_2}u_{\ell_3}u_{\ell_4}\frac{dr}{r^2}$$

where u_ℓ are radial wave functions.

On specializing to J = 0 we have $X(j_1 j_2 0) = \hat{j}_1(-)^{\ell_1}$ and

$$\langle(j_1^2)0+|v|(j_3^2)0+\rangle = \frac{V}{8\pi}(-)^{\ell_1+\ell_3}\,\hat{j}_1\hat{j}_3\,I(\ell_1\ell_1\ell_3\ell_3)$$

Thus requirement (b) may be checked immediately by computing the radial integrals. This has been done (with other results given below) by J. N. Bardsley, and the results are given in Table 1-1 for the set of particle states $3s_{1/2}$, $2d_{3/2}$, $2d_{5/2}$, $1g_{7/2}$, $1h_{11/2}$ that occur between magic numbers 50 and 82. First, we note that the phase $(-)^{\ell_1+\ell_3}$

Table 1-1

Values of $I(\ell_1 \ell_1 \ell_3 \ell_3)$ in Units of $2^{-10}(2\pi)^{-1/2}\left(\frac{\hbar}{M\omega}\right)^{-3/2}$

ℓ_1 \ ℓ_3	1g	2d	3s	1h
1g	312	180	148	268
2d		376	282	167
3s			619	139
1h				255

means that the four matrix elements between the $1h_{11/2}$ state and the others have the wrong sign for (b). However this sign can be brought in line with (b) by reversing the phase of the $(1h_{11/2}{}^2)_{0+}$ state, this being conventional. The values in Table 1-1 are computed with oscillator wave functions, and ω is the oscillator frequency. It can be seen that, apart from the $3s_{1/2}{}^2$ diagonal element, the dispersion of values is quite small. Since, in practice, the matrix elements appear with the weight $(2j_3 + 1)$, the effect of the one large matrix element will be small. Notice that off-diagonal values decrease as $|\ell_1 - \ell_3|$ increases.

To test requirement (a), the quantities $X(j_1 j_2 J)$ have been computed for $J = 2+$. Their squares are given in Table 1-2, and are to be compared with the value $\hat{j}_1{}^2$ for $J = 0$. It can be seen that the values of diagonal terms are about four times less than those for $J = 0+$. The nondiagonal ones are only about two to three times less. If all integrals I were the same, this means that matrix elements for $J = 2+$ are about three or four times less than for $J = 0+$. We may avoid considering integrals I by comparing values of $\langle (j_1 j_2)2+ |v| (j_1 j_2)2+ \rangle_{A.S.}$ with $\langle (j_1{}^2)0+ |v| (j_2{}^2)0+ \rangle_{A.S.}$. This is done in Table 1-3. It can be

Table 1-2

Values of $|X(j_1 j_2 J)|^2$ for $J = 2$

j_2 \ j_1	$1g_{7/2}$	$2d_{5/2}$	$2d_{3/2}$	$3s_{1/2}$	$1h_{11/2}$
$1g_{7/2}$	$\frac{40}{21}$	$\frac{16}{35}$	$\frac{144}{35}$		
$2d_{5/2}$		$\frac{48}{35}$	$\frac{24}{35}$	$\frac{12}{5}$	
$2d_{3/2}$			$\frac{4}{5}$	$\frac{8}{5}$	
$3s_{1/2}$					
$1h_{11/2}$					$\frac{420}{143}$

Table 1-3

Ratios $\langle (j_1 j_2)2+ | v | (j_1 j_2)2+ \rangle_{A.S.} / \langle (j_1^2)0+ | v | (j_2^2)0+ \rangle_{A.S.}$

j_2 \ j_1	$1g_{7/2}$	$2d_{5/2}$	$2d_{3/2}$	$3s_{1/2}$	$1h_{11/2}$
$1g_{7/2}$	$\frac{147}{616}$	$\frac{21}{311}$	$\frac{185}{253}$		
$2d_{5/2}$		$\frac{120}{564}$	$\frac{65}{461}$	$\frac{169}{209}$	
$2d_{3/2}$			$\frac{75}{376}$	$\frac{113}{181}$	
$3s_{1/2}$					
$1h_{11/2}$					$\frac{187}{763}$

Table 1-4

Values of $|X(j_1 j_2 J)|^2$ for $J > 2$

j_1	j_2	$\lvert X(j_1 j_2 4)\rvert^2$
$1g_{7/2}$	$1g_{7/2}$	$\frac{72}{77}$
$2d_{5/2}$	$1g_{7/2}$	$\frac{80}{77}$
$2d_{3/2}$	$1g_{7/2}$	$\frac{80}{63}$
$3s_{1/2}$	$1g_{7/2}$	$\frac{16}{9}$
$2d_{5/2}$	$2d_{5/2}$	$\frac{4}{7}$
$2d_{5/2}$	$2d_{3/2}$	$\frac{16}{7}$
$1h_{11/2}$	$1h_{11/2}$	$\frac{224}{143}$

j_1	j_2	$\lvert X(j_1 j_2 6)\rvert^2$
$1g_{7/2}$	$1g_{7/2}$	$\frac{200}{429}$
$2d_{5/2}$	$1g_{7/2}$	$\frac{400}{143}$
$1h_{11/2}$	$1h_{11/2}$	$\frac{2400}{2431}$

j_1	j_2	$\lvert X(j_1 j_2 8)\rvert^2$
$1h_{11/2}$	$1h_{11/2}$	$\frac{29400}{46189}$

seen that the pairing force matrix elements exceed the others by factors varying from 1.3 to 15, the mean value being about 5.

In Table 1-4 we give factors $|X(j_1 j_2 J)|^2$ for $J > 2$. These have roughly the same mean value as $|X(j_1 j_2 2)|^2$ given above, and the same remarks apply.

1-4 EFFECT OF PAIRING FORCES ON STATES OF TWO PARTICLES ALLOWING CONFIGURATION MIXING

Suppose that the particles may be in any of Ω pair states, which are not all degenerate. The single particle energy will be written $\epsilon_{jm} \equiv \epsilon_\alpha$, so the energy of the pair $(\alpha, -\alpha)$ is $2\epsilon_\alpha$.

The effects of pairing forces can be solved exactly in this simple case of two particles. The eigenvalues and vectors are solutions of

$$(2\epsilon_\alpha - E_n)a_{n\alpha} - |G| \sum_{\alpha' > 0} a_{n\alpha'} = 0$$

$$|2\underline{\epsilon} - E\underline{1} - |G|\,\underline{I}| = 0$$

where $\underline{I}$ is the matrix with one in all places. Writing K_n for $\Sigma_{\alpha' > 0}\, a_{n\alpha'}$, we have

$$a_{n\alpha} = +\,|G|\, K_n / (2\epsilon_\alpha - E_n)$$

whence

$$\sum_{\alpha > 0} \frac{|G|}{2\epsilon_\alpha - E} = 1$$

This latter equation gives the eigenvalues $E = E_n$. In Fig. 1-4 one sees the characteristic depression of the ground state. If some of the

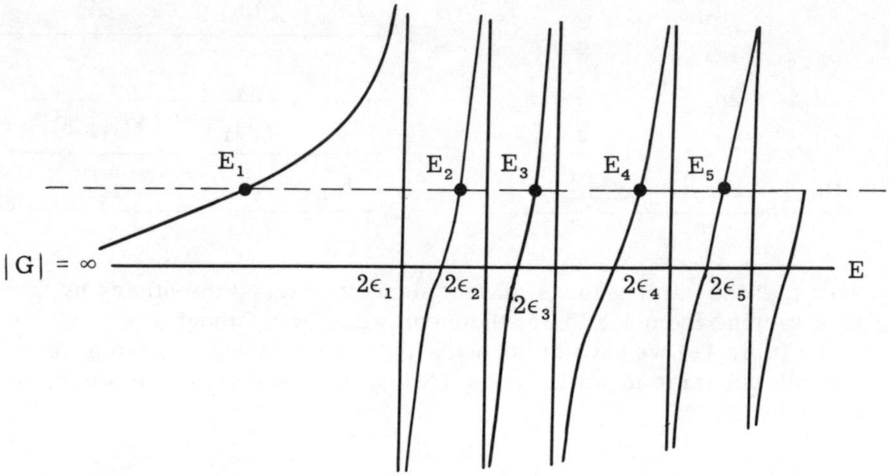

Figure 1-4 Plot of $\{\Sigma_{\alpha > 0}(2\epsilon_\alpha - E)^{-1}\}$. The eigenvalues are the energies at which this function equals the value of $|G|^{-1}$. A typical set of eigenvalues are shown, being intercepts with a horizontal line. The depression of the extreme eigenvalue can be seen.

ϵ_α are degenerate (equal to ϵ_j), the effect is to change the eigenvalue equation to

$$\sum_j |G|\, n_j \Big/ (2\epsilon_j - E) = 1$$

where n_j is the weight of state j. In j − j coupling, n_j is $\frac{1}{2}(2j+1)$. All states a_n above have J = 0. States of J ≠ 0 are not affected by the pairing force.

1-5 CASE OF THREE PARTICLES WITH CONFIGURATION MIXING

This can also be solved exactly and is similar to the last case. All states with nonzero interactions have the form $|\alpha'(\alpha')_t A\rangle$. The matrix for given total component m breaks into parts corresponding to the A of the odd particle. (Clearly the pair interaction has zero matrix elements when A changes.) Thus the matrix for any given A is just that for the case of two particles above, except for the fact that symmetry eliminates the state $|A(A_t)A\rangle$. When the odd particle is in the A state the eigenvectors satisfy

$$\left(2\epsilon_\alpha + \epsilon_A - E_n{}^A\right) a_{n\alpha}{}^A - |G| \sum_{\alpha' > 0} a_{n\alpha'}{}^A = 0$$

where $a_{nA}{}^A$ does not occur. Solving this set of $(\Omega - 1)$ equations leads to

$$a_{n\alpha}{}^A = +|G|\, K_n{}^A \Big/ \left(2\epsilon_\alpha + \epsilon_A - E_n{}^A\right)$$

$$K_n{}^A = \sum_{\alpha' > 0} a_{n\alpha'}{}^A$$

$$\sum_{\substack{\alpha > 0 \\ (\alpha \neq A)}} \frac{|G|}{2\epsilon_\alpha + \epsilon_A - E_n{}^A} = 1$$

When α labels the states jm of j − j coupling we have

$$\sum_j |G| \left(2j + 1 - 2\,\delta_{jA}\right) \Big/ \left(2\epsilon_j + \epsilon_A - E_n{}^A\right) = 2$$

where $\delta_{jA} = 1$ if A belongs to the j orbit, 0 otherwise.

In the case when all α are degenerate, the energy gap is $(\Omega - 1)|G|$, the reduction from $\Omega|G|$ being due to the fact that the presence of the odd particle A prevents one pair state from being occupied.

When there are two nondegenerate states j_1 and j_2 with energies ϵ_1 and ϵ_2 ($\epsilon_2 > \epsilon_1$), then the separation between the lowest eigenvalues E_0^1 and E_0^2 is found to be

$$E_0^2 - E_0^1 = \delta - \left\{\sqrt{(1 + x/2)^2 - (2j_2 - 1)|G|/\delta} - \sqrt{(1 + x/2)^2 - (2j_2 + 1)|G|/\delta}\right\}\delta$$

where

$$\delta = \epsilon_2 - \epsilon_1 \qquad \Delta = (\Omega - 1)|G| = (j_1 + j_2)|G| \qquad x = \Delta/\delta$$

The absolute energy of the lowest state is

$$E_0^1 = 3\epsilon_1 - \Delta + \delta\left\{(1 + x/2) - \sqrt{(1 + x/2)^2 - (2j_2 + 1)|G|/\delta}\right\}$$

When x is small, the last terms in these two formulas are $|G|$ and $\frac{1}{2}(2j_2 + 1)|G|$ to lowest order. When x is large they are $2\delta/(\Omega - 1)$ and $\delta(2j_2 + 1)/(\Omega - 1)$. In all cases, these are small compared to the leading terms. Of particular interest is the fact that, for large x, $(E_0^2 - E_0^1)$ is reduced below the value δ by the fractional amount $1 - 2/(\Omega - 1)$. This compression of the particle spectrum will be later seen to be a general effect, valid for any odd number of particles. The physical reason for the effect is easy to see. When only a pair is present, it spends most time in the lower level, which consequently contributes the larger part of the pairing energy. When an odd particle is put in this level, it "blocks" one substate of it for the pair, and this costs part of the pairing energy. When put in the upper state, it costs part of its contribution to the pairing energy, which is smaller. Hence the particle levels are compressed by the difference in contributions to the pairing energies from a substate in the two levels.

For three particles, the depressed states have exactly the form of an odd particle and a pair (antisymmetrized). In Chap. 3 we show that, for > three particles, and nondegenerate ϵ_α, such solutions (i.e., a number of pairs with at most one odd particle) are not exact, but they are valid to a good approximation. In Chap. 2 we show that, if the particle spectrum ϵ_α is degenerate, they are exact. In Sec. 3-6 we describe a method for obtaining exact solutions in the nondegenerate case, provided that the number of particles (or holes) and the number of particle energies are not very big.

2

EFFECT OF PAIRING FORCES ON STATES OF N PARTICLES IN DEGENERATE PARTICLE STATES

From the above case of two particles, one guesses that the lowest state of $N \equiv 2p$ particles in degenerate orbitals is

$$\Psi_N = \mathcal{A}[(1,2)_{0+}(3,4)_{0+} \cdots \text{ p pairs}]$$

$$(1,2)_{0+} = \sum_{\alpha} \psi_{\alpha}(1)\,(\psi_{\alpha}(2))_t$$

where ψ_α are the particle states. This guess is correct but, because of the presence of the antisymmetrizing operator $\mathcal{A}$, it is awkward to deal with in this form. For this reason we switch to the formalism of creation and destruction operators which has the merit that all states are automatically antisymmetric. Furthermore it is especially convenient when the force matrix elements in the problem are equal, as with the pairing force (see below).

Formalism

If the Hamiltonian in the coordinate space representation is

$$H = \sum_i T_i + \sum_{(ij)} v_{ij}$$

where the sums are over particles i, and the particle pairs (ij), the same thing in the new representation is†

† The potential energy term may be written in three equivalent ways:

(1) $$\sum_{(\alpha\beta),(\gamma\delta)} \langle \alpha\beta | v | \gamma\delta \rangle_{\text{A.S.}} \; a_\alpha^+ a_\beta^+ a_\delta a_\gamma$$

(sums over different pairs of states, matrix element antisymmetric)

$$H = \sum_{\alpha\beta} \langle \alpha | T | \beta \rangle a_\alpha^+ a_\beta + \sum_{(\alpha\beta)(\gamma\delta)} \langle \alpha\beta | v | \gamma\delta \rangle_{\text{A.S.}} a_\alpha^+ a_\beta^+ a_\delta a_\gamma$$

where α, β, γ, δ label particle states, $(\alpha\beta)$ and $(\gamma\delta)$ state pairs, and the operators a_α^+ (creation) and a_α (destruction) satisfy

$$\left[a_\alpha^+, a_\beta\right]_+ = \delta_{\alpha\beta} \qquad \left[a_\alpha^+, a_\beta^+\right]_+ = 0 \qquad \left[a_\alpha, a_\beta\right]_+ = 0$$

The states $\langle \alpha\beta |, | \gamma\delta \rangle$ are antisymmetrized. Whereas the first H has the number of particles N built into it, the second does not but commutes with the number operator n:

$$n = \sum_\alpha a_\alpha^+ a_\alpha$$

i.e., $[H,n] = 0$. Any wave function $a_\alpha^+ a_\beta^+ \ldots |0\rangle$ in this formalism is automatically antisymmetric. The single-particle Hamiltonian becomes

$$\sum_\alpha \epsilon_\alpha a_\alpha^+ a_\alpha$$

The pairing force Hamiltonian† will be taken as

---

(2) $\frac{1}{2} \sum_{\alpha\beta\gamma\delta} \langle \alpha\beta | v | \gamma\delta \rangle_{\text{not A.S.}} a_\alpha^+ a_\beta^+ a_\delta a_\gamma$

(sums over all particle states, matrix element not A.S.)

(3) $\frac{1}{4} \sum_{\alpha\beta\gamma\delta} \langle \alpha\beta | v | \gamma\delta \rangle_{\text{A.S.}} a_\alpha^+ a_\beta^+ a_\delta a_\gamma$

(sums over all particle states, matrix element A.S.)

†One might have guessed that the pairing force

$$V' = \tilde{G} \sum_{jj'} A^+(j'^2) A(j^2)$$

where

$$A^+(j^2) = \sum_m (jmj - m | 00) a_{jm}^+ a_{j-m}^+$$

was more "natural." This force contains weighting factors $(2j + 1)^{1/2}$, which cancel the Ω_j factor in the energy gap. Since a δ-function force produces a gap $\propto (2j + 1)$, the force V in the text is the more physical. In any case, the problem with V′ cannot be solved with the present method when different j occur. It can be solved with the general Belyaev method (see Sec. 3-3), which allows G to depend on j,j′ in arbitrary fashion.

$$H = \sum_{\alpha>0} \epsilon_\alpha \left(a_\alpha{}^+ a_\alpha + a_{\bar\alpha}{}^+ a_{\bar\alpha}\right) - |G| \sum_{\alpha,\alpha'>0} a_{\alpha'}{}^+ a_{\bar\alpha'}{}^+ a_{\bar\alpha} a_\alpha$$

i.e.,

$$\langle \alpha\beta |v| \gamma\delta\rangle_{A.S.} = -|G|\, \delta_{\alpha,\bar\beta}\, \delta_{\gamma,\bar\delta}$$

$a_{\bar\alpha}{}^+, a_{\bar\alpha}$ are the creation, destruction operators for the state $\bar\alpha$ that is the time-reverse (α_t) of α. At present, all ϵ_α are assumed equal. The second term, which we call V, may be written

$$V = -|G|\, A^+ A$$

where A^+ is the pair creation operator for states with equal weight to all substates:

$$A^+ = \sum_{\alpha>0} a_\alpha{}^+ a_{\bar\alpha}{}^+$$

It is easy to show that

$$[V,A^+] = -|G|\,(\Omega + 2 - n)\,A^+$$

where Ω is the number of pair states (i.e., number of $\alpha > 0$). If $\Psi_{0,0}$ is the vacuum state, we have

$$[V,A^+]\Psi_{0,0} = -|G|\,(\Omega + 2 - n)\,A^+\Psi_{0,0}$$

writing $A^+\Psi_{0,0} \equiv \Psi_{2,0}$:

$$V\Psi_{2,0} = -|G|\,\Omega\Psi_{2,0}$$

Thus the ground-state energy of two particles is $-|G|\,\Omega$.

As general notation we write $\Psi_{N,s}$ as a state of N particles, seniority s (seniority[1] is the number of unpaired particles). From the result,

$$[V,A^{+2}] = A^+[V,A^+] + [V,A^+]A^+$$
$$= -2|G|\,(\Omega + 2 - n)\,A^{+2} - |G|\,(nA^{+2} - A^+ nA^+)$$

We find, operating on $\Psi_{0,0}$,

$$\Psi_{4,0} = -2|G|\,(\Omega - 2)\,\Psi_{4,0} - |G|\,(4\Psi_{4,0} - 2\Psi_{4,0})$$
$$= -2|G|(\Omega - 1)\,\Psi_{4,0}$$

Thus the ground-state energy of four particles is $-2|G|(\Omega - 1)$. [The occurrence of $(\Omega - 1)$ rather than Ω can be traced to the fact that a state occupied by one pair is not available to the others.] Generally we have $\Psi_{N,0} = (A^+)^{N/2}\Psi_{0,0}$.

Energies of Excited States

We define B_x^+ as the set of pair creation operators producing states orthogonal to the pair state produced by A^+, i.e., $\langle 0 | AB_x^+ | 0 \rangle = 0$. (For the set of particle states in a spherical well labeled by jm, A^+ produces the state of J = 0, M = 0; x may be taken to label J,M with J ≠ 0.) Expanding B_x^+:

$$B_x^+ = \sum_{\alpha\alpha'} B_{x\alpha\alpha'} a_\alpha^+ a_{\alpha'}^+$$

where $B_{x\alpha\alpha'} = -B_{x\alpha'\alpha}$, this means that $\Sigma_{\alpha>0} B_{x\alpha\bar{\alpha}} = 0$. From this condition, it follows that $AB_x^+\Psi_{0,0} = 0$, so

$$VB_x^+\Psi_{0,0} = 0$$

Thus the $(\Omega - 1)$ excited states $\Psi_{2,2}$ have zero energy. Also

$$VA^+B_x^+\Psi_{0,0} = -|G|(\Omega - 2)A^+B_x^+\Psi_{0,0}$$

$A^+B_x^+\Psi_{0,0}$ is thus the state $\Psi_{4,2}$ (N.B.: The state $B_x^+A^+\Psi_{0,0}$ is not a good state.) Thus states $\Psi_{4,2}$ with (four particles, one pair) have energy $-|G|(\Omega - 2)$. The energy of states $\Psi_{4,4}$ can be found from the fact that

$$\text{Trace } V = -\tfrac{1}{2}\Omega(\Omega - 1)2|G|$$

$$= E_{4,0} + (\Omega - 1)E_{4,2} + \tfrac{1}{2}\Omega(\Omega - 3)E_{4,4}$$

whence $E_{4,4} = 0$.

States of Odd Number of Particles

Since $Va_\alpha^+\Psi_{0,0} = 0$, we have

$$VA^+a_\alpha^+\Psi_{0,0} = [V,A^+]a_\alpha^+\Psi_{0,0}$$

$$= -|G|(\Omega - 1)A^+a_\alpha^+\Psi_{0,0}$$

Thus $A^+a_\alpha\Psi_{0,0}$ is the state $\Psi_{3,1}$ with energy $-|G|(\Omega - 1)$. This is easily extended to more particles using the methods above. States $\Psi_{3,3}$ are $B^+a_\alpha^+\Psi_{0,0}$.

General Number of Particles

The ground state is $(A^+)^{N/2}\,\Psi_{0,0}$ for N even and $(A^+)^{[(N-1)/2]} \times a_\alpha^+ \Psi_{0,0}$ for N odd. The energy of any state of seniority s is

$$E_{N,s} = -\frac{|G|}{4}(N - s)(2\Omega - N - s + 2)$$

For even N, the excitation energy of the first excited state is always $|G|\,\Omega$; $-E_{N,0}$ rises to a maximum of $|G|\,(\Omega/2)\,[(\Omega/2) + 1]$ at mid-shell $N = \Omega$, then falls to $|G|\,\Omega$ at the full shell $N = 2\Omega$.

Evaluation of Matrix Elements

Consider the single-particle operator diagonal in representation α:

$$Q = \sum_\alpha q_{\alpha\alpha'} a_\alpha^+ a_{\alpha'}$$

with $q_{\alpha\alpha'} = q_\alpha\,\delta_{\alpha\alpha'}$. It is a straightforward exercise to show that, for N even:

$$\langle \Psi_{N,0}|Q|\Psi_{N,0}\rangle = \langle \Psi_{0,0}|A^{N/2}\,Q(A^{N/2})^+|\Psi_{0,0}\rangle$$

$$= \frac{(\Omega - 1)!\left(\frac{N}{2}\right)!\,\frac{N}{2}}{\left(\Omega - \frac{N}{2}\right)!}\left(\sum_\alpha q_\alpha\right)$$

Since a single-particle operator cannot change s by more than 2, all transitions from the s = 0 state must lead to s = 2. Thus

$$\sum_\lambda \langle \Psi_{N,2,\lambda}|Q|\Psi_{N,0}\rangle^2 = \langle \Psi_{N,0}|Q^2|\Psi_{N,0}\rangle$$

$$= \langle \Psi_{0,0}|A^{N/2}\,Q^2(A^{N/2})^+|\Psi_{0,0}\rangle$$

$$= \frac{\frac{N}{2}\left(\Omega - \frac{N}{2}\right)}{\Omega - 1}\left(\frac{1}{\Omega}\sum_\alpha q_\alpha^2\right)$$

This is $\sim N/2$ times the single-particle value for $N < \Omega/2$, illustrating that the pairing forces can give rise to collective effects in the wave function.

3

EFFECT OF PAIRING FORCES ON STATES OF N PARTICLES IN NONDEGENERATE PARTICLE STATES

This problem cannot be solved exactly but can be solved to a good approximation. There are several different mathematical ways to arrive at the (approximate) solution, those of Bayman,[8] Kerman,[11] Belyaev[4] and Bogoliubov,[41,42] Pal[10] and Anderson,[45] and Migdal[39] and Sawicki.[9] The solution that always emerges is the one that one would arrive at by guessing. We have seen in Sec. 1-4 that the general solution for two particles has the form

$$\Psi_2 = \left(\sum_{\alpha > 0} C_\alpha a_\alpha^+ a_{\bar{\alpha}}^+ \right)^p \Psi_0$$

where Ψ_0 is the vacuum state, and where C_α depend on the single-particle energy spectrum $\epsilon_1, \epsilon_2, \ldots$. The guess for an even number $N \equiv 2p$ particles is

$$\Psi_N = \left(\sum_{\alpha > 0} C_\alpha{}^p a_\alpha^+ a_{\bar{\alpha}}^+ \right)^p \Psi_0$$

where the coefficients $C_\alpha{}^p$ depend on p and are determined by minimizing the energy. This function is antisymmetric automatically. Further we know from the results above that the form is correct in both extreme limits: $|G|$ large, $C_{\alpha_1}{}^p$ equal for all α; $|G|$ small, $C_\alpha{}^p = 0$ except for the set $C_{\alpha_1}{}^p \ldots C_{\alpha_p}{}^p$. [In this latter case, the state is

$$p!\, C_{\alpha_1}{}^p \cdots C_{\alpha_p}{}^p \left(a_{\alpha_1}^+ a_{\bar{\alpha}_1}^+ \right) \cdots \left(a_{\alpha_p}^+ a_{\bar{\alpha}_p}^+ \right) \Psi_0]$$

See Bayman.

Unfortunately, it is difficult to evaluate $\langle \Psi_N | H | \Psi_N \rangle$ directly in the general case, so various indirect methods have been developed.

3-1 BAYMAN VARIATIONAL METHOD

In the Bayman method, we set up the generating function:

$$\Psi(z) = \prod_{\alpha > 0} \left(V_\alpha + z^{1/2} V_\alpha a_\alpha^+ a_{\bar{\alpha}}^+\right)\Psi_0$$

and notice that it may be written

$$\Psi(z) = U \sum_p \Psi_N \frac{z^{p/2}}{p!}$$

U being $(\Pi_{\alpha > 0} U_\alpha)$, and where the coefficients $C_\alpha{}^p$ in Ψ_N are

$$C_\alpha{}^p = \frac{V_\alpha}{U_\alpha}$$

Notice that the Ψ_N are not normalized. $\Psi(z)$ is a linear combination of states of different numbers of particles and has the properties

$$\langle\Psi(z)\,|\,\Psi(z)\rangle = \prod_{\alpha > 0} (U_\alpha{}^2 + zV_\alpha{}^2)$$

$$\langle\Psi(z)\,|n|\,\Psi(z)\rangle = 2\left[\prod_{\alpha > 0} (U_\alpha{}^2 + zV_\alpha{}^2)\right] \times \left[\sum_{\beta > 0} zV_\beta{}^2 \Big/ (U_\beta{}^2 + zV_\beta{}^2)\right]$$

The matrix element of H can also be written explicitly. If 0 is any operator preserving the number of particles, the matrix element in state Ψ_N can be picked out from that in $\Psi(z)$ by

$$\langle\Psi_N\,|0|\,\Psi_N\rangle = \oint z^{-p-1}\,\langle\Psi(z)\,|0|\,\Psi(z)\rangle\,dz$$

where the contour includes the origin. Thus the energy of the state Ψ_N is

$$E_N = \langle\Psi_N|H|\Psi_N\rangle \Big/ \langle\Psi_N|n|\Psi_N\rangle\,(1/N)$$

This is evaluated by the saddle-point method, and Bayman finds

$$E_N = \sum_{\alpha > 0} \frac{2\epsilon_\alpha z_0 V_\alpha{}^2}{W_\alpha{}^2} - |G|\left(\sum_{\alpha > 0} \frac{z_0{}^{1/2} U_\alpha V_\alpha}{W_\alpha{}^2}\right)^2 - |G| \sum_{\alpha > 0} \left(\frac{z_0 V_\alpha{}^2}{W_\alpha{}^2}\right)^2$$

where $W_\alpha^2 \equiv U_\alpha^2 + z_0 V_\alpha^2$ and the saddle point z_0 is given by

$$\sum_{\alpha > 0} \frac{z_0 V_\alpha^2}{W_\alpha^2} = P \ (\equiv N/2)$$

This last equation may be regarded as a subsidiary condition when E_N is minimized with respect to the U_α and V_α. Since z_0 occurs only with V_α^2, we may set $z_0 = 1$. Since the equations are unchanged if U_α and V_α are multiplied by the same factor, we cannot determine $(U_\alpha^2 + V_\alpha^2)$ and so set this equal to 1. Using the Lagrange multiplier λ, we must minimize:

$$E_N - \lambda N = \sum_{\alpha > 0} 2(\epsilon_\alpha - \lambda) V_\alpha^2$$

$$- |G| \left(\sum_{\alpha > 0} U_\alpha V_\alpha \right)^2 - |G| \sum_{\alpha > 0} V_\alpha^4$$

and determine λ from

$$\sum_{\alpha > 0} V_\alpha^2 = p$$

This last relation shows that V_α^2 is to be interpreted as the probability that pair state α is occupied. Then $U_\alpha^2 \equiv 1 - V_\alpha^2$ is the probability of it being unoccupied. On minimizing,

$$2(\epsilon_\alpha - \lambda) U_\alpha V_\alpha - |G| (U_\alpha^2 - V_\alpha^2) \left(\sum_{\beta > 0} U_\beta V_\beta \right)$$

$$- 2 |G| V_\alpha^3 U_\alpha = 0$$

The error in the saddle-point method is $0(1/\Omega)$, and so the accuracy is high for large Ω. If U_α and V_α are assumed positive numbers, large Ω means that the last term in the last equation is $\ll$ second term. If it is dropped (or incorporated in the first term by replacing ϵ_α by $\tilde{\epsilon}_\alpha \equiv \epsilon_\alpha - |G| V_\alpha^2$, we have

$$2(\tilde{\epsilon}_\alpha - \lambda) U_\alpha V_\alpha - |G| (U_\alpha^2 - V_\alpha^2) \left(\sum_{\beta > 0} U_\beta V_\beta \right) = 0$$

For two particles V_α^2 is $0(1/\Omega)$ and $U_\alpha^2 \sim 1$, so that to $0(1/\Omega)$ this is the same as the eigenvector equations in Sec. 1-4, with

$$C_\alpha = k V_\alpha$$

Comparison of the two normalization conditions fixes constant k as unity. Thus the present results are checked by the (exact) solution for two particles to the expected order of accuracy.

The solution of the last equation is

$$U_\alpha^2 = \tfrac{1}{2}\left(1 + \frac{\tilde{\epsilon}_\alpha - \lambda}{\sqrt{(\tilde{\epsilon}_\alpha - \lambda)^2 + \Delta^2}}\right)$$

$$V_\alpha^2 = \tfrac{1}{2}\left(1 - \frac{\tilde{\epsilon}_\alpha - \lambda}{\sqrt{(\tilde{\epsilon}_\alpha - \lambda)^2 + \Delta^2}}\right)$$

where the quantity Δ is defined as

$$\Delta = |G| \sum_{\alpha > 0} U_\alpha V_\alpha$$

The energy is

$$E_N = \sum_{\alpha > 0} 2\tilde{\epsilon}_\alpha V_\alpha^2 - \frac{\Delta^2}{|G|}$$

Inserting the values for U_α and V_α in that for Δ we have either $\Delta = 0$ or

$$\sum_{\alpha > 0} \frac{1}{\sqrt{(\tilde{\epsilon}_\alpha - \lambda)^2 + \Delta^2}} = \frac{2}{|G|} \tag{A}$$

The condition $\Sigma_{\alpha > 0} V_\alpha^2 = p$ leads to the relation

$$\sum_{\alpha > 0} \left(1 - \frac{(\epsilon_\alpha - \lambda)}{\sqrt{(\tilde{\epsilon}_\alpha - \lambda)^2 + \Delta^2}}\right) = 2p \tag{B}$$

Conditions (A) and (B) must be solved together to give values of λ and Δ.

Conditions for Solution of (A) and (B)

If (A) is taken alone, it has a solution if and only if $\Sigma_{\alpha > 0} |G|/|\tilde{\epsilon}_\alpha - \lambda| > 2$. For a discrete spectrum $\tilde{\epsilon}_\alpha$, this can always be satisfied by choosing λ sufficiently close to one of the $\tilde{\epsilon}_\alpha$. In general, however, condition (B) restricts the choice of λ, so there is a minimum value of $|G|$, $|G|_{crit}$, say, below which there is no solution of (A) and (B). In other words, $\Delta = 0$ and no superconducting state occurs. An exceptional case occurs when several states α are degenerate at energy $\tilde{\epsilon}_\alpha$ and when not all of these states are filled. In this case, (A) and (B) have a solution for all values of $|G|$ so that one can pass continuously from the superconducting state to the weak coupling limit (shell model). This applies to the case of jm states in spherical nuclei, where states of different m have the same energy $\tilde{\epsilon}_j$.

Condition for Convergence of (A) and (B)

Condition (B) is such that the summand is $\sim \tilde{\epsilon}_\alpha^{-2}$ for large $\tilde{\epsilon}_\alpha$. The density of $\tilde{\epsilon}_\alpha$ is $\sim \tilde{\epsilon}_\alpha^{1/2}$, so the sum always converges. In contrast, condition (A) will diverge if the sum is unrestricted, so that the sum must be cut off. The same is true of the first term in E_N. This exposes a grave weakness of the present extreme version of the pairing force model, in which all pairing force matrix elements are equal (viz., $= |G|$). The model can only be used if the sum over α is cut off in (A). In spherical nuclei, this may be done with some plausibility at the levels at magic numbers, but in deformed nuclei it is highly arbitrary. We shall see in Sec. 3-3 that it is possible to relax the extreme pairing force assumption to allow $\langle \alpha\bar{\alpha} | \mathcal{G} | \alpha'\bar{\alpha}' \rangle$ to depend on α, α'. This automatically disposes of the convergence problem both in condition (A) and E_N.

Strong Coupling Limit

When Δ or $(\tilde{\epsilon}_\alpha - \lambda)$ is $\gg$ range of values of $\tilde{\epsilon}_\alpha$, we have, with $\bar{\epsilon}$ = mean of $\tilde{\epsilon}_\alpha$,

$$\bar{\epsilon} - \lambda = |G| (\Omega/2 - p) \qquad \Delta = |G| \sqrt{p(\Omega - p)}$$

$$V_\alpha^2 = p/\Omega \qquad E_N = 2p\bar{\epsilon} - \Delta^2/|G|$$

Comparing with the results in Sec. 3, E_N differs by $2p(\bar{\epsilon} - \epsilon) + p|G|$. This checks with the above statement that the present results are correct to $0(1/\Omega)$.

Energy Gap and the Spectra of Even and Odd Nuclei

In the state so far considered, the ground state, all particles are paired off and can occupy all the available pair states. Let us enquire about the energy needed to take a pair and to put the two particles in two definite orbits α_1 and α_2, thereby excluding these orbits from remaining pairs. Referring back to the expression for the total energy E_N, this may be written identically as

$$E_N = E'_{2(p-V_1^2-V_2^2)} + 2\tilde{\epsilon}_1 V_1^2 + 2\tilde{\epsilon}_2 V_2^2 - 2(U_1V_1 + U_2V_2)\Delta$$
$$+ |G| (U_1V_1 + U_2V_2)^2$$

The last term is less than the previous one by a factor

$$\frac{U_1V_1 + U_2V_2}{2\Delta/|G|}$$

Referring back to the definition of Δ we see that, if all Ω levels in the sum over $\alpha > 0$ contribute appreciably, then the denominator is $\sim\Omega$. In general, however, not all the levels will contribute; for the levels more distant from the Fermi surface, $U_\alpha V_\alpha$ will be small, i.e., $\ll$ the typical surface value of 0.5. Thus we define[51] an effective number of levels, Ω_{eff}, by

$$\Omega_{\text{eff}} \equiv \frac{2\Delta}{|G|}$$

The last term in the above expression is less than the preceding one by $0(1/\Omega_{\text{eff}})$ and we now assume that it is small and drop it. *The approximation of dropping terms $0(1/\Omega_{eff})$ is the basic one in deriving the usual results of the pairing force model.* Sometimes, corrections arising from this source are serious and must be taken into account. We discuss this in connection with excited states in Sec. 3-2.

The energy of the excited state is

$$E_N^* = E_{(N-2)}' + \tilde{\epsilon}_1 + \tilde{\epsilon}_2$$

The prime signifies that the states α_1 and α_2 are excluded. Thus E_x' is the energy:

$$E_x' = \sum_{\alpha>0}' 2\tilde{\epsilon}_\alpha V_\alpha'^2 - |G| \left(\sum_{\alpha>0} U_\alpha' V_\alpha' \right)$$

where $\Sigma_{\alpha>0}' V_\alpha'^2 = \frac{1}{2}x$. (Note that E_{N-2}' may be taken as the minimized energy, but $E_{2(p-V_1^2-V_2^2)}$ is not, since it contains the V_α's that minimize E_N.) Since $\delta(E_x' - \lambda' x) = 0$ for variation of V_α', and since $\delta E_x' = \lambda\ \delta x$ for variation of x:

$$E_{N-2}' - E_{2(p-V_1^2-V_2^2)}' = 2\lambda(V_1^2 + V_2^2 - 1)$$

It follows that

$$E_N^* - E_N = e_{\alpha_1} + e_{\alpha_2} - \frac{|G|}{4}\Delta^2\left(\frac{1}{e_{\alpha_1}} + \frac{1}{e_{\alpha_2}}\right)^2$$

where

$$e_\alpha = \sqrt{(\tilde{\epsilon}_\alpha - \lambda)^2 + \Delta^2}$$

Thus the energy needed to break a pair and put the particles in orbits α_1 and α_2 has the form of a sum $(e_{\alpha_1} + e_{\alpha_2})$ provided we drop the last term, which is small, i.e., $0(1/\Omega)$. Since the state so formed has spin $J \neq 0$, it will be orthogonal to the ground state. Excited states formed in this way are the lowest excited states, and the excitation energy is called the "energy gap." Near midshell, it is $\sim 2\Delta$ and can be $\gg$ the spacing of particle levels.

By similar arguments one may show that the ground energy $E_{(N+1),\alpha}$ of an odd number, $(2p + 1)$, of particles with the odd particle in a definite orbit α is

$$E_{(N+1)\alpha} = E_N + \lambda + \sqrt{(\tilde{\epsilon}_\alpha - \lambda)^2 + \Delta^2}$$

This demonstrates the well-known compression effect of single-particle levels. If $(\tilde{\epsilon}_{\alpha_2} - \tilde{\epsilon}_{\alpha_1})$ is $\ll \Delta$ or λ, then

$$\frac{E_{(N+1)\alpha_2} - E_{(N+1)\alpha_1}}{\tilde{\epsilon}_{\alpha_2} - \tilde{\epsilon}_{\alpha_1}} = \frac{1}{\sqrt{1 + (\Delta/\overline{\epsilon} - \lambda)^2}}$$

where $\overline{\epsilon} = \frac{1}{2}(\tilde{\epsilon}_{\alpha_2} + \tilde{\epsilon}_{\alpha_1})$. This effect is significant if $\Delta \gtrsim |\overline{\epsilon} - \lambda|$. Near midshell $[\Delta/(\overline{\epsilon} - \lambda)] \sim \Omega$, and the effect can be very strong.

The above results may be specialized to the case of degenerate particle levels (all $\tilde{\epsilon}_\alpha$ equal). The excitation energy needed to break a pair is

$$\begin{aligned} E_N^* - E_N &= 2\overline{e} \\ &= 2\sqrt{(\overline{\epsilon} - \lambda)^2 + \Delta^2} \\ &= |G|\,\Omega \end{aligned}$$

where we have used the previous results that $\overline{\epsilon} - \lambda = [(\Omega/2) - p]\,|G|$ and $\Delta = |G|\sqrt{p(\Omega - p)}$. This agrees with the exact result derived earlier. Note that 2Δ is not equal to the energy gap $|G|\,\Omega$ in general. It is equal to it at midshell $(p = \Omega/2)$ but is less otherwise.

We return to the result that the energy needed to break a pair and put the particles in orbits α_1 and α_2 has the form of a sum $e_{\alpha_1} + e_{\alpha_2}$. This strongly suggests that we introduce the notion of "quasi-particle," the energy of which includes the effects of pairing forces (through Δ) in addition to the particle energy $\tilde{\epsilon}_\alpha$, i.e., the quasi-particle is "clothed." From this point of view, the ground state is the vacuum state of the quasi-particles; the energy needed to create a particle in state α is e_α.

3-2 QUASI-PARTICLES AND AN ALTERNATIVE APPROACH TO THE PAIRING FORCE PROBLEM

The ground state is the *vacuum* state of the quasi-particles, not a product state of N quasi-particles. This difference, although vital, is simple enough to explain. Given a state Ψ_N of N independent particles and a set of particle states α. Suppose states α' are occupied, while the rest, α'', are empty. We may now make the transformation from the real particle operators a_α to the quasi-particle operators b_α:

$$b_\alpha = \begin{cases} a_\alpha & \text{for } \alpha = \alpha'' \\ a_{(\alpha)_t}^{+} \equiv a_{\bar{\alpha}}^{+} & \text{for } \alpha = \alpha' \end{cases}$$

Whereas we had

$$a_\alpha \Psi_N = 0, \; a_\alpha^{+} \Psi_N = \Psi_{N+1} \qquad \text{for } \alpha = \alpha'''$$

$$\left\{ \begin{aligned} a_\alpha \Psi_N &= \Psi_{N-1} \\ a_\alpha^{+} \Psi_N &= 0 \end{aligned} \right\} \qquad \text{for } \alpha = \alpha'$$

we now have $b_\alpha \Psi_N = 0$ for all α. Thus Ψ_N is the vacuum state for the new particles. We write this $|0)$, with a parenthesis, and the state of one quasi-particle α as

$$b_\alpha^{+} \Psi_N \equiv b_\alpha^{+} |0) \equiv |\alpha)$$

For $\alpha = \alpha''$, the quasi-particle state $|\alpha)$ is the real particle state α'' in the presence of the filled states α'; for $\alpha = \alpha'$, it is the absence of the real particle state $(\alpha)_t$ [i.e., the presence of the hole state $(\alpha)_t$] in the set of filled states α'. b_α^{+} is always a creation operator in the sense that, for $\alpha = \alpha''$ it creates a particle; for $\alpha = \alpha'$ it creates a hole. Clearly, however, operation by any operator like

$$\sum_\alpha Q_\alpha b_\alpha \qquad \sum_\alpha Q_\alpha b_\alpha^{+} \qquad \sum_{\alpha\beta} Q_{\alpha\beta} b_\alpha b_\beta^{+}$$

etc., will not give an eigenstate of the number of real particles. The reason for using the true-reversed state when $\alpha = \alpha'$ is that b_α^{+} can be said to always "add α" to the state on which it acts [e.g., when α is $\mathbf{k}$, b_α^{+} for $\alpha = \alpha''$ creates a particle $\mathbf{k}$. For $\alpha = \alpha'$, it creates a hole $(\mathbf{k})_t = -\mathbf{k}$, i.e., it destroys particle $(\mathbf{k})_t = -\mathbf{k}$. If the total vector for the original system is $\mathbf{K}$, it changes it to $\mathbf{K} - (-\mathbf{k})$, i.e., to $\mathbf{K} + \mathbf{k}$].

The above transformation from a_α to b_α is such that b_α acting on the ground state gives zero. We now try to preserve this result in the more general case when the ground state contains correlations between particles. The effect of these correlations is to smooth out the sharp Fermi surface so that, instead of being 100 per cent occupied or unoccupied, the various particle states have a certain probability of being occupied. The simplest generalization[41,42] of the above transformation that includes this effect and seems reasonable is

$$b_\alpha = U_\alpha a_\alpha - V_\alpha a_{\bar{\alpha}}^+ \qquad \text{for all } \alpha \text{ where } U_\alpha \text{ and } V_\alpha \text{ are real.}$$

The condition $[b_\alpha, b_\alpha^+]_+ = 1$ gives the relation $U_\alpha^2 + V_\alpha^2 = 1$. We expect U_α^2 to go from zero for states well below the mean particle energy to unity for those well above. V_α^2 must behave in the opposite fashion and is evidently related to the probability that state α is occupied. In the above case of no correlations, we get the correct transformation by taking $U_\alpha = 0,1$ for states α below, above the Fermi surface.

For the state $\bar{\alpha}$, we have

$$b_{\bar{\alpha}} = U_{\bar{\alpha}} a_{\bar{\alpha}} - V_{\bar{\alpha}} a_\alpha^+$$

The quantities V_α and $U_{\bar{\alpha}}$ are not independent if $[b_\alpha, b_{\bar{\alpha}}] = 0$, but satisfy

$$\frac{U_\alpha}{V_\alpha} + \frac{U_{\bar{\alpha}}}{V_{\bar{\alpha}}} = 0$$

Belyaev[4] chooses the convention that U_α and V_α are always positive numbers and $V_{\bar{\alpha}} = -V_\alpha$, $U_{\bar{\alpha}} = U_\alpha$, so, for $\alpha > 0$,

$$\left.\begin{aligned} b_\alpha &= U_\alpha a_\alpha - V_\alpha a_{\bar{\alpha}}^+ \\ b_{\bar{\alpha}} &= U_\alpha a_{\bar{\alpha}} + V_\alpha a_\alpha^+ \end{aligned}\right\} \rightarrow \left\{\begin{aligned} a_\alpha &= U_\alpha b_\alpha + V_\alpha b_{\bar{\alpha}}^+ \\ a_{\bar{\alpha}} &= U_\alpha b_{\bar{\alpha}} - V_\alpha b_\alpha^+ \end{aligned}\right.$$

We shall work with this convention from now on. We note that the state $(U_\alpha + V_\alpha a_\alpha^+ a_{\bar{\alpha}}^+)\Psi_0$, for $\alpha > 0$, is such that

$$b_\alpha\left(U_\alpha + V_\alpha a_\alpha^+ a_{\bar{\alpha}}^+\right)\Psi_0 = 0$$

$$b_{\bar{\alpha}}\left(U_\alpha + V_\alpha a_\alpha^+ a_{\bar{\alpha}}^+\right)\Psi_0 = 0$$

where Ψ_0 is the vacuum state of real particles. It follows immediately that the vacuum state $|0)$ of the quasi-particles corresponding to the operators b_α is

$$|0) = \prod_{\alpha > 0} \left(U_\alpha + V_\alpha a_\alpha^+ a_{\bar{\alpha}}^+\right) \Psi_0$$

since this has the required property:

$$b_\alpha |0) = 0 \qquad b_{\bar{\alpha}} |0) = 0$$

Since the operators b_α and $(U_\alpha + V_\alpha a_\alpha^+ a_{\bar{\alpha}}^+)$ leads to a superposition of states of different even numbers of real particles, it is clear that $|0)$ is not an eigenstate of the number of real particles, and therefore cannot be equal to the state Ψ_N introduced above. This is the basic difficulty of the present approach and is inavoidable in that it is implied in the transformation from a_α to b_α. Nevertheless, if used properly, the present method will give the required results, as we shall show. We now show how the variables U_α can be chosen to make the vacuum state $|0)$ as good an eigenstate of H as possible.

If the transformation is inserted in the Hamiltonian H, it becomes (from simple algebra, using Wick's theorem)

$$H = U + H_{20} + H_{11} + H_{int}$$

P. 30. $H = \sum_{\alpha\beta} \langle\alpha|T|\beta\rangle a_\alpha^+ a_\beta + \sum_{(\alpha\beta)(\gamma\delta)} \langle\alpha\beta|V|\gamma\delta\rangle a_\alpha^+ a_\beta^+ a_\delta a_\gamma$

where U is the constant:

$$U = \sum_{\alpha > 0} \left(\epsilon_\alpha - \frac{|G|}{2} V_\alpha^2\right) 2V_\alpha^2 - |G| \left(\sum_{\alpha > 0} U_\alpha V_\alpha\right)^2$$

H_{20} and H_{11} are quadratic in the b's:

$$H_{20} = \sum_{\alpha > 0} \left[\left(\epsilon_\alpha - |G| V_\alpha^2\right) 2U_\alpha V_\alpha - \left(|G| \sum_{\alpha_1 > 0} U_{\alpha_1} V_{\alpha_1}\right)\left(U_\alpha^2 - V_\alpha^2\right)\right]\left(b_\alpha^+ b_{\bar{\alpha}}^+ + b_{\bar{\alpha}} b_\alpha\right)$$

$$H_{11} = \sum_{\alpha > 0} \left[\left(\epsilon_\alpha - |G| V_\alpha^2\right)\left(U_\alpha^2 - V_\alpha^2\right) + \left(|G| \sum_{\alpha_1 > 0} U_{\alpha_1} V_{\alpha_1}\right) 2U_\alpha V_\alpha\right]\left(b_\alpha^+ b_\alpha + b_{\bar{\alpha}}^+ b_{\bar{\alpha}}\right)$$

The sums are over positive values of α, α_1 only. The form of H_{int} is complicated and will not be given. It is fourth power in the b's. In terms of a's it is

$$-|G| \sum_{\alpha\alpha' > 0} N(a_\alpha^+ a_{\bar{\alpha}}^+ a_{\bar{\alpha}'} a_{\alpha'})$$

where N is normal product with respect to b's.

While all four terms of H are kept, it commutes with the number operator, n. When we drop H_{int}, it no longer does so, and the eigenstates are mixtures of states of different numbers of particles. In order to pick out the state Ψ with the closest relation to the correct state Ψ_N for a given number of particles, we insist that Ψ satisfies the condition

$$\langle \Psi | n | \Psi \rangle = N$$

Mathematically this can be done if we use a Lagrange multiplier λ and work with

$$H' \equiv H - \lambda n$$

instead of H, which means that U, H_{20}, and H_{11} are replaced by

$$U' \equiv U - \lambda \sum_{\alpha > 0} 2V_\alpha^2$$

$$H'_{20} \equiv H_{20} - 2\lambda \sum_{\alpha > 0} U_\alpha V_\alpha (b_\alpha^+ b_{\bar{\alpha}} + b_{\bar{\alpha}} b_\alpha)$$

$$H'_{11} \equiv H_{11} - \lambda \sum_{\alpha > 0} (U_\alpha^2 - V_\alpha^2)(b_\alpha^+ b_\alpha + b_{\bar{\alpha}}^+ b_{\bar{\alpha}})$$

The subsidiary condition in terms of the b's is $\langle \Psi | n | \Psi \rangle = N$, with

$$n = \sum_{\alpha > 0} \{2V_\alpha^2 + (U_\alpha^2 - V_\alpha^2)(b_\alpha^+ b_\alpha + b_{\bar{\alpha}}^+ b_{\bar{\alpha}})$$

$$+ 2U_\alpha V_\alpha (b_\alpha^+ b_{\bar{\alpha}}^+ + b_{\bar{\alpha}} b_\alpha)\}$$

If we drop H_{int} and demand that the vacuum state $|0)$ of the quasiparticles is an eigenstate of H', then

$$H_{20}' = 0$$

This gives a condition on the U's and V's:

$$(\epsilon_\alpha - \lambda - |G| V_\alpha^2) 2U_\alpha V_\alpha - \left(|G| \sum_{\beta > 0} U_\beta V_\beta\right)(U_\alpha^2 - V_\alpha^2) = 0$$

which is precisely the condition found in the previous method. The subsidiary condition applied to the vacuum state $|0)$ is

$$\sum_{\alpha>0} 2V_\alpha^{\,2} = N$$ — ② From ① and ②, U, V can be found.

—again the same as before.

Defining as before the gap parameter

$$\Delta = |G| \sum_{\alpha>0} U_\alpha V_\alpha$$

and the quasi-particle energy

$$e_\alpha = \sqrt{(\tilde{\epsilon}_\alpha - \lambda)^2 + \Delta^2}$$

we find that $U_\alpha^{\,2} = \frac{1}{2}(1 + (\tilde{\epsilon}_\alpha - \lambda)/e_\alpha)$, and that H_{11}' transforms to $\Sigma_{\alpha>0}\, e_\alpha (b_\alpha^{\,+} b_\alpha + b_{\bar{\alpha}}^{\,+} b_{\bar{\alpha}})$. Thus the transformed Hamiltonian is now (dropping H_{int}):

$$H = U' + \sum_{\alpha>0} e_\alpha (b_\alpha^{\,+} b_\alpha + b_{\bar{\alpha}}^{\,+} b_{\bar{\alpha}}) + \lambda n$$

and the ground-state (vacuum) energy is

$$U = U' + \lambda N = \sum_{\alpha>0} \left(\tilde{\epsilon}_\alpha + \frac{|G|}{2} V_\alpha^{\,2}\right) 2V_\alpha^{\,2} - \frac{\Delta^2}{G}$$

This is just the same as before. Thus the present results check on all points with the previous ones. It only remains to check on the basic condition for the validity of the present approach; viz., the range of numbers of particles in $|0)$ is small. We can easily show that

$$(n^2) - (n)^2 = \sum_{\alpha>0} 4U_\alpha^{\,2} V_\alpha^{\,2} = \sum_{\alpha>0} \frac{\Delta^2}{(\tilde{\epsilon}_\alpha - \lambda)^2 + \Delta^2}$$

When $|G|$ is large (the degenerate case), this is $N/2[1 - (N/2\Omega)]$, which is $< N/2$, so that

$$\frac{(n^2) - (n)^2}{(n)^2} < \frac{1}{2N}$$

which is small, and decreases as N increases.

One can see directly from the expression for the vacuum state $|0)$ that the component of this state with a given (even) number of particles M is

$$\left[\sum_{\alpha>0} (V_\alpha/U_\alpha)\, a_\alpha{}^+ a_{\bar{\alpha}}{}^+\right]^{M/2} \Psi_0$$

where we remember that U_α and V_α are dependent on the prescribed mean number N.

The fact that states are not eigenstates of n gives rise to the occurrence of spurious components in excited states, i.e., parts not independent of other states and the ground state. We know that, if $|0')$ is an actual ground state, that $n|0')$ does not correspond to a new state. Thus any components of $n|0)$ in excited states are spurious. Sometimes, such components occur nearly all in one state with large total strength, in which case that state must be omitted as spurious.

Excited States and Odd N Nuclei

Such states are made by creating quasi-particles in the vacuum state. The energies follow immediately from the above form of H. Choosing (n) to be the same in state $|\alpha_1\alpha_2)$ as in $|0)$, the excitation energy of $|\alpha_1\alpha_2)$ is $\left(e_{\alpha_1} + e_{\alpha_2}\right)$. Passing from the even nucleus $|0)$ to the odd one $|\alpha)$, we choose (n) to be one more; then the excitation energy of the state $|\alpha)$ is $e_\alpha + \lambda$. Notice that these energies are, strictly speaking, subject to small corrections, arising from the fact that the U_α are somewhat different in the excited state (since certain particle states are blocked). These corrections are $0(1/\Omega_{eff})$ and can often be ignored. However, as pointed out by Soloviev[49,50] and Nilsson and Prior,[51] the correction may be large (~ 30 per cent) in some cases. This may happen in particular in deformed nuclei where, although there may be 20 levels in the particle spectrum, only 4 or 5 contribute appreciably to sums (e.g., in $\Delta = |G|\,\Sigma_{\alpha>0}\, U_\alpha V_\alpha$). Clearly the blocking of 1 or 2 such levels in such a case has a large effect, so that one cannot equate the excitation energies to quasi-particle energies, but must evaluate the total excited state energy and subtract the vacuum energy (for the same N) from it. For two-quasi-particle states, the corrected energy (~1.4 MeV) is always less than the quasi-particle energy (~1.7 MeV), but more than the free-particle energy (~ 0.15 MeV). One trouble that arises in this corrected theory, in which the U_α are appreciably different in the ground and excited states, is that states are no longer automatically orthogonal. Two-quasi-particle states of spin 0+ are not orthogonal to the ground state. States of other spins are orthogonal on grounds of spin, so this corrected theory is satisfactory for these.

The wave functions of the various states are found by acting on the vacuum with appropriate b^+ operators. Acting with a single $b_\alpha{}^+$ gives

$$|\alpha) \equiv b_\alpha{}^+|0) = \prod_{\substack{\alpha'>0\\ \alpha'\neq\alpha}} \left(U_{\alpha'} + V_{\alpha'}\, a_{\alpha'}{}^+ a_{\bar{\alpha}'}{}^+\right)\left(-V_\alpha\, a_\alpha{}^+\right)\Psi_0$$

This is a system with N odd. Determining the V_α and $V_{\alpha'}$ to minimize the energy gives $V_\alpha = 1$, and the usual formula for $V_{\alpha'}$, except that state α is not taken into account. We see that a state of an odd nucleus has the odd (real) particle in a definite orbit α just as in the shell model, whereas other particles are paired off.

Suppose now that we wish to identify excited states of an even-N system. These may be taken to have the form

$$|\alpha_1\alpha_2) \equiv b_{\alpha_1}^+ b_{\alpha_2}^+ \; |0)$$

$$= \prod_{\substack{\alpha' \neq \alpha_1,\alpha_2 \\ \alpha' > 0}} \left(U_{\alpha'} + V_{\alpha'} a_{\alpha'}^+ a_{\bar{\alpha}'}^+\right) a_{\alpha_1}^+ a_{\alpha_2}^+ \Psi_0$$

where the $V_{\alpha'}$ are given by the usual formula except that states α_1 and α_2 are not included in the sum in Δ. If we demand that the state $|\alpha_1\alpha_2)$ has N real particles in it, it follows that

$$\sum_{\substack{\alpha' \neq \alpha_1,\alpha_2 \\ \alpha' > 0}} 2V_{\alpha'}^2 = N - 2$$

This means in general that the $V_{\alpha'}$ are not quite the same as those for the ground state of the N-particle system which satisfy

$$\sum_{\substack{\alpha' \neq \alpha_1,\alpha_2 \\ \alpha' > 0}} 2V_{\alpha'}^2 = N - 2V_{\alpha_1}^2 - 2V_{\alpha_2}^2$$

Clearly the differences are least when $V_{\alpha_1}^2$ and $V_{\alpha_2}^2$ are $\sim \frac{1}{2}$, i.e., when the states α_1 and α_2 are at the Fermi surface. In any case, the state $|\alpha_1\alpha_2)$ is orthogonal to the ground state on grounds of spin (provided $\alpha_1 \neq \alpha_2$).

When $\alpha_1 = \bar{\alpha}_2$, special considerations apply:

$$|\alpha\bar{\alpha}) \equiv b_\alpha^+ b_{\bar{\alpha}}^+ \; |0)$$

$$= \prod_{\substack{\alpha' \neq \alpha \\ \alpha' > 0}} \left(U_{\alpha'} + V_{\alpha'} a_{\alpha'}^+ a_{\bar{\alpha}'}^+\right) \left(U a_\alpha^+ a_{\bar{\alpha}}^+ - V_\alpha\right) \Psi_0$$

The condition of N real particles is

$$\sum_{\substack{\alpha' \neq \alpha \\ \alpha' > 0}} 2V_{\alpha'}^2 + 2U_\alpha^2 = N$$

whereas in the ground state it is

$$\sum_{\substack{\alpha' \neq \alpha \\ \alpha' > 0}} 2V_{\alpha'}^{\,2} + 2V_{\alpha}^{\,2} = N$$

This means that $V_{\alpha'}$ will be the same in the two states only if $V_\alpha^{\,2} \approx \frac{1}{2}$. If $V_\alpha^{\,2}$ differs from $\frac{1}{2}$, the two sets of $V_{\alpha'}$ are different. When state α is nearly unoccupied in the vacuum (i.e., $\tilde{\epsilon}_\alpha \gg \lambda$), then $V_\alpha \approx 0$ and the excited state $|\alpha\bar{\alpha})$ is essentially two real particles added to the vacuum state of (N − 2) particles. When state α is nearly occupied in the vacuum (i.e., $\tilde{\epsilon}_\alpha \ll \lambda$), then $V_\alpha \approx 1$, and the excited state $|\alpha\bar{\alpha})$ is essentially two holes in the vacuum state of (N + 2) particles.

In summary, it has been shown that the ground state may be regarded as the vacuum state of the quasi-particles. Excited states are made by creating quasi-particles in the vacuum. This approach gives a close relation between the present general case and the case of degenerate ϵ_α through the seniority number s, which classifies the states and may be defined as the number of quasi-particles present.

When three or more quasi-particles are present, one has the problem of classifying their states. One may do this by a seniority number just as one does for real particles. However this only classifies states. There is no reason to believe that it diagonalizes the residual quasi-particle interactions.

3-3 MORE GENERAL APPLICATION OF THE QUASI-PARTICLE TRANSFORMATION

The arguments leading to the introduction of the transformation to quasi-particles in Sec. 3-2 did not depend on pairing forces but apply to any kind of internuclear forces. It is thus of interest to transform a general nuclear Hamiltonian to see if anything useful emerges. Belyaev[4] has done this, and we follow his work. Other authors[6,43] have also studied this problem.

First of all, Belyaev generalizes the approach in a different respect: He includes the problem of determining the best set of particle states α with which to work.

In terms of creation and destruction operators for any arbitrary set of particle states α,

$$H = \sum_{\alpha\alpha'} \langle \alpha | T | \alpha' \rangle a_\alpha^{+} a_{\alpha'} + \sum_{\substack{\alpha_1\alpha_2 \\ \alpha_1'\alpha_2'}} \langle \alpha_1 \alpha_2 | v | \alpha_1' \alpha_2' \rangle a_{\alpha_1}^{+} a_{\alpha_2}^{+} a_{\alpha_2'} a_{\alpha_1'}$$

where the states in the matrix elements are A.S.

The transformation to the quasi-particles gives

$$H' = H - \lambda n$$

$$H' = U' + H_{20}' + H_{11}' + H_{\text{int}}$$

where

$$U' = \sum_{\alpha > 0} \Bigg(\langle \alpha | T | \alpha \rangle - \lambda + \tfrac{1}{2} \sum_{\alpha_1 > 0} [\langle \alpha\bar{\alpha}_1 | v | \alpha\bar{\alpha}_1 \rangle + \langle \alpha\alpha_1 | v | \alpha\alpha_1 \rangle] V_{\alpha_1}^2 \Bigg) 2V_\alpha^2 + \sum_{\alpha\alpha_1 > 0} \langle \alpha\bar{\alpha} | v | \alpha_1\bar{\alpha}_1 \rangle U_{\alpha_1} V_{\alpha_1} U_\alpha V_\alpha$$

$$H_{20}' = \sum_{\alpha\alpha' > 0} \Bigg\{ \Bigg(\langle \alpha | T | \alpha' \rangle - \lambda\, \delta_{\alpha\alpha'} + \sum_{\alpha_1 > 0} [\langle \alpha\bar{\alpha}_1 | v | \alpha'\bar{\alpha}_1 \rangle + \langle \alpha\alpha_1 | v | \alpha'\alpha_1 \rangle] V_{\alpha_1}^2 \Bigg) \times \left(U_\alpha V_{\alpha'} + U_{\alpha'} V_\alpha\right) + \sum_{\alpha_1 > 0} \langle \alpha\bar{\alpha}' | v | \alpha_1\bar{\alpha}_1 \rangle U_{\alpha_1} V_{\alpha_1} \left(U_\alpha U_{\alpha'} - V_\alpha V_{\alpha'}\right) \Bigg\} \times \left(b_\alpha^+ b_{\bar{\alpha}'}^+ + b_{\bar{\alpha}} b_{\alpha'}\right)$$

$$H_{11}' = \sum_{\alpha\alpha' > 0} \Bigg\{ \Bigg(\langle \alpha | T | \alpha' \rangle - \lambda\, \delta_{\alpha\alpha'} + \sum_{\alpha_1 > 0} [\langle \alpha\bar{\alpha}_1 | v | \alpha'\bar{\alpha}_1 \rangle + \langle \alpha\alpha_1 | v | \alpha'\alpha_1 \rangle] V_{\alpha_1}^2 \Bigg) \times \left(U_\alpha U_{\alpha'} - V_\alpha V_{\alpha'}\right) - \sum_{\alpha_1 > 0} \langle \alpha\bar{\alpha}' | v | \alpha_1\bar{\alpha}_1 \rangle U_{\alpha_1} V_{\alpha_1} \left(U_\alpha V_{\alpha'} + V_\alpha U_{\alpha'}\right) \Bigg\} \times \left(b_\alpha^+ b_{\alpha'} + b_{\bar{\alpha}'}^+ b_{\bar{\alpha}}\right)$$

All sums are over positive values only. H_{int} is fourth-order in the b's. The states in the matrix elements are A.S.

The condition that the ground state is the vacuum state of the quasi-particles is $H_{20}' = 0$, i.e.,

$$\Big\{ \langle \alpha | T | \alpha' \rangle - \lambda \delta_{\alpha\alpha'} + \sum_{\alpha_1 > 0} [\langle \alpha\bar{\alpha}_1 | v | \alpha'\bar{\alpha}_1 \rangle + \langle \alpha\alpha_1 | v | \alpha'\alpha_1 \rangle] V_{\alpha_1}{}^2 \Big\} \times \left(U_\alpha V_{\alpha'} + U_{\alpha'} V_\alpha\right) + \sum_{\alpha_1 > 0} \langle \alpha\bar{\alpha}' | v | \alpha_1\bar{\alpha}_1 \rangle U_{\alpha_1} V_{\alpha_1} \left(U_\alpha U_{\alpha'} - V_\alpha V_{\alpha'}\right) = 0$$

for all pairs α, α',

In principle, this condition can be solved for the states α and the U_α, V_α, giving a very powerful method. In practice this has not been done in general but only partially. For example, in the Hartree-Fock problem we assume values for U_α and V_α:

$$U_\alpha = 0, \; V_\alpha = 1 \qquad \text{for occupied states}$$

$$V_\alpha = 0, \; U_\alpha = 1 \qquad \text{for all other states}$$

and solve for states α only. The ground-state energy is

$$U = \sum_\alpha{}' \langle \alpha | T | \alpha \rangle + \tfrac{1}{2} \sum_{\alpha\alpha_1}{}' \langle \alpha\alpha_1 | v | \alpha\alpha_1 \rangle$$

where the prime denotes sum over occupied states only and the condition $H_{20}' = 0$ leads to

$$\langle \alpha | T | \alpha' \rangle + \Big\langle \alpha \Big| \sum_{\alpha_1}{}' \langle \alpha_1 | v | \alpha_1 \rangle \Big| \alpha' \Big\rangle = 0$$

where α is occupied, α' unoccupied, or vice versa. We may now introduce the one-particle potential V_p, defined by

$$\langle \alpha | V_p | \alpha' \rangle \equiv \sum_{\alpha_1}{}' \langle \alpha\alpha_1 | v | \alpha'\alpha_1 \rangle$$

whereupon the energy is

$$U = \sum_\alpha{}' \langle \alpha | T + \tfrac{1}{2} V_p | \alpha \rangle$$

and the condition becomes

$$\langle \alpha \,|\, T + V_p \,|\, \alpha' \rangle = 0$$

for α occupied, α' unoccupied (or vice versa). Since there are no other restrictions on α, α' we may choose† a set α^0 so that this condition is satisfied for all $\alpha^0 \neq \alpha^{0\prime}$; i.e., states α^0 diagonalize $T + V_p$:

$$(T + V_p - \epsilon_{\alpha^0}) \,|\alpha^0\rangle = 0$$

The pairing force problem treated previously makes the opposite specialization to that in the Hartree-Fock picture: It assumes states α are given, and determines the U_α and V_α.

For general forces, this is not a correct procedure, and it can be shown[40,54,56] that the condition cited above must be solved for states α and coefficients U_α simultaneously. It is legitimate for the special case of forces with the pairing force property

$$\langle \alpha\bar{\alpha}' \,|\, v \,|\, \alpha_1\bar{\alpha}_1 \rangle = \langle \alpha\bar{\alpha} \,|\, v \,|\, \alpha_1\bar{\alpha}_1 \rangle \, \delta_{\alpha\alpha'}$$

In this case, the second part of the condition $H_{20}' = 0$ for $\alpha \neq \alpha'$ is zero identically and the first part becomes

$$\langle \alpha \,|\, T \,|\, \alpha' \rangle + \sum_{\alpha_1} \langle \alpha\alpha_1 \,|\, v \,|\, \alpha'\alpha_1 \rangle \, V_{\alpha_1}^2 = 0$$

This leads to a definition of the particle potential $\tilde{V}_p$:

$$\langle \alpha \,|\, \tilde{V}_p \,|\, \alpha' \rangle \equiv \sum_{\alpha_1} \langle \alpha\alpha_1 \,|\, v \,|\, \alpha'\alpha_1 \rangle \, V_{\alpha_1}^2$$

which is a natural extension of that given previously. The condition $H_{20}' = 0$ for $\alpha = \alpha'$ is

$$(\tilde{\epsilon}_\alpha - \lambda)\, 2U_\alpha V_\alpha - (U_\alpha^2 - V_\alpha^2)\, \Delta_\alpha = 0$$

where $\tilde{\epsilon}_\alpha$ are the eigenvalues of $(T + \tilde{V}_p)$.

This is just the same as before. The only difference is that Δ_α is now

---

†A general set satisfying the basic condition is such that its occupied states are linear orthogonal combinations of occupied states α^0 (similarly with unoccupied states). Occupied and unoccupied states are not mixed because of the condition $\langle \alpha \,|\, T + V_p \,|\, \alpha' \rangle = 0$. Since V and U have the form of traces over occupied states, it is clear that they are invariant to charge in the basis α. The particular choice α^0 is made only for convenience, not necessity.

$$\Delta_\alpha = -\sum_{\alpha_1>0} \langle\alpha\bar{\alpha}|v|\alpha_1\bar{\alpha}_1\rangle U_{\alpha_1}V_{\alpha_1}$$

The solutions for U_α and V_α are the same as in the pairing force problem, except that Δ in U_α has a subscript α; it satisfies

$$\Delta_\alpha = -\tfrac{1}{2}\sum_{\alpha_1>0} \frac{\langle\alpha\bar{\alpha}|v|\alpha_1\bar{\alpha}_1\rangle}{\sqrt{(\tilde{\epsilon}_{\alpha_1}-\lambda)^2+\Delta_{\alpha_1}^{\ 2}}}\,\Delta_{\alpha_1}$$

The Hamiltonian becomes

$$H = U' + \lambda n + \sum_{\alpha>0} e_\alpha\left(b_\alpha^{\ +}b_\alpha + b_{\bar{\alpha}}^{\ +}b_{\bar{\alpha}}\right)$$

with

$$e_\alpha = \sqrt{(\tilde{\epsilon}_\alpha-\lambda)^2+\Delta_\alpha^{\ 2}}$$

The ground-state energy U becomes

$$U = U' + \lambda N = \sum_{\alpha>0}\langle\alpha|T+\tfrac{1}{2}\tilde{V}_p|\alpha\rangle\, 2V_\alpha^{\ 2} - \sum_{\alpha>0} U_\alpha V_\alpha \Delta_\alpha$$

We see that the assumption of the extreme pairing force

$$\langle\alpha\bar{\alpha}'|\mathcal{G}|\alpha_1\bar{\alpha}_1\rangle = -|G|\,\delta_{\alpha\alpha'}$$

is stronger than is necessary. We may allow G to depend on α and α_1, and still obtain a solution. At the same time the assumption (for $\alpha \neq \alpha'$)

$$\overline{|\langle\alpha\bar{\alpha}'|v|\alpha_1\bar{\alpha}_1\rangle|} \ll \overline{|\langle\alpha\bar{\alpha}|v|\alpha_1\bar{\alpha}_1\rangle|}$$

is retained, and this is the crucial one upon which the validity of the theory depends. One particular advantage of the present formulation is that it is not necessary to arbitrarily restrict sums in order to ensure convergence, because this is guaranteed by the presence of the factor $\langle\alpha\bar{\alpha}|v|\alpha_1\bar{\alpha}_1\rangle$ in Δ_α. The first term in U also converges; it is like $\int\epsilon_\alpha(\Delta_\alpha^{\ 2}/\epsilon_\alpha^{\ 2})\,\epsilon_\alpha^{\ 1/2}\,d\epsilon_\alpha$ for large ϵ_α, and this converges if Δ_α falls off faster than $\epsilon_\alpha^{\ 1/4}$.

It is important that the terms $\langle\alpha\bar{\alpha}|v|\alpha_1\bar{\alpha}_1\rangle$ give rise to an entirely new effect which cannot be included in the over-all field V_p. This is the "superconductivity" effect.

Effect of Nonequality of $\langle \alpha\bar{\alpha} | v | \alpha'\bar{\alpha}' \rangle$ in a Numerical Example

In Sec. 1-3 we have given the values of matrix elements $\langle (j_1{}^2)\,0+ | v | (j_3{}^2)\,0+ \rangle$ for a δ-function force. Specializing the above equation for Δ_α to the (jm) representation [with $\hat{j} \equiv (2j+1)^{1/2}$],

$$\hat{j}\,\Delta_j = -\tfrac{1}{2}\sum_{j_1} \frac{\langle (j^2)\,0+ | v | (j_1{}^2)\,0+ \rangle}{\sqrt{(\epsilon_{j_1} - \lambda)^2 + \Delta_{j_1}{}^2}}\,\hat{j}_1\,\Delta_{j_1}$$

J. N. Bardsley has solved this in conjunction with the number equation:

$$\sum_{j_1} \left(1 - \frac{\epsilon_{j_1} - \lambda}{\sqrt{(\epsilon_{j_1} - \lambda)^2 + \Delta_{j_1}{}^2}} \right) = \frac{N}{2}$$

for $N = 17$, and the states $2d_{5/2}$, $1g_{7/2}$, $3s_{1/2}$, $2d_{3/2}$, and $1h_{11/2}$. This corresponds to the treatment by Kisslinger and Sorensen,[19] of Sn^{117}. The particle energies are taken as: 0, 0.22, 1.9, 2.2, and 2.8 MeV, respectively. The strength of interaction V is fixed by choosing it so that the mean value of matrix elements $|\langle m\bar{m} | v | m'\bar{m}' \rangle_{A.S.}|$ equals the value of $|G|$ used by the above authors: $|G| = 0.187$ MeV. We have

$$\sum_{jj'} \hat{j}\hat{j}' \langle (j^2)\,0+ | v | (j'^2)\,0+ \rangle$$

$$= \sum_{jm,j'm'} \langle jm(jm)_t | v | j'm'(j'm')_t \rangle_{A.S.}$$

$$= -\left(2 \sum_{jj'} \tfrac{1}{4}\,\hat{j}^2\,\hat{j}'^2 \right) |G|$$

The results are given in Table 3-1.

It can be seen that all differences are $\lesssim 0.05$ MeV, which is quite small compared to other sources of error. It may be that matrix elements from finite-range forces will give more serious corrections than those arising from δ-function forces, but no estimates have yet been made. On the basis of the present example, one may fairly conclude that the effects of nonequality of matrix elements $\langle \alpha\bar{\alpha} | v | \alpha'\bar{\alpha}' \rangle$ are small, and that calculations with the extreme pairing force model are quite accurate in this respect.

Table 3-1
Values of Δ_j and $e_j \equiv \sqrt{(\epsilon_j - \lambda)^2 + \Delta_j{}^2}$ for δ-Function Force and Pairing Force for Sn^{117} (all in MeV)
(λ is 1.84, 1.81 MeV for the two cases, respectively)

j	Δ_j (δ)	Δ_j (p.f.)	e_j (δ)	e_j (p.f.)
$3s_{1/2}$	0.983	1.00	0.985	1.004
$2d_{3/2}$	1.049	1.00	1.109	1.073
$1h_{11/2}$	0.932	1.00	1.338	1.407
$1g_{7/2}$	1.013	1.00	1.910	1.878
$2d_{5/2}$	1.049	1.00	2.118	2.068

3-4 THE "BOSON" AND "QUASI-BOSON" APPROXIMATIONS

If the number of real particles N is small compared to the number of pair states Ω, we can solve the pairing force problem to a good approximation by treating pairs of particles as bosons.[38]

The pairing Hamiltonian is

$$H = \sum_{\alpha > 0} \epsilon_\alpha \bar{n}_\alpha - |G| \sum_{\alpha,\alpha' > 0} A_{\alpha'}{}^+ A_\alpha$$

where

$$\bar{n}_\alpha = a_\alpha{}^+ a_\alpha + a_{\bar{\alpha}}{}^+ a_{\bar{\alpha}} \equiv n_\alpha + n_{\bar{\alpha}}$$

$$A_\alpha{}^+ = a_\alpha{}^+ a_{\bar{\alpha}}{}^+$$

A_α satisfies the commutation relations

$$[A_\alpha, A_{\alpha'}{}^+] = \delta_{\alpha\alpha'}(1 - \bar{n}_\alpha)$$

$$[\bar{n}_\alpha, A_{\alpha'}{}^+] = 2\delta_{\alpha\alpha'} A_\alpha{}^+ \qquad [\bar{n}_\alpha, A_{\alpha'}] = -2\delta_{\alpha\alpha'} A_\alpha$$

True boson operations A_α would satisfy the commutation relation

$$[A_\alpha, A_{\alpha'}{}^+] = \delta_{\alpha\alpha'}$$

The correction term $\bar{n}_\alpha$ arises from the Pauli principle, acting on the constituent fermions to prevent two of them occupying the same state. If the number of states is large and the number of particles small, the chance of this is small, so the Pauli principle correction is small, and we can set $(1 - \bar{n}_\alpha) \approx 1$. This is the *boson approximation*. The above H now represents a system of noninteracting bosons in a one-body potential. This is a problem of known solution. The energies for exciting a pair are solutions of

$$-\frac{1}{|G|} = \sum_{\alpha > 0} \frac{1}{E - 2\epsilon_\alpha}$$

which is just the same equation as occurs in the two-particle problem in Sec. 1-4, where it is exact.

When the number of particles is not small compared to the number of states, we cannot use this approach. Instead we must make the transformation to quasi-particles as in Sec. 3-2. This procedure gives a good but not exact solution. There are interactions between the quasi-particles which are neglected. We may now treat these interactions to some extent by combining quasi-particles into quasi-bosons, and repeating the boson approximation above. This is the *quasi-boson approximation,* and it enables us to improve on the solution of Sec. 3-2.

We make the definitions:

$$B_\alpha{}^+ = b_\alpha{}^+ b_{\bar{\alpha}}{}^+ \qquad \bar{n}_\alpha = b_\alpha{}^+ b_\alpha + b_{\bar{\alpha}}{}^+ b_{\bar{\alpha}}$$

These operators satisfy

$$[B_\alpha, B_{\alpha'}{}^+] = (1 - \bar{n}_\alpha)\, \delta_{\alpha\alpha'}$$

$$[\bar{n}_\alpha, B_{\alpha'}{}^+] = 2\delta_{\alpha\alpha'} B_\alpha{}^+ \qquad [\bar{n}_\alpha, B_{\alpha'}] = -2\delta_{\alpha\alpha'} B_\alpha$$

As we saw in Sec. 3-2, the Hamiltonian may be written in terms of the b's—or of the B's. It contains terms of zero, first, and second order in the operators B and $\bar{n}$. In the quasi-particle approximation, the second-order term is ignored. It is the interaction between quasi-particles and may be written

$$H_{int} = H_c + H_{res}$$

where

$$H_c = -|G| \sum_{\alpha\alpha' > 0} (U_\alpha{}^2 B_\alpha{}^+ - V_\alpha{}^2 B_\alpha)$$
$$\times (U_{\alpha'}{}^2 B_{\alpha'} - V_{\alpha'}{}^2 B_{\alpha'}{}^+)$$

$$H_{res} = +|G| \sum_{\alpha\alpha'>0} U_\alpha V_\alpha \{\bar{n}_\alpha(U_{\alpha'}{}^2 B_{\alpha'} - V_{\alpha'}{}^2 B_{\alpha'}{}^+) + (U_{\alpha'}{}^2 B_{\alpha'}{}^+ - V_{\alpha'}{}^2 B_{\alpha'})\bar{n}_\alpha\} - |G| \sum_{\alpha\alpha'>0} U_\alpha V_\alpha U_{\alpha'} V_{\alpha'} \bar{n}_\alpha \bar{n}_{\alpha'}$$

The part of the total Hamiltonian H' of first order in B_α has been made to vanish by the choice of U_α, and we have

$$H' = U + \sum_{\alpha>0} e_\alpha \bar{n}_\alpha + H_c + H_{res}$$

Writing

$$q_\alpha = \sqrt{\tfrac{1}{2}}\,(B_\alpha + B_\alpha{}^+)$$

$$p_\alpha = -i\sqrt{\tfrac{1}{2}}\,(B_\alpha - B_\alpha{}^+)$$

we have

$$H_c = -\tfrac{1}{2}|G| \sum_{\alpha>0} \omega_\alpha + \widetilde{H}$$

$$\widetilde{H} = -\tfrac{1}{2}|G| \left\{ \left(\sum_{\alpha>0} \omega_\alpha q_\alpha \right)^2 + \left(\sum_{\alpha>0} p_\alpha \right)^2 \right\}$$

where

$$\omega_\alpha = U_\alpha{}^2 - V_\alpha{}^2 = (\epsilon_\alpha - \lambda)/e_\alpha$$

Quite generally, if

$$[H', q_\alpha] = -i \sum_{\alpha'>0} x_{\alpha\alpha'} p_{\alpha'}$$

$$[H', p_\alpha] = +i \sum_{\alpha'>0} y_{\alpha\alpha'} q_{\alpha'}$$

then if we find a transformation

$$Q_\ell = \sum_{\alpha>0} \lambda_{\ell\alpha} q_\alpha$$

$$P_\ell = \sum_{\alpha>0} \mu_{\ell\alpha} p_\alpha$$

so that

$$\left[Q_\ell, P_k\right] = i\,\delta_{\ell k}$$

$$\left[H', Q_\ell\right] = -iB_\ell P_\ell \qquad \left[H', P_\ell\right] = iC_\ell Q_\ell$$

it follows that the operator

$$O_\ell^+ = \sqrt{C_\ell}\,Q_\ell - i\sqrt{B_\ell}\,P_\ell$$

is such that $O_\ell|0') = 0$ and that the eigenstate $O_\ell^+|0')$ has an energy equal to $W_\ell \equiv \sqrt{B_\ell C_\ell}$ more than the energy of the ground state $|0')$.

The required transformation satisfies

$$\underline{\tilde{x}}\,\underline{\lambda}_\ell = B_\ell\,\underline{\mu}_\ell$$

$$\underline{\tilde{y}}\,\underline{\mu}_\ell = C_\ell\,\underline{\lambda}_\ell$$

In our problem, $[H', q_i]$ and $[H', p_i]$ have the required form if we neglect H_{res} and if we make the quasi-boson approximation

$$[B_\alpha, B_{\alpha'}^+] = \delta_{\alpha\alpha'}$$

Using the latter, we have

$$\left[q_\alpha, q_{\alpha'}\right] = \left[p_\alpha, p_{\alpha'}\right] = 0$$

$$\left[q_\alpha, p_{\alpha'}\right] = i\,\delta_{\alpha\alpha'}$$

$$\left[\bar{n}_\alpha, q_{\alpha'}\right] = -2i\,\delta_{\alpha\alpha'}\,p_\alpha$$

$$\left[\bar{n}_\alpha, p_{\alpha'}\right] = 2i\,\delta_{\alpha\alpha'}\,q_\alpha$$

whence

$$x_{\alpha\alpha'} = 2e_\alpha\,\delta_{\alpha\alpha'} - |G|$$

$$y_{\alpha\alpha'} = 2e_\alpha\,\delta_{\alpha\alpha'} - |G|\,\omega_\alpha\omega_{\alpha'}$$

It is straightforward to solve the above matrix equations. Writing

$$\sum_{\alpha>0} \lambda_{\ell\alpha} = X_\ell \qquad \sum_{\alpha>0} \omega_\alpha\mu_{\ell\alpha} = Y_\ell$$

we have

$$\lambda_{\ell\alpha} = \frac{X_\ell e_\alpha + Y_\ell \omega_\alpha B_\ell}{W_\ell^{\,2} - e_\alpha^{\,2}} \qquad \mu_{\ell\alpha} = \frac{X_\ell C_\ell + Y_\ell \omega_\alpha e_\alpha}{W_\ell^{\,2} - e_\alpha^{\,2}}$$

Inserting these back in X_ℓ and Y_ℓ, the consistency condition for X_ℓ/Y_ℓ is

$$W_\ell^{\,2}(W_\ell^{\,2} - 4\Delta^2)\, a_\ell^{\,2} = W_\ell^{\,2} b_\ell^{\,2}$$

where

$$a_\ell = \sum_{\alpha > 0} [2e_\alpha (4e_\alpha^{\,2} - W_\ell^{\,2})]^{-1}$$

$$b_\ell = \sum_{\alpha > 0} \omega_\alpha (4e_\alpha^{\,2} - W_\ell^{\,2})^{-1}$$

For our problem we may assume $W_\ell \neq 0$, so

$$b_\ell = a_\ell \sqrt{W_\ell^{\,2} - 4\Delta^2}$$

i.e.,

$$\sum_{\alpha > 0} e_\alpha^{-1} \{e_\alpha \sqrt{W_\ell^{\,2} - 4\Delta^2} + 2\omega_\alpha\}^{-1} = 0$$

This is the eigenvalue condition determining the quantities W_ℓ, which are the spacings between the ground state and the various excited states. In the limit in which H_c is neglected, these are states of two like quasi-particles. In spherical nuclei, all states involved are 0+ states.

An important feature of this last equation is that it has $(p - 1)$, not p solutions, where p is the number of nondegenerate levels. Thus the spurious state does not occur. This inclusion of the term H_c with the quasi-boson method removes the spurious state that occurs in the quasi-particle approximation.

Hogaasen-Feldman[38] has applied the quasi-boson method to the case of two shells of equal degeneracy with half the maximum number of particles present. He compares the spectra with those obtained by other approximations.

3-5 TREATMENT USING LINEARIZATION METHOD

In most published accounts of the pairing force problem and the collective vibration problem, the mathematical methods used have been quite distinct. The former is tackled with the Bogoliubov transformation, and the second with the method of linearization. Anderson,[45] and also Valatin[40] and Pal,[10] have pointed out that the second method (as described in Chap. 12) can be used to solve the pairing force problem. The Hamiltonian is

$$H = \sum_{\alpha} \epsilon_\alpha a_\alpha^+ a_\alpha - |G| \sum_{\alpha\alpha' > 0} a_{\alpha'}^+ a_{\bar{\alpha}'}^+ a_{\bar{\alpha}} a_\alpha$$

and

$$[H, a_\alpha^+] = \epsilon_\alpha a_\alpha^+ - |G| \sum_{\alpha' > 0} a_{\alpha'}^+ a_{\bar{\alpha}'}^+ a_{\bar{\alpha}}$$

To apply the method, we try to pick out from the last term some terms linear in a_α^+ or $a_{\bar{\alpha}}$ (other $a_{\alpha'}$ cannot occur because of angular momentum conservation). Assume that the a operators are transformed linearly into b operators:

$$a_\alpha = \sum_{\alpha'} \left(p_{\alpha\alpha'} b_{\alpha'} + r_{\alpha\alpha'} b_{\alpha'}^+ \right)$$

Because of angular momentum conservation

$$p_{\alpha\alpha'} = p_\alpha \delta_{\alpha\alpha'} \qquad r_{\alpha\alpha'} = r_\alpha \delta_{\bar{\alpha}\alpha'}$$

Wick's theorem says that

$$a_{\alpha'}^+ a_{\bar{\alpha}'}^+ a_{\bar{\alpha}} = N(a_{\alpha'}^+ a_{\bar{\alpha}'}^+ a_{\bar{\alpha}}) + (0 | a_{\alpha'}^+ a_{\bar{\alpha}'}^+ | 0) a_{\bar{\alpha}}$$

$$+ (0 | a_{\bar{\alpha}'}^+ a_{\bar{\alpha}} | 0) a_{\alpha'}^+ - (0 | a_{\alpha'}^+ a_{\bar{\alpha}} | 0) a_{\bar{\alpha}'}^+$$

Here the normal product is with respect to the b operators, and the vacuum expectation values $(\cdots)$ are with respect to the vacuum of the b operators. These values vanish unless $\alpha = \pm\alpha'$, and we have

$$[H, a_\alpha^+] = \tilde{\epsilon}_\alpha a_\alpha^+ - \Delta a_{\bar{\alpha}} + \text{normal product term}$$

where

$$\tilde{\epsilon}_\alpha = \epsilon_\alpha - |G| N_\alpha$$

$$N_\alpha = (0 | a_\alpha^+ a_\alpha | 0)$$

$$\Delta = G \sum_{\alpha > 0} P_\alpha$$

$$P_\alpha = (0 | a_\alpha^+ a_{\bar{\alpha}}^+ | 0)$$

Now we neglect the normal product term. This corresponds to Belyaev's neglect of the term of fourth order in the quasi-particle operators. The form of $[H,a_\alpha^+]$ is now that required for the application of the linearization method (see Chap. 8). We have

$$[H,a_{\bar{\alpha}}] = -\tilde{\epsilon}_\alpha a_{\bar{\alpha}} - \Delta a_\alpha^+$$

Taking the two together, the excitation energy matrix is

$$\begin{pmatrix} \tilde{\epsilon}_\alpha & -\Delta \\ -\Delta & -\tilde{\epsilon}_\alpha \end{pmatrix}$$

with positive root $e_\alpha = \sqrt{\tilde{\epsilon}_\alpha^2 + \Delta^2}$ and eigenvector (u_α, v_α) satisfying

$$\tilde{\epsilon}_\alpha u_\alpha - \Delta v_\alpha = e_\alpha u_\alpha$$

$$-\Delta u_\alpha - \tilde{\epsilon}_\alpha v_\alpha = e_\alpha v_\alpha$$

The step-up operator is now

$$b_\alpha^+ = u_\alpha a_\alpha^+ + v_\alpha a_{\bar{\alpha}}$$

and the step-down operator

$$b_\alpha = u_\alpha a_\alpha + v_\alpha a_{\bar{\alpha}}^+$$

The choice of normalization

$$(b_\alpha b_\alpha^+) = 1$$

leads to

$$u_\alpha^2 + v_\alpha^2 = 1$$

whence

$$u_\alpha^2 = \frac{1}{2}\left(1 + \frac{\tilde{\epsilon}_\alpha}{\sqrt{\tilde{\epsilon}_\alpha^2 + \Delta^2}}\right)$$

$$v_\alpha^2 = \frac{1}{2}\left(1 - \frac{\tilde{\epsilon}_\alpha}{\sqrt{\tilde{\epsilon}_\alpha^2 + \Delta^2}}\right)$$

The only difference between these results and those derived by previous methods is that we have taken no account of the fact that the solution (i.e., the vacuum state of the b operators) is not an eigenstate of the number of particles. This is allowed for by replacing H by $H - \lambda n$, and then $\tilde{\epsilon}_j \to \tilde{\epsilon}_j - \lambda$ and the results are the same as the previous ones. It can be seen that the method could also be used for the generalized pairing force problem of Sec. 3-3.

The method may be used further to study the question of extending the pairing force model to include neutron-proton pairing effects. In this connection, we note that the quasi-particle solutions do *not* have isotopic spin T as a good quantum number. This is evident for like particles, since 2T equals N, the number of particles, which is not quantized. It is also evident from the above equation for $[H, a_\alpha^+]$. If H conserved number then the term $a_{\bar{\alpha}}$ on the right could not occur, since it destroys a particle rather than creates one. Since the fact that isotopic spin is not a quantum number does not upset the usefulness of the pairing solution for like particles provided $(\langle T^2\rangle - \langle T\rangle^2) \ll \langle T\rangle^2$, we may assume that the above expression for $[H, a_\alpha^+]$ for this case is then $[H, a_{\alpha n}^+] = A_\alpha a_{\alpha n}^+ + B_\alpha a_{\bar{\alpha} n} + C_\alpha a_{\alpha p}^+ + D_\alpha a_{\bar{\alpha} p}$. Valatin and Bremond[44] have recently described a method for pairing effects of mixed particles which seems related to this. (See Sec. 5-1 for further discussion.)

3-6 KERMAN'S TREATMENT WITH QUASI-SPINS

In cases where the numbers of nondegenerate energies ϵ_α and of particles (or holes) are limited (say five or so), a feasible procedure is to diagonalize the term $\Sigma_\alpha \epsilon_\alpha a_\alpha^+ a_\alpha$ in a representation of states appropriate to the degenerate case. In this way an *exact* solution can be found for a fixed number of particles. Kerman[11,21] has shown that it is especially easy to carry out this program if one introduces the idea of "quasi-spins" to label the representation.

We assume that $\alpha \equiv jm$; i.e., we are using a spin-orbit classification with a spherical potential. The pairing Hamiltonian may be written

$$H = \sum_j \epsilon_j \left(\Omega_j + 2S_{jo}\right) - |G|\, S_+ S_-$$

where

$$S_{j+} = \sum_{m>0} a_{jm}^+ a_{(jm)_t}^+$$

$$S_{j-} = \sum_{m>0} a_{(jm)_t} a_{jm}$$

$$S_{jo} = \tfrac{1}{2} \sum_{m>0} \left\{ a_{jm}^+ a_{jm} - a_{(jm)_t} a_{(jm)_t}^+ \right\} = \tfrac{1}{2}\left(n_j - \Omega_j\right)$$

and $\mathbf{S} = \Sigma_j \mathbf{S}_j$. The point of this notation is that S_+, S_-, S_0 have the commutation properties of angular momentum, so we may refer to $\mathbf{S}$ as the "quasi-spin." S_{j+} is the same as the operator A used in Chap. 2, and the use of $\mathbf{S}$ below gives a more systematic derivation of results already derived in Chap. 2.

The commutation relations are

$$\left[S_{i+}, S_{j-}\right] = 2S_{jo}\ \delta_{ij} = (n_i - \Omega_i)\ \delta_{ij}$$

$$\left[S_{io}, S_{j+}\right] = S_{j+}\ \delta_{ij}$$

$$\left[S_{io}, S_{j-}\right] = -S_{j-}\ \delta_{ij}$$

Thus

$$\left[H, S_{j+}\right] = 2\epsilon_j S_{j+} + 2|G|\, S_+ S_{jo}$$

If we can assume $N_j \ll \Omega_j$, and so put $S_{jo} = -\frac{1}{2}\Omega_j$, then the last equation is linear and we may apply the results of the linearization method described in Chap. 8. The eigenvalue matrix is

$$\begin{pmatrix} 2\epsilon_1 - |G|\,\Omega_1 & -\ \ |G|\,\Omega_1 & -\ \ |G|\,\Omega_1 & \cdots \\ -\ \ |G|\,\Omega_2 & 2\epsilon_2 - |G|\,\Omega_2 & -\ \ |G|\,\Omega_2 & \cdots \\ -\ \ |G|\,\Omega_3 & -\ \ |G|\,\Omega_3 & 2\epsilon_3 - |G|\,\Omega_3 & \cdots \\ \vdots & \vdots & \vdots & \end{pmatrix}$$

This is precisely the energy matrix that we found in Secs. 1-4 and 3-4 for the two-particle problem. Thus the case where the number of particles is small relative to the number of orbits in each degenerate group can be solved using the two-particle solution. This approximation is the "boson" approximation. It amounts to ignoring the Pauli principle and treating pairs of fermions as bosons with operators $S_{i+} \equiv A_i^+$ satisfying $[A_i^+, A_j] = \Omega_i\ \delta_{ij}$.

Returning to the exact solution, we see that H commutes with S_j^2 so that the spin of each subgroup is a good quantum number. On the other hand, S_{jo} is not, since it does not commute with the pairing part of H, although it does with the first term. Thus, if we use the representation

$$|\,\mathcal{S}_1 M_1, \mathcal{S}_2 M_2, \ldots\rangle$$

where $\mathcal{S}_r, M_r$ are the spin and component of the j_r group, the pairing force gives rise to terms nondiagonal in the M's. An alternative representation is

$$|(\mathcal{S}_1\mathcal{S}_2)\mathcal{S}_{12}(\mathcal{S}_3)\mathcal{S}_{123}\cdots\mathcal{S}M\rangle$$

where $\boldsymbol{\mathcal{S}}_{12} = \boldsymbol{\mathcal{S}}_1 + \boldsymbol{\mathcal{S}}_2$, $\boldsymbol{\mathcal{S}}_{123} = \boldsymbol{\mathcal{S}}_{12} + \boldsymbol{\mathcal{S}}_3$, etc., and $\mathcal{S}$,M are the total spin and component. This diagonalizes the pairing force, but the first term in H has terms nondiagonal in $\mathcal{S}_{12}$, $\mathcal{S}_{123}$, . . . , $\mathcal{S}$ (but diagonal in M). Kerman uses this latter representation. The contribution of the pairing force to the energy of a state in this representation is easily seen to be

$$-|G|\{\mathcal{S}(\mathcal{S}+1) - M(M+1)\}$$

which is independent of $\mathcal{S}_{12}$, $\mathcal{S}_{123}$, etc., for given $\mathcal{S}$.

If n_j is the number operator for the j shell, we have

$$S_{jo} = \tfrac{1}{2}\left(n_j - \Omega_j\right)$$

and

$$|S_{jo}| \le S_j \le \tfrac{1}{2}\Omega_j$$

The lowest state for any value of n_j is that of maximum S_j, viz.,

$$S_j = \tfrac{1}{2}\Omega_j$$

and this corresponds to all particles paired. In the degenerate case, the lowest state (i.e., the superconducting state of seniority zero) is that in which $\mathcal{S}_{12}$, $\mathcal{S}_{123}$ . . . , $\mathcal{S}$ all have their maximum value, viz., $\mathcal{S}_{12} = \tfrac{1}{2}(\Omega_1 + \Omega_2)$, $\mathcal{S}_{123} = \tfrac{1}{2}(\Omega_1 + \Omega_2 + \Omega_3)$ . . . , $\mathcal{S} = \tfrac{1}{2}\Sigma_j\,\Omega_j$. The nondegeneracy of the ϵ_j mixes this state with states of other values of $\mathcal{S}_{12}$, $\mathcal{S}_{123}$ . . . , $\mathcal{S}$.

Kerman, Lawson, and Macfarlane[21] have compared the exact energies of states of the Pb isotopes with those derived by Kisslinger and Sorensen[19] from the quasi-particle approximation. They find that the absolute energy of the ground state differs between the two calculations by 250 keV. The excitation energy of the first excited states of even isotopes varies by up to 400 keV, the mean difference being about 200 keV.

They have also examined the overlap between the exact wave functions and those from the quasi-particle approximation. When the component of the latter for the correct number of particles is isolated, the overlap amplitude is 0.99 or better, in spite of the fact that the component may account for only 40 per cent of the wave function.

4

PREDICTION OF PROPERTIES OF NONCOLLECTIVE LEVELS AND COMPARISON WITH DATA

We shall ignore for the present levels that are especially sensitive to the multipole parts of the nuclear forces, e.g., collective quadrupole vibrations. There are a number of different items that are predicted by the pairing force theory and can be compared directly to experiment. We illustrate this by quoting the results of Kisslinger and Sorensen[19] for the case of the Pb isotopes. Since these have a magic number of protons and we ignore mixing across major shell closures, the problem of treating the effects of the N-P interaction does not arise. In Fig. 4-1 we give the single particle spectrum ($\tilde{\epsilon}_j$)

0	$3p_{1/2}$
−0.57	$2f_{5/2}$
−0.90	$3p_{3/2}$
- - - - - -	$\bar{\epsilon}_j = -1.42$
−1.63	$1i_{13/2}$
−2.35	$2f_{7/2}$

Figure 4-1 Single-particle spectrum ($\tilde{\epsilon}_j$) assumed for N between 100 and 126.

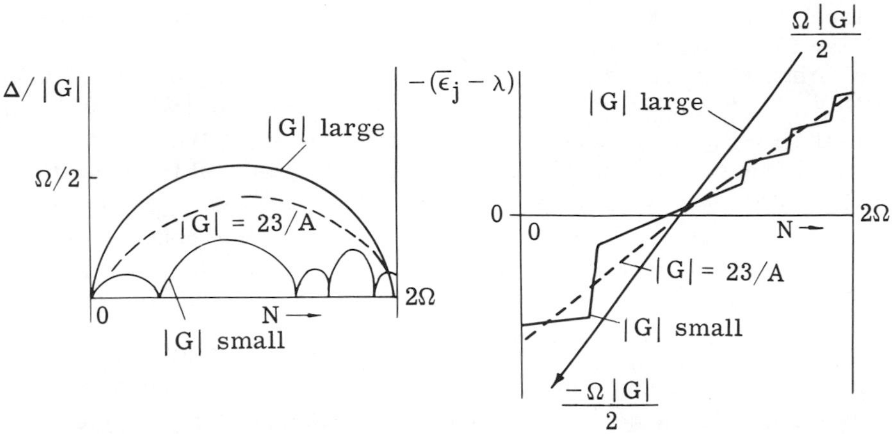

Figure 4-2 Behavior of Δ and $(\overline{\epsilon}_j - \lambda)$ as major shell fills for $|G|$ small, intermediate, and large (i.e., $|G| \ll d$, $|G| \sim d$, $|G| \gg d$, where d is mean sublevel spacing).

that is assumed. (In inverted form it is the spectrum of the single hole system Pb^{207}.) The mean energy $\overline{\epsilon}_j$ is 1.43 MeV below the $3p_{1/2}$ level. The $1h_{9/2}$ level is ignored. According to a recent paper by Mukherjee and Cohen,[27] it is $2\frac{1}{2}$ MeV below the $2f_{7/2}$ level.

In Fig. 4-2 we give the behavior of $(\overline{\epsilon}_j - \lambda)/|G|$ and $\Delta/|G|$ as functions of mass number. These are obtained from the relations†

$$\frac{|G|}{2} \sum_j \frac{(j + \frac{1}{2})}{\sqrt{(\widetilde{\epsilon}_j - \lambda)^2 + \Delta^2}} = 1$$

$$\sum_j (j + \tfrac{1}{2}) \frac{(\widetilde{\epsilon}_j - \lambda)}{\sqrt{(\widetilde{\epsilon}_j - \lambda)^2 + \Delta^2}} = \Omega - N$$

†Strictly the pair of equations for λ and Δ apply to even isotopes only, but Kisslinger and Sorensen have used them for all isotopes. The correct equations for odd isotopes are easy to derive. The wave function is

$$|\alpha) \equiv b_\alpha^+ |0) = \prod_{\alpha' > 0}{}' \, (U_{\alpha'} + V_{\alpha'} a_{\alpha'}^+ a_{\overline{\alpha}'}^+) a_\alpha^+ \Psi_0$$

where Π' means that the term $\alpha' = \alpha$ is excluded, and we have put a factor $(U_\alpha^2 - V_\alpha^2)$ equal to 1. This state has a *real* particle in state α, while the rest of the state is constructed as for an even nucleus, except that α is excluded, and $U_{\alpha'}$ and $V_{\alpha'}$ are somewhat different. The quantity $(\alpha |H| \alpha)/(\alpha|\alpha)$ can be minimized to determine $U_{\alpha'}$ and $V_{\alpha'}$. The results are given in Ref. 21, where it is shown that the corrections to the above procedure are small. The number of pair levels considered is $\Omega = 17$, and the strength $|G|$ is taken as 0.11 MeV (for reasons given below).

When G is very large (i.e., $\gg$ mean level spacing, which is ~ 0.15 MeV), $(\bar{\epsilon}_j - \lambda)/|G| \rightarrow [(\Omega/2) - p] \equiv \frac{1}{2}(\Omega - N)$ and $\Delta/|G| \rightarrow \sqrt{p(\Omega - p)} \equiv \frac{1}{2}\sqrt{N(2\Omega - N)}$, and these are shown for comparison. When $|G|$ is very small, λ moves in jumps from the vicinity of one level to the next. When near the energy $\tilde{\epsilon}_j$ we have $(\tilde{\epsilon}_j - \lambda)/|G| = -(p' - \frac{1}{2}\Omega')$ and $\Delta/|G| = \sqrt{p'(\Omega' - p')}$. Here we assume that the level contains Ω' degenerate pair levels of which p' are occupied. (*N.B.:* When $|G|$ is small, no solution of the equations exists for filled j-shells; see Chap. 3).

In the plot for $|G| = 23/A = 0.11$ MeV, there is no trace of structure in $(\bar{\epsilon}_j - \lambda)$, so we may assume that the pairing effects are appreciable. At the same time we note that λ moves with A at the rate that it does for $|G|$ small, the only difference being the absence of jumps. In other words, λ stays near the zero-order Fermi surface, which means that the limit $|G|$ large (i.e., $\gg$ mean sublevel spacing) is not reached.

Energy Gap

Taking this as $2\sqrt{(\tilde{\epsilon}_j - \lambda)^2 + \Delta^2}$, where $\tilde{\epsilon}_j$ is the level nearest to λ, this increases from 0.50 MeV for Pb^{206} to 1.0 MeV for Pb^{204}, then flattens off but slowly increases to 1.3 MeV for Pb^{197}. Ignoring 2+ levels, which may be specially positioned by collective effects, there is very little data in even-A isotopes. About the only relevant item is the fact that there is a 4+ state in Pb^{204} and Pb^{202} at about 1.3 MeV. In the pure shell model, these would be states of $(2f_{5/2})^2$ and $(2f_{5/2})^4$. Probably (for the same $|G| = 0.11$ MeV) the excited 4+ states on this model would be lower, but their energy could be raised by increasing $|G|$. Thus there is only weak evidence for pairing force mixing from the energy gap in even-even nuclei.

Spurious States

A good example of the kind of spurious state that may be introduced by the quasi-particle approach occurs in Pb^{206}. This is a two-particle problem, so may be treated exactly. There are five states of spin 0+ which are orthogonal mixtures of $(3p_{1/2})^{-2}$, $(2f_{5/2})^{-2}$, $(3p_{3/2})^{-2}$, $(1i_{13/2})^{-2}$, $(2f_{7/2})^{-2}$. In the quasi-particle approach, one generates excited 0+ states by exciting quasi-particle pairs in the vacuum state. There are five such states, giving six in all with the ground state. The five excited states must contain components of the ground state which in toto add up in intensity to unity. If the pairing force mixing in the ground state were strong, this spurious part of each excited state would be only ~ 20 per cent and so relatively weak. For the actual nucleus, however, with $|G| = 0.11$ MeV, the ground state is nearly pure $(3p_{1/2})^{-2}$, so that nearly all the spurious components are concentrated in the excited state of $2(3p_{1/2})$ quasi-particles, which must be therefore ignored.

Odd Nuclei

The predicted spectrum of an odd nucleus is obtained directly by computing $e_j \equiv \sqrt{(\tilde{\epsilon}_j - \lambda)^2 + \Delta^2}$ for the nucleus for the various j. In the case $|G| = 0$, Δ is zero, and λ proceeds in jumps as each shell fills. As N increases from 0 to 2Ω, a typical level falls in energy relative to the ground state, becomes the ground state while its shell fills, then increases again. For larger $|G|$, this general behavior is maintained with two changes: The jumps are smoothed out, and the various levels are compressed together. This is illustrated with reference to the Pb isotopes in Fig. 4-3. For $G = 0$, the spread in energy of all levels at midshell is less than at the extremes by a factor ~ 2. For sufficiently large G it approaches a factor Ω.

In comparing with the data, there is no dramatic evidence for strong pairing effects but, in making a best fit, one derives the value $|G| = 0.11$ MeV that has been used above. The most striking fact is the fall of the $1i_{13/2}$ level as A falls, but this is roughly given by $|G| = 0$, the only difference being the occurrence of jumps at A = 196, 200, 206.

The phenomenon of orbits of high spin filling in pairs and not giving rise to ground-state spins of odd nuclei has been recognized from the early days of the shell model. It is included in the pairing force model to some extent. For example, if high spin level (like $1h_{11/2}$) occurs just above a low spin level (like $3s_{1/2}$), then, for one to seven particles, λ occurs nearer the $3s_{1/2}$ level than the $1h_{11/2}$, and the lowest state spin is $\frac{1}{2}+$. For > seven particles, however, λ rises above

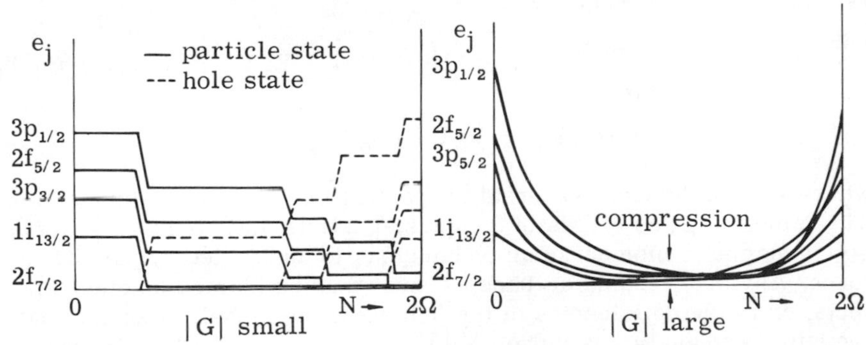

Figure 4-3 Spectra of odd nuclei for $|G|$ small and large.

the $1h_{11/2}$ level and so the lowest state spin is $\frac{11}{2}-$. If there were a low spin level just above the $1h_{11/2}$, then its spin would become the ground-state spin, so that only one or two nuclei would have $J = \frac{11}{2}-$. Experimentally *none* do, so the theoretical picture with pairing forces is not complete. Kisslinger and Sorensen[19] find that the quadrupole force is mainly responsible for large spins not occurring.

Even-Odd Effect in Binding Energies

For any N, our formulas give for ground-state energies:

$$E_{N+2} = E_N + 2\lambda$$

$$E_{N+1} = E_N + \lambda + e_\alpha$$

It follows that

$$\left(E_{N+2} + E_N - 2E_{N+1}\right) = 2e_\alpha$$

For $G = 0$, this vanishes. For $|G| \neq 0$ it is positive. Experimentally it is ~ 2 MeV for $Z = 50$, ~ 0.8 MeV for $Z = 82$. Comparison with the data for nuclei near $Z = 50$, $N = 82$, $Z = 82$ accords quite well with the value $|G| = 23/A$ MeV used above.

Total Binding Energy to Major Closed Shell

From the binding of Pb^{204} and Pb^{206} in Pb^{208}, one finds that $|G| = 23/A$ MeV gives a satisfactory fit, but is not very sensitively determined.

Magnetic Dipole Moments

The magnetic dipole (M1) moment operator for the quasi-particle is $Q_{LM\pi}$ with $L = 1$, $M = 0$, $\pi = +$:

$$Q_{10+} \equiv \mu = \sum_{\alpha\alpha' > 0} \langle \alpha | \mu | \alpha' \rangle \Big[(U_\alpha U_{\alpha'} + V_\alpha V_{\alpha'})(b_\alpha{}^+ b_{\alpha'} - b_{\bar{\alpha}'}{}^+ b_{\bar{\alpha}}) + (U_\alpha V_{\alpha'} - V_\alpha U_{\alpha'})(b_\alpha{}^+ b_{\bar{\alpha}'}{}^+ - b_{\bar{\alpha}} b_{\alpha'}) \Big]$$

where we use the time-reversal properties of M1 matrix elements. The value $(\alpha | \mu | \alpha)$ of this in the quasi-particle state α is $\langle \alpha | \mu | \alpha \rangle$, so the magnetic moment of an odd nucleus is unaffected by pairing force. Any observed discrepancies must thus be blamed on other effects, or to the deficiencies of the pairing force model. It seems that the latter explanation is more likely, since Blin-Stoyle[28] has shown that simple configuration mixing calculations with a δ-function force produce large effects on magnetic moments. Kisslinger and Freed[20] have computed the effects of admixing small amounts of those three quasi-particle states involving spin-orbit flip, since large effects from such mixing have been found previously. The pairing force cannot produce such admixture but a more realistic force like a δ-function can.

Electromagnetic Transition Rates

For a transition between quasi-particle states j and j′, pairing correlations introduce a factor $(U_j U_{j'} \pm V_j V_{j'})$ in the matrix element (+ for ML, − for EL):

$$(\alpha \,|Q_{LM\pi}|\, \alpha') = \left(U_j U_{j'} \pm V_j V_{j'}\right) \langle \alpha \,|Q_{LM\pi}|\, \alpha' \rangle$$

Thus a qualitative effect of introducing pairing force mixing is to make matrix elements vary smoothly with mass number instead of fluctuating, as in the pure shell model. This is especially true of M4 transitions in odd nuclei (e.g., $1i_{13/2} \to 2f_{5/2}$ in the Pb isotopes). Thus pairing forces help to explain the well-known phenomenon of the constancy of M4 matrix elements.

Ikegami and Udegawa[37] have analyzed the values of the width of a forbidden E2 transition in Sn^{120} with the pairing force model. This is the transition 2.49 (7−) → 2.29 (5−) and the width is about 0.2 per cent of the single-particle value. Theoretically the states are two-quasi-particle states:

$$7-: \quad 1h_{11/2}\, 2d_{3/2}$$

$$5-: \quad 1h_{11/2}\, 3s_{1/2}$$

and so the transition is the quasi-particle transition $2d_{3/2} \to 3s_{1/2}$. The effect of pairing correlations appears in a factor

$$\left(U_j U_{j'} - V_j V_{j'}\right)^2$$

where j and j′ are the two orbits involved. This is ~1 when j and j′ are both well above (or well below) the Fermi level λ, but it can be ≪ 1 when j and j′ are near the Fermi level. The analysis of Kisslinger and Sorensen[19] implies that this factor is 4 per cent, and is sensitive to small changes in parameters. Thus a fit may be obtained.

This example stresses the qualitative point that pairing correlations may inhibit electric transitions between quasi-particle levels near the Fermi surface. At the same time, they may enhance other transitions (e.g., two quasi-particles → vacuum).

Reduced Widths for Nucleons

These have been studied theoretically by Yoshida[22] and by Belyaev and Zakhariev.[23]

If we ignore that fact that the U_α are slightly different for neighboring odd and even nuclei (as mentioned at the beginning of this section), then it is easy to evaluate reduced widths with the pairing force model.

In units of the single-particle reduced width, any reduced width is

$$\langle \Psi_{JM} | \Phi_{JM}(j,J_0) \rangle^2$$

This is called the spectroscopic factor $S(J,jJ_0)$. Ψ_{JM} is the parent and Φ_{JM} is the coupled "channel state" of nucleon j and daughter nucleus J_0.

When the parent is odd, and Ψ_{JM} is the quasi-particle state of spin $J = j$, $M = m$:

$$\Psi_{jm} = \prod_{\alpha > 0}{}' (U_\alpha + V_\alpha a_\alpha^+ a_{\bar{\alpha}}^+) a_{jm}^+ \Psi_0$$

where the prime indicates that state $\alpha = jm$ is excluded. The channel state is

$$\Phi_{jm} = a_{jm}^+ \prod_{\alpha > 0} (U_\alpha' + V_\alpha' a_\alpha^+ a_{\bar{\alpha}}^+) \Psi_0$$

$$= \prod_{\alpha > 0}{}' (U_\alpha' + V_\alpha' a_\alpha^+ a_{\bar{\alpha}}^+) U_{jm} a_{jm}^+ \Psi_0$$

Ignoring the difference between U_α and U_α' we have

$$S(j,j0) = U_{jm}^2 \;\left(= U_j^2\right)$$

This says, reasonably enough, that the probability of an even nucleus picking up a nucleon in state jm is determined by the probability that the state is vacant.

When the parent is even, and Ψ_{JM} is the vacuum state,

$$\Psi_{00} = \prod_{\alpha > 0} (U_\alpha + V_\alpha a_\alpha^+ a_{\bar{\alpha}}^+) \Psi_0$$

The channel state is

$$\Phi_{00} = \frac{1}{\hat{j}} \sum_m a_{jm}^+ \prod_{\alpha > 0}{}' (U_\alpha' + V_\alpha' a_\alpha^+ a_{\bar{\alpha}}^+) a_{\overline{jm}}^+ \Psi_0$$

Ignoring the difference between U_α and U_α', it follows that

$$S(0,jj) = \left[\sum_m V_{jm} \Big/ \hat{j}\right]^2 = (2j + 1) V_j^2$$

The interpretation is that the probability of an even nucleus losing a j-nucleon is determined by the probability of j-nucleons occurring in the nucleus.

In the special case of degenerate levels,

$$S(j,j0) = 1 - N/2\Omega$$

$$S(0,jj) = (2j + 1)N/2\Omega$$

Cohen and Price[24] show how one can fit (d,p) and (d,t) data in some situations to get a value for U_j that is not affected by the absolute errors in the stripping and pickup theories.

For instance, if (d,p) and (d,t) reactions exciting the particle states $j = \ell \pm \frac{1}{2}$ are measured, then

$$[(2j + 1)^{-1}\sigma(d,p)]_+ / [(2j + 1)^{-1}\sigma(d,p)]_- = U_+^2/U_-^2$$

$$[(2j + 1)^{-1}\sigma(d,t)]_+ / [(2j + 1)^{-1}\sigma(d,t)]_- = V_+^2/V_-^2$$

in obvious notation. These can be solved for U_+ and U_-. We have assumed only that the single-particle stripping cross section depends on ℓ, not j, and is independent of Q-value. The last assumption may be corrected by adding a factor A^{Q_+}/A^{Q_-}, where A is found to be about 1.2. As another example, if the (d,p) reaction from the j state of an odd target to the ground state of the even nucleus is studied along with the (d,p) reaction from the same even nucleus to the j state in the next odd nucleus, then

$$\frac{\sigma_o(d,p)}{\sigma_e(d,p)} = \frac{V_j^2}{(2j + 1) U_j^2}$$

where o and e denote odd and even target.

Similarly for (d,t) reactions:

$$\frac{\sigma_o(d,t)}{\sigma_e(d,t)} = \frac{U_j^2}{(2j + 1) V_j^2}$$

When these special cases involving ratios do not apply, one must analyze the absolute value of $\sigma(d,p)$ or $\sigma(d,t)$. This can be done to obtain U_j^2 if the absolute single-particle cross sections are specified. At present, distorted-wave Born approximation theory gives good agreement with experimental data, so one can make reliable estimates of the latter.

Cohen and Price[24] have studied (d,p) and (d,t) reactions on Sn isotopes A-116, 118, 120, 122, and 124, giving data on particle levels in odd isotopes between 115 and 125, inclusive. The levels concerned are $2d_{5/2}$, $1g_{7/2}$, $3s_{1/2}$, $2d_{3/2}$, and $1h_{11/2}$. ℓ-values to groups in the (d,p) data are assigned by comparing with standard angular patterns for $\ell = 0, 2, 4,$ and 5. The standards are patterns to levels of known spin and are well differentiated (see Fig. 4-4). A similar treatment for (d,t) reactions was not possible, so ℓ-values had to be assigned. This was done assuming that the groups corresponded to the same particle-hole states already identified in (d,p) studies. To correct for Q-value effects it is assumed that

$$\sigma(\theta,Q) = \sigma(\theta)A^{-Q} \qquad \text{for (d,p)}$$

$$\sigma(\theta,Q) = \sigma(\theta)A^{Q} \qquad \text{for (d,t)}$$

where A is a constant of about 1.2 and Q is in MeV. All general trends (see Fig. 4-5) agree with calculations of Kisslinger and Sorensen,[19] as do many of the details. One discrepancy is that V_j^2 for the $2d_{5/2}$ and $1g_{7/2}$ levels is somewhat too small in the lighter isotopes (0.78 compared to 0.92), but a private communication from Sorensen indicates that multipole ($\ell = 2$) force effects can account for this.

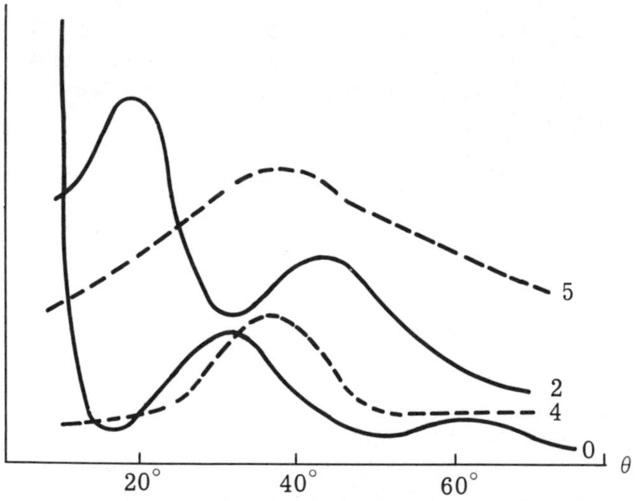

Figure 4-4 Stripping patterns for $\ell_n = 0, 2, 4, 5$.

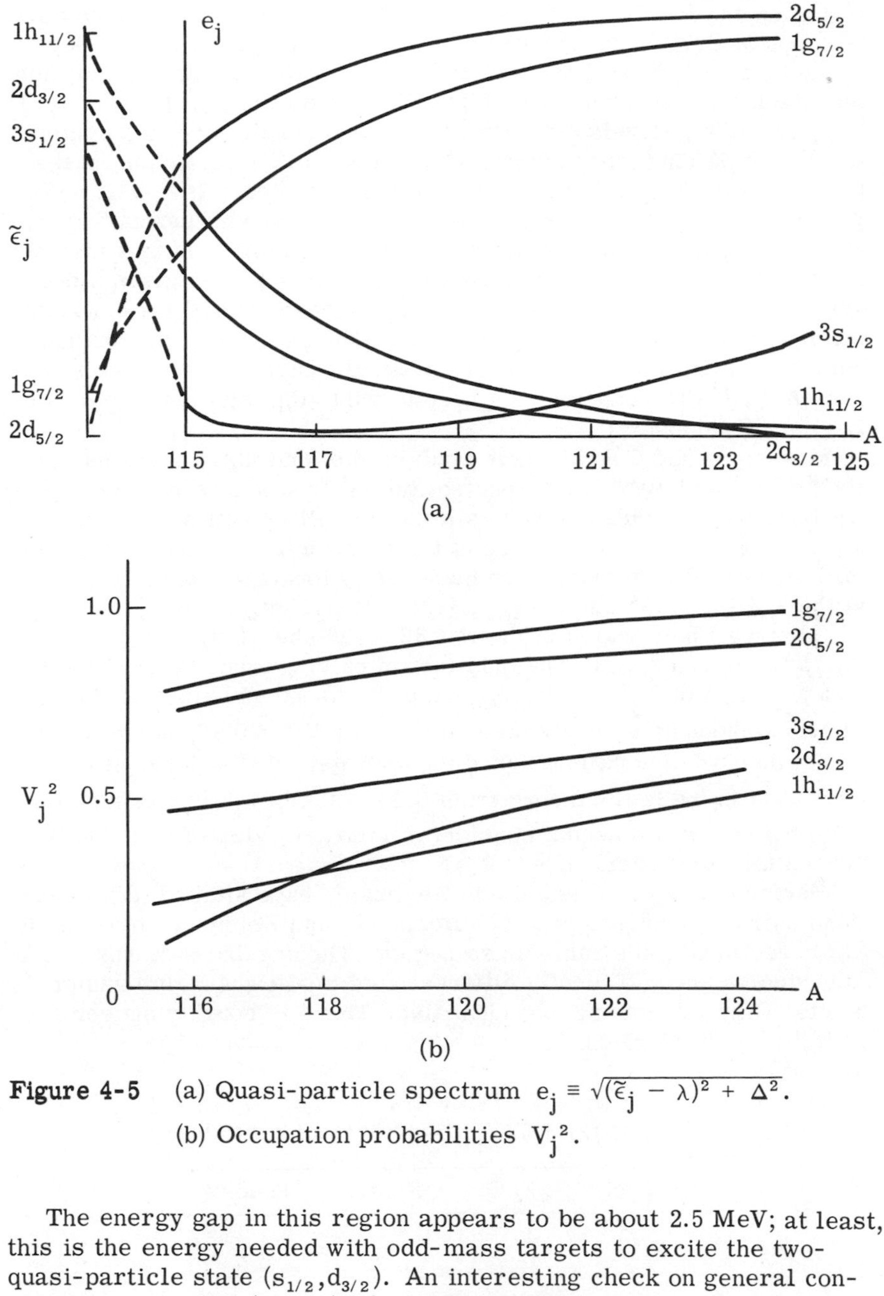

Figure 4-5 (a) Quasi-particle spectrum $e_j \equiv \sqrt{(\tilde{\epsilon}_j - \lambda)^2 + \Delta^2}$. (b) Occupation probabilities V_j^2.

The energy gap in this region appears to be about 2.5 MeV; at least, this is the energy needed with odd-mass targets to excite the two-quasi-particle state $(s_{1/2}, d_{3/2})$. An interesting check on general consistency is that $\Sigma_j\ (2j + 1)V_j^2$ should equal the number of neutrons involved. This is found to be well satisfied.

Cohen and Hamburger[25] have studied (d,p) and (d,t) reactions on isotopes of Zr. These isotopes do not have a magic number of particles (except Zr^{90} with N = 50) and so we must make the assumption that the forty protons are "stable" although nonmagic. The $2d_{5/2}$, $2d_{3/2}$, and $3s_{1/2}$ levels are identified, and generally good agreement found with pairing force theory. One remarkable effect found is that the $1g_{7/2}$ state is much higher than in the Sn isotopes (see Fig. 4-5). Such sharp falls in single-particle-level position with increasing A, are, in fact, to be expected, as remarked by Talmi.[29] In this instance the filling of the $1g_{9/2}$ proton orbital between Zr and Sn gives a deepening of the over-all nuclear potential in just the radial region where the $1g_{7/2}$ wave function is concentrated. The same general idea has been used[30] to explain fluctuations of single-particle-level positions near A = 60. [The experiments here are the (d,p) studies of Schiffer, Lee, and Zeidman.[31]]

Mukherjee and Cohen[27] have studied (d,p) and (d,t) reactions on $Pb^{206,207,208}$ and Bi^{209}. As expected, the neutron single-particle spectra from (d,p) studies are very similar for all targets in the same mass region. The same is true of the neutron single hole states from (d,t) studies. The authors have managed to locate all particle states in the N = 126 - 184 shell ($2g_{9/2}$, $1i_{11/2}$, $1j_{15/2}$, $3d_{5/2}$, $4s_{1/2}$, $2g_{7/2}$, $3d_{3/2}$) and all hole states in the N = 82 - 126 shell ($1h_{9/2}$, $2f_{5/2}$, $3p_{3/2}$, $2f_{5/2}$, $1i_{13/2}$, and $3p_{1/2}$). The only test of pairing force theory has been measurement of V_j^2 for the $p_{1/2}$ state in the ground state of Pb^{206}. Three methods give nearly the same value: $V_j^2 \approx 0.46$, whereas shell-model theory[32] and pairing force theory[19] gave $V_j^2 \approx 0.27$. If Δ is increased in the latter theory from 0.25 to 0.40, V_j^2 is increased to 0.37, but this would need a considerably larger value of $|G|$ than is needed for other data.

Macfarlane, Raz, Yntema, and Zeidman[26] have studied (d,t) reactions on Fe and Ni isotopes. Schiffer, Lee, and Zeidman[31] have studied (d,p) reactions in the same mass region. The angular patterns in the (d,t) studies are sufficiently differentiated to allow ℓ-value assignments. Only $\ell = 1$ and 3 are identified. There is roughly agreement with theory (Table 4-1).

Table 4-1

Values of $(2j + 1)V_j^2$ (≡ number of particles)

Target	j	Expt.	Theory
Ni^{58}	2p	1.7	1.4
	$1f_{5/2}$	0.3	0.6
Ni^{60}	2p	3.1	2.5
	$1f_{5/2}$	0.9	1.4

Both (d,p) and (d,t) reactions give a measure of the ratio of U_j^2 for Ni^{58} and Ni^{60}. These agree, thereby giving support to the general approach.

Reduced Widths for Nucleon Pairs

Yoshida[33] has studied the question of how pairing correlations affect transfer reaction cross sections with two like nucleons transferred, e.g., (t,p).

First, he expresses the parent state in terms of daughter states with expansion coefficients $B(Jj_1j_2)$ defined by

$$\Psi_{J_fM_f}(A+2) = \sum_{Jj_1j_2} B(Jj_1j_2)\left[\Psi_{J_iM_i}(A)\,\Phi_{JM}(2)\right]_{J_fM_f}$$

where $\Phi_{JM}(2)$ is the two-particle wave function

$$\Phi_{JM}(2) = \left[\varphi_{j_1m_1}\varphi_{j_2m_2}\right]_{JM}$$

where the notation $[\ \ ]_{JM}$ means "vector coupled to JM." We have, in Born approximation,

$$\frac{d\sigma_L}{d\Omega} = \cdots \left|\sum_{Jj_1j_2} B(Jj_1j_2)(\cdots)\int R_{j_1}R_{j_2}j_L(Qr)\,r^2\,dr\right|^2$$

where $(\cdots)$ represents some vector coupling factors.

We have

$$B(Jj_1j_2) = \sum_m \left(J_iM_iJM\,|\,J_fM_f\right)\left\langle \Psi_{J_fM_f}\,|A^+(j_1j_2JM)|\,\Psi_{J_iM_i}\right\rangle$$

where A^+ is the pair creation operator:

$$A^+(j_1j_2JM) = \frac{1}{\sqrt{1+\delta_{j_1j_2}}}\sum_{m_1m_2}(j_1m_1j_2m_2\,|\,JM)\,a_{j_1m_1}^+a_{j_2m_2}^+$$

This may be written in terms of quasi-particle operators b_{jm} using the usual transformation, and then B can be evaluated in various situations:

(a) vacuum → vacuum:

$$B(0jj) = \sqrt{j+\tfrac{1}{2}}\;U_j(A)V_j(A+2)$$

(b) vacuum → two-quasi-particle state $|j_1 j_2\rangle$:

$$B(J j_1 j_2) = -\sqrt{2J+1}\, V_{j_1}(A+2)\, V_{j_2}(A+2)$$

(c) two-quasi-particle state → vacuum:

$$B(J j_1 j_2) = U_{j_1}(A)\, U_{j_2}(A)$$

(d) one-quasi-particle state J_f → one-quasi-particle state J_i:

$$B(J j_1 j_2) = \sqrt{\frac{2J+1}{2J_f+1}}\, V_{j_1} U_{j_2}\, \delta_{J_i j_1}\, \delta_{J_f j_2} \sqrt{1+(-)^J \delta_{J_i J_f}}$$

$$+ \sqrt{j_1 + \tfrac{1}{2}}\, V_{j_1} U_{j_1}\, \delta_{J_i J_f}\, \delta_{j_1 j_2}\, \delta_{J0}$$

The cross section in case (a) contains the factor

$$\left| \sum_j (j + \tfrac{1}{2})\, U_j(A) V_j(A+2) \right|^2$$

if we make the small-Q approximation: $j_0(QR) \approx 1$, so only $j_1 = j_2$ occurs. Neglecting the difference between $V_j(A+2)$ and $V_j(A)$, this is

$$\sim \left(\frac{2\Delta}{|G|} \right)^2$$

which, for Sn isotopes, is ~ 115. For pure shell-model states, the same factor is ~ 10, so we see that pairing correlations increase the cross section by ~ 10.

No analysis of data with this approach has been reported, but it should be useful in the future.

5

FURTHER QUESTIONS AND PROBLEMS

5-1 EFFECTS OF NEUTRON-PROTON INTERACTION

The neglect of the neutron-proton interaction is the major weakness of the pairing force theory. This interaction is just as strong as that between a pair of like nucleons. (In fact, in the $T = 0$ state, it is stronger.) The only possible circumstance that might vitiate its effects is that its matrix elements may be made relatively small by the poor overlap between neutron and proton orbitals. This assertion has had very little numerical substantiation; if anything, available numbers suggest that the matrix elements are hardly smaller than those between orbits in the same major shell. In any case, in lighter nuclei ($A < 100$), neutrons and protons fill the same shell together and so there are no possible grounds for neglecting the interaction between them.

Another argument sometimes used to justify the neglect of the N-P interaction is that if all neutrons are paired off by their pairing forces, and so are all protons, then they have a stability against disturbance by the N-P force. This argument cannot be right, since the N-P force is stronger than the N-N or P-P pairing force, so that it may give rise to N-P correlation effects, stronger than N-N or P-P pairing.

There are two basic difficulties in trying to extend the present pairing force theory to include both neutrons and protons:

1. The N-P force is not equal to the N-N force (except in $T = 1$ states) and does not have the simple property of depressing one state below the others. For a given two-particle configuration j^2, several of the various states of $T = 0$ (viz., those with $J = 1, 3, \ldots, 2j$) occur in energy near the $J = 0$, $T = 1$ pairing state. Furthermore the state $J = 0$ does not occur for $T = 0$, so there is no evident way to extend the usual pairing force $-|G|\, A^{+}A$ (where A^{+} creates $J = 0$ pairs). The

best one can do is to revert to L-S coupling and use the form $-|G|A^+A$, where A^+ creates $L = 0$ pairs (both of $S = 0$, $T = 1$ and $S = 1$, $T = 0$). Even so, this is a poor treatment of the $T = 0$ part of the actual force, since one knows that $L \neq 0$ states are also strongly affected by it.

2. The simplicity and form of the Bogoliubov transformation arises essentially from the facts that, for identical nucleons: (1) if there is a particle in state α, no second particle can occur in the state; (2) a particle in state α interacts only with a particle in state $\overline{\alpha}$. When neutrons and protons are present, there are four interacting states rather than two; viz., αn, $\overline{\alpha}$n, αp, $\overline{\alpha}$p. Thus any analogous transformation must involve operators for all four states and thus be considerably more complicated. Several authors have considered this problem in light nuclei:

a. Bolsterli and Evans[34] have considered the force

$$H = \sum_{\alpha\alpha'} G_{\alpha\alpha'} A_\alpha^{\;+} A_{\alpha'}$$

where

$$A_\alpha = a_{\alpha m_t} a_{\overline{\alpha}\overline{m}_t} \qquad \alpha \equiv jm$$

This is an interaction between N-P pairs only (not N-N or P-P) and so is not charge-independent. On the other hand, it is more general than the usual pairing force, in that G depends on m,m′; i.e., the interaction is not restricted to $J = 0$ pairs. A transformation of the essential form

$$B_\alpha = \left[\prod_{\alpha' m'_t} \pm \left(1 - 2n_{\alpha' m'_t}\right)\right] A_\alpha$$

where

$$n_{\alpha' m'_t} = a_{\alpha' m'_t}^{\;+} a_{\alpha' m'_t}$$

is used. The B's satisfy Fermi commutation rules and H can be written approximately as $\Sigma_{\alpha\alpha'}\, g_{\alpha\alpha'} B_\alpha B_{\alpha'}$. Results are derived only for the case of two particles interacting with the particles in a closed shell (e.g., F^{18}). The values of $g_{\alpha\alpha'}$ are obtained from a δ-function force.

b. Soloviev[13] has tackled the problem by inventing a Hamiltonian which has a form identical to the pairing Hamiltonian, except that each operator a_α now represents a neutron *pair* or proton *pair*. The usual pairing-type solution applies to these pairs. Clearly, in treating the N-P force quite independently of the N-N and P-P force, isotopic spin is abandoned.

c. Flowers[14] has directly tried to modify the Bogoliubov transformation to include both types of particle but has found formidable difficulties. He has made some progress by following the idea that the main effect of the interactions is to introduce alpha-particle-type correlations into the wave function. If this is correct, then perhaps it would be best to abandon the Bogoliubov approach, and to build the correlations into the shell wave functions explicitly as done by Wildermuth.[35]

All the above attempts to include N-P interactions have been directed at light nuclei where neutrons and protons are filling the same shell. It is just as important to solve the problem in heavier nuclei. Experimentally, Cohen and Price[24] have found evidence that the properties of neutron groups in nuclei are affected by changing the number of protons. For example, the (d,p) spectra on Cd^{114} and Sn^{116} show marked differences. The same is true of Cd^{116} and Sn^{118}, and also of (d,t) reactions on these pairs. This stresses the necessity of taking N-P interactions into account.

Pal and Mitra[46] have studied the low-lying states of ${}_{59}Pr_{84}{}^{143}$, which has two neutrons and nine protons outside major closed shells. They treat the neutron and proton systems separately with pairing force theory, and then take into account the N-P interaction as a perturbation. They find that the predicted spectrum is remarkably stable for a wide range of variation of the latter interaction, and agrees with the data.

Recently Bremond and Valatin[44] have given a theory for including the N-P interaction. To describe this, let us first return to the theory without such interaction. The wave function is $\Psi_{N,P} = \Pi_{\alpha>0} 0_\alpha^+ \Psi$, where $0_\alpha^+ = 0_{\alpha p}^+ 0_{\alpha n}^+ = (V_{\alpha p} + V_{\alpha p} a_{\alpha p}^+ a_{\bar{\alpha} p}^+)(V_{\alpha n} + V_{\alpha n} a_{\alpha n}^+ a_{\bar{\alpha} n}^+)$, i.e., a product of neutron and proton pairing force wave functions. For given numbers N and P of neutrons and protons

$$\sum_{\alpha>0} 2V_{\alpha p}^2 = P \qquad \sum_{\alpha>0} 2V_{\alpha n}^2 = N$$

If the wave function has the product form, no neutron-proton pairing effects occur, either in the wave function or in the energy. The general Hamiltonian contains matrix elements of types

(a) $\langle \alpha n \ \beta n \,|v|\, \gamma n \ \delta n \rangle$

(b) $\langle \alpha p \ \beta p \,|v|\, \gamma p \ \delta p \rangle$

(c) $\langle \alpha n \ \beta p \,|v|\, \gamma n \ \delta p \rangle$

When its expectation value is taken in the product-type wave function, we find factors like $\langle 0_{\alpha n} | V | 0_{\gamma n}^+ \rangle$, $\langle 0_{\alpha p} | V | 0_{\gamma p}^+ \rangle$, $\langle 0_{\alpha n} 0_{\beta n} | V | 0_{\alpha n}^+ 0_{\beta n}^+ \rangle$, $\langle 0_{\alpha p} 0_{\beta p} | V | 0_{\alpha p}^+ 0_{\beta p}^+ \rangle$, $\langle 0_{\alpha n} 0_{\beta p} | V | 0_{\alpha n}^+ 0_{\beta p}^+ \rangle$, and no others survive. These give matrix elements of the types (a) with $\alpha = \bar{\beta}$, $\gamma = \bar{\delta}$, (b) with $\alpha = \bar{\beta}$, $\gamma = \bar{\delta}$, (a) with $\alpha = \gamma$, $\beta = \delta$, (b) with $\alpha = \gamma$, $\beta = \delta$, and (c) with $\alpha = \gamma$, $\beta = \delta$. Of these five classes, the first two are pairing-force-type matrix elements and the last three are contributions to the self-consistent potential, i.e., to the single-particle energies. The important fact is that the only N-P interaction effect is in the single-particle energies. Apart from this, the calculation is essentially two independent pairing force calculations for the separate neutron and proton systems.

Bremond and Valatin[44] suggest that we can generalize this by replacing the product form of $0_\alpha{}^+$ by

$$0_\alpha{}^+ = A_\alpha + B_\alpha a_{\alpha p}{}^+ a_{\bar{\alpha} p}{}^+ + C_\alpha a_{\alpha n}{}^+ a_{\bar{\alpha} n}{}^+$$

$$+ D_\alpha (a_{\alpha p}{}^+ a_{\bar{\alpha} p}{}^+)(a_{\alpha n}{}^+ a_{\bar{\alpha} n}{}^+)$$

where A_α, B_α, C_α, and D_α are not subject to any condition like $A_\alpha D_\alpha = B_\alpha C_\alpha$. Unfortunately this only represents a neutron-proton correlation of a very special kind. This can be seen by evaluating the energy. Factors occurring are now $\langle 0_\alpha | V | 0_\beta{}^+ \rangle$, $\langle 0_\alpha 0_\beta | V | 0_\alpha{}^+ 0_\beta{}^+ \rangle$. These do not involve any new matrix elements. The only new effect is that elements (c) with $\alpha = \bar{\beta} = \gamma = \bar{\delta}$ now give a pairing effect, whereas before they contributed only to the single-particle energies. Such elements are only a particular small set of those elements (c) that one expects to contribute to N-P pairing, viz., those with $\alpha = \bar{\beta}$, $\gamma = \bar{\delta}$. In the sense that elements $\langle \alpha n\ \bar{\alpha} p | v | \gamma n\ \bar{\gamma} p \rangle$ with $\alpha \neq \gamma$ do not occur, the suggested theory does not seem satisfactory. In order to include such elements with the present approach, it would seem to be essential to include a term $E(a_{\alpha n}{}^+ a_{\bar{\alpha} p}{}^+ + a_{\alpha p}{}^+ a_{\bar{\alpha} n}{}^+)$ in $0_\alpha{}^+$. The implications of this have not been examined.

Even if such a modification were possible, it is not certain that a sufficiently realistic treatment of the N-P force would be achieved. In the present theories, the coefficients A_α, B_α, etc. are independent of m (i.e., $A_\alpha = A_j$) and this means that all operators $a_{\alpha p}{}^+ a_{\bar{\alpha} p}{}^+$ finally occur coupled to $J = 0\ (\Sigma_m a_{\alpha p}{}^+ a_{\bar{\alpha} p}{}^+)$, and the total state has $J = 0$. If the N-P force were such that the $J = 0$ (i.e., $T = 1$) state of the N-P system occurred below all others (as, e.g., in Sc^{42}) then the same would be true in the extended theory. However, the lowest N-P state may have $J \neq 0$ (e.g., Li^6, F^{18}), so the state of the total system with minimized energy should involve N-P pairs with $J \neq 0$. To include such pairs would need a radical extension of the pairing theory. In fact, such an extension would no longer be a pairing theory in the sense that the interaction in states other than the pair states $|\alpha\bar{\alpha}\rangle$ is included. This is, of course, no argument against trying to make an extension. One must face the fact that a pairing force theory for the N-P interaction may be too unrealistic to be of any use. We saw in Sec. 1-4 that this is possibly true for the N-N interaction (since matrix elements for $J \neq 0$ states are not much smaller than for $J = 0$), so it is even more possible for the N-P case. However this conclusion may be too gloomy in view of the fact that all even-even nuclei have spin zero. If the pairing force has no validity, it is hard to explain this.

In Sec. 3-5 we have suggested a method[48] for including N-P pairing effects, which is a straightforward extension of the linearization approach to the pairing force problem for like particles. This may be more satisfactory than the above method in that it could include matrix elements $\langle \alpha n, \bar{\alpha} p \,|\, v \,|\, \beta n, \bar{\beta} p \rangle$, with $\alpha \neq \beta$. On the other hand, it is still a pairing force treatment and subject to the last criticism above. If this turns out to be a valid criticism, one may find a useful theory by using the generalized linearization method (the "Higher Random-Phase Approximation"), described in Part II.

Baranger[43] has also recently studied the matters related to the question of including N-P pairing effects. He suggests that one consider the form

$$\left(\sum_{\alpha\beta\gamma\delta} A_{\alpha\beta\gamma\delta}\, a_{\alpha n}^{+} a_{\beta n}^{+} a_{\alpha p}^{+} a_{\delta p}^{+} \right)^{p} \Psi_0$$

for a self-conjugate nucleus, but is not very optimistic about the practical usefulness of this form.

5-2 EFFECT OF PAIRING CORRELATIONS ON THE OPTICAL POTENTIAL

The effect on the real part, V, has been studied by Sawicki.[18] It enters through the mixed density function

$$\rho(r,r') = \sum_{\alpha} V_{\alpha}^{2} \phi_{\alpha}^{*}(r)\phi_{\alpha}(r')$$

occurring in the expression for V. Also the t-matrix is somewhat affected through the exclusion of occupied states. As might be guessed, the effect is small, $<$ 1 per cent.

Terasawa[53] has studied the imaginary part, W, and finds that pairing correlations are much more important. In their absence, W is reduced greatly by the Pauli principle if a sharp Fermi surface is assumed. Pairing correlations smear the surface, and W is increased at the nuclear surface by a factor which may be as large as 2.

5-3 FUNDAMENTAL DETERMINATION OF STRENGTHS OF PAIRING FORCE AND ENERGY GAP

So far these have been determined empirically. In principle they can be determined from the nucleon-nucleon interaction, or, more precisely, from the effective interaction in nuclear matter (the t-matrix).

Brueckner et al.[15] have found that the theoretical gap for like nucleons is much too small (~ eV). This is due to the repulsion in the $^{31}S_0$ state (for the *effective* interaction). They solve for the gap in terms of $|G|$, using the extreme pairing force model, G being determined from the matrix elements of the interaction. Unfortunately this approach involves cutting off the energy integrals in an arbitrary fashion.

Fano and Tomasini[16] determine the gap directly from the interaction matrix elements using the more general theory of Sec. 3-3. The gap contains an exponential, the exponent being determined by the t-matrix, so the gap is very sensitive to the interaction. Emery[36] has also demonstrated these facts, and agrees with the other authors that the theoretical value of the gap for like particles would appear to be much too small.

Emery[36] has pointed out the relation between the existence of an energy gap and the existence of a pole in the t-matrix. Balian and Mehta[17] have studied this point and shown that the Bogoliubov transformation leads to a t-matrix that is free of poles.

It is to be stressed that all these calculations are concerned with infinite nuclear matter, and assume a pairing force of the kind

$$\langle \mathbf{k}_1 \mathbf{k}_2 | v | \mathbf{k}_3 \mathbf{k}_4 \rangle = v(\mathbf{k}_1, \mathbf{k}_3)\ \delta_{\mathbf{k}_1, -\mathbf{k}_2}\ \delta_{\mathbf{k}_3, -\mathbf{k}_4}$$

For a normal two-body force, we have

$$\langle \mathbf{k} \quad -\mathbf{k} | v | \mathbf{k}' \quad -\mathbf{k}' \rangle = \sum_{\ell} P_{\ell}(\cos \widehat{\mathbf{k}\mathbf{k}'})\ \langle j_{\ell}(kr) | v | j_{\ell}(k'r) \rangle$$

where the new matrix element is taken in relative coordinate r only, and irrelevant factors are dropped. Thus we see that each partial wave component of the two-nucleon interaction contributes to the pairing force. There is no very close relation between this pairing force and the one we have been concerned with in finite nuclei. Thus the failure of the above calculations to obtain a gap near the observed value (~ 1 MeV) is not significant, since the observed one depends essentially on the finiteness of nuclei. We have seen that the δ-function force $v = V\,\delta(\mathbf{r})$ reproduces matrix elements similar to those of the pairing force model. If we use Table 1-1 to equate the two we find, for $A \approx 120$,

$$V \approx -130\,|G|\,b^3$$

where b is the oscillator size parameter $\hbar/M\omega$. The empirical value of $|G|$, $-23/A$ MeV, gives a value $-25b^3$ MeV f^{+3} for the effective singlet interaction V between nucleons. This agrees well with the value from earlier shell-model fitting; e.g., de Shalit and Goldhaber[47] find $V \approx -22b^3$ MeV f^3. This is of the same order as that for free nucleons ($V \sim 500$ MeV f^3) but larger than that calculated for nuclear matter.[15]

References

1. G. Racah, *Phys. Rev.*, **62**, 438 (1942).
2. Bohr, Mottelson, and Pines, *Phys. Rev.*, **110**, 936 (1958).
3. B. Mottelson, "The Many-Body Problem," University of Grenoble, 1958 (Lectures at Les Houches Summer School) (Dunod, Paris, 1959), p. 259.
4. S. T. Belyaev, *Mat. Fys. Medd.*, **31**, 11 (1959).
5. R. A. Ferrell, *Phys. Rev.*, **107**, 1631 (1957); also S. Fallieros, Thesis, U. of Maryland, 1959.
6. M. Baranger, *Phys. Rev.*, **120**, 957 (1960).
7. D. J. Thouless and J. G. Valatin, *Nucl. Phys.*, **31**, 211 (1962).
8. B. F. Bayman, *Nucl. Phys.*, **15**, 33 (1960).
9. J. Sawicki, *Ann. Phys.*, **13**, 237 (1961).
10. K. Pal, unpublished (1962).
11. A. Kerman, *Ann. Phys.*, **12**, 300 (1961).
12. H. J. Lipkin, to be published.
13. V. G. Soloviev, *Nucl. Phys.*, **18**, 161 (1960).
14. B. H. Flowers, Proc. Rutherford Jubilee Conf., Manchester, 1961, Paper S2/1.
15. Brueckner, Soda, Anderson, and Morel, *Phys. Rev.*, **118**, 1442 (1960).
16. G. Fano and A. Tomasini, *Nuovo Cimento*, **18**, 1247 (1960).
17. R. Balian and M. L. Mehta, *Nucl. Phys.*, **31**, 587 (1962).
18. J. Sawicki, *Nuovo Cimento*, [X] **15**, 504 (1960).
19. L. S. Kisslinger and R. A. Sorensen, *Mat. Fys. Medd.*, **32**, 9 (1960).
20. N. Freed and L. S. Kisslinger, *Nucl. Phys.*, **25**, 611 (1961).
21. Kerman, Lawson, and Macfarlane, *Phys. Rev.*, **124**, 162 (1961).
22. S. Yoshida, *Phys. Rev.*, **123**, 2122 (1961).
23. S. T. Belyaev and B. N. Zakhariev, Dubna preprint, 1961.
24. B. L. Cohen and R. E. Price, *Phys. Rev.*, **121**, 1441 (1961).

25. B. L. Cohen and E. W. Hamburger, *Phys. Rev.*, **125**, 1358 (1961).
26. Macfarlane, Raz, Yntema, and Zeidman, *Phys. Rev.*, **127**, 204 (1962).
27. Mukherjee and Cohen, *Phys. Rev.*, **127**, 1284 (1962).
28. R. J. Blin-Stoyle, *Rev. Mod. Phys.*, **28**, 75 (1956).
29. I. Talmi, private communication to B. L. Cohen, quoted in Ref. 25.
30. A. M. Lane (unpublished, 1959).
31. Schiffer, Lee, and Zeidman, *Phys. Rev.*, **115**, 427 (1959).
32. Guman, Kharitonov, Sliv, and Sogomonova, *Nucl. Phys.*, **28**, 192 (1961).
33. S. Yoshida, *Nucl. Phys.*, to be published.
34. M. Bolsterli and J. A. Evans, Proc. Rutherford Jubilee Conf., Manchester, 1961, Paper C2/29.
35. Tang, Wildermuth, and Pearlstein, *Nucl. Phys.*, **32**, 499 (1962).
36. V. J. Emery, *Nucl. Phys.*, **19**, 154 (1960).
37. H. Ikegami and T. Udegawa, *Phys. Rev.*, **124**, 1518 (1961).
38. J. Hogaasen-Feldman, *Nucl. Phys.*, **28**, 258 (1961).
39. A. B. Migdal, *Nucl. Phys.*, **30**, 239 (1962).
40. J. G. Valatin, *Phys. Rev.*, **122**, 1012 (1961).
41. N. N. Bogoliubov, *Nuovo Cimento*, **7**, 794 (1958).
42. J. G. Valatin, *Nuovo Cimento*, **7**, 843 (1958).
43. M. Baranger, *Phys. Rev.*, **130**, 1244 (1963).
44. B. Bremond and J. G. Valatin, *Nucl. Phys.*, **41**, 640 (1963).
45. P. W. Anderson, *Phys. Rev.*, **112**, 1900 (1958).
46. D. Mitra and M. K. Pal, *Nucl. Phys.*, **42**, 221 (1963).
47. A. de Shalit and M. Goldhaber, *Phys. Rev.*, **92**, 1211 (1953).
48. A. M. Lane and M. K. Pal, to be published.
49. V. G. Soloviev, *Mat. Fys. Medd.*, **1**, No. 11 (1961).
50. C. J. Gallacher, Jr., and V. G. Soloviev, *Mat. Fys. Medd.*, **2**, No. 2 (1962).
51. S. G. Nilsson and O. Prior, *Mat. Fys. Medd.*, **32**, No. 16 (1961).
52. J. J. Griffin and M. Rich, *Phys. Rev. Letters*, **3**, 342 (1959); and *Phys. Rev.*, **118**, 850 (1960).
53. T. Terasawa, *Nucl. Phys.*, **39**, 563 (1962).
54. M. Baranger, *Phys. Rev.*, **122**, 992 (1961).
55. Arvieu, Baranger, Veneroni, Baranger, and Gillet, *Phys. Rev. Letters*, **4**, 119 (1963).
56. N. Bogoliubov, *Soviet Phys. Usp.*, **2**, 236 (1959).

PART II

COLLECTIVE MOTIONS

6

NUCLEAR COLLECTIVE MOTION

Nuclear collective motion is fairly distinctive in physics. There is some similarity with the phenomena of oscillations of a classical liquid drop and with electron gas oscillations, but there are also essential differences. Unlike the liquid drop, the nucleus is a quantum system, and its collective parameters differ considerably from hydrodynamic values. The most obvious difference with the plasma is that the nucleus is a relatively small system, so that its collective modes are characterized by angular rather than linear momenta, and also by parity. A further difference arises from the existence of two types of nuclear particle. These may oscillate in phase or out of phase. In the language of isotopic spin, we say that the two types of oscillation are "T = 0" and "T = 1."

Multipole Modes

Nuclear collective modes are thus classified by $\mathcal{L} \equiv (T, L, \pi)$ (isotopic spin, angular momentum, parity). We refer to $\mathcal{L}$ as the multipole order. Experimentally the only well-established modes are those with parity $\pi = (-)^L$, i.e., in electromagnetic terminology, "electric multipoles" such as E3 signifying $L = 3$, $\pi = -$. For such modes it is convenient to define "multipole operators":

$$Q_{TLM} = \begin{cases} \sum_i r_i{}^L Y_{LM}(\Omega_i) & \text{for } T = 0 \\ \sum_i \tau_{3i} r_i{}^L Y_{LM}(\Omega_i) & \text{for } T = 1 \end{cases}$$

Q_{0LM} is the "mass multipole operator." The "charge multipole operator" (which refers to protons only) is

$$Q_{ELM} = \tfrac{1}{2}(Q_{0LM} - Q_{1LM})$$

Criteria for Collective Motion

In surveying the data on nuclei in a given mass region, there are two basic criteria used for deciding whether collective phenomena occur:

1. Regularities in spectra characteristic of collective modes. The simplest are the uniform spacing of the vibrator and the $J(J+1)$-type spectrum of the rotator. A less decisive criterion is the systematic occurrence of a given type of level in different nuclei.

2. Strong electromagnetic matrix elements, either diagonal (e.g., E2 moments) or nondiagonal (e.g., EL transitions). By "strong" here, we mean at least several times larger than a typical value for a single proton. The matrix element for a proton transition between a particle state of orbital angular momentum L and one of $L = 0$ is:

$$\langle LM | Q_{0LM} | 00 \rangle = \frac{1}{\sqrt{4\pi}} \int_0^\infty \left[u_L(r)\, r^L u_0(r) \right] r^2\, dr$$

where the u's are radial wave functions. For a rough estimate, we may replace the integral by the Lth moment of the density distribution $\rho(r)$ of the nucleus concerned:

$$\langle r^L \rangle \equiv \int r^L \rho(r)\, d\mathbf{r} \Big/ \int \rho(r)\, d\mathbf{r}$$

Sum Rules

An alternative version of criterion (2) is that the transition exhausts at least a fair fraction (say $\gtrsim 5$ per cent) of a sum rule. There are two sum rules that are relevant; in obvious notations, these are

$$\sum_n |\langle n | Q_{TL0} | 0 \rangle|^2 = \langle 0 | (Q_{TL0})^2 | 0 \rangle \equiv S_{NEW}{}^{TL}$$

$$\sum_n (E_n - E_0) |\langle n | Q_{TL0} | 0 \rangle|^2$$

$$= \tfrac{1}{2} \langle 0 | [Q_{TL0}, [H, Q_{TL0}]] | 0 \rangle \equiv S_{EW}{}^{TL}$$

We call these the non-energy-weighted (NEW) and energy-weighted (EW) sum rules. The only sum that can be evaluated exactly (i.e., without reference to a model) is the EWS[1,2] for $T = 0$:

$$S_{EW}{}^{0L} = \frac{\hbar^2 A}{8\pi M} L(2L+1) \langle r^{2L-2} \rangle$$

The only assumption is that H contains no explicitly velocity-dependent forces (exchange forces are permitted). Strictly, this value is obtained when the ground state has spin 0, but any correction for nonzero spin is small. It is fortunate that most observed modes appear to be (or are assumed to be) T = 0. The exception is the E1 mode, which is T = 1. Exchange forces contribute to $S_{EW}{}^{1L}$, and a model is needed for their evaluation. This has been done by Bethe and Levinger[3] for the E1 mode using the independent-particle model. The same model can be used to evaluate $S_{NEW}{}^{TL}$:

$$\left(S_{NEW}{}^{TL}\right)_{\text{shell model}} = \frac{A}{4\pi}\langle r^{2L}\rangle\, z$$

The factor z lies between $\frac{1}{2}$ and 1, but depends on multipole order and the nucleus in general. It represents the correction due to the contribution from the cross terms $r_i{}^L r_j{}^L Y_L(i)\, Y_L(j)$ in Q^2; for odd multipoles such terms contribute only through antisymmetrization. For even multipoles they contribute anyway, and can be obtained from $\langle 0\,|\,Q\,|\,0\rangle^2 = 0$ (for spin 0).

This value for $S_{NEW}{}^{TL}$ has been observed to be violated by single transitions (e.g., E2 transitions[4] in Ni^{58}, Ni^{60}), so that it is not reliable. This is not surprising, since it is likely that the zero-point motion for the appropriate multipole mode, although small, could increase $S_{NEW}{}^{TL}$ considerably if it were included in the wave function. In Chap. 7 we find that this motion gives

$$\left(S_{NEW}{}^{TL}\right)_{\text{coll. model}} = \left(\frac{A(2L+1)}{4\pi}\frac{\langle r^{2L-2}\rangle}{R^{L-2}}\right)^2 \frac{1}{2}\left(\frac{\hbar^2}{B_L{}' C_L{}'}\right)^{1/2}$$

For suitable values of $B_L{}'$, $C_L{}'$, this can exceed the above shell-model value of $S_{NEW}{}^{TL}$. Unfortunately, one does not have any independent source at present for the evaluation of $B_L{}'$, $C_L{}'$. Thus the NEW sum rule cannot be used, since we do not know its sum, but only a lower limit, viz., the shell-model value.

Observed Facts

The criteria (1) and (2) have led to the identification of various collective modes from the data. The following kinds have been discussed, but not all confirmed by experiment.

E1(T = 1). The E1 "giant dipole" resonance was the first nuclear collective mode to be identified. The suggestion that it be visualized as a collective oscillation of neutrons against protons (i.e., T = 1) was made in 1948 by Goldhaber and Teller.[5] (The corresponding T = 0 mode for E1 is of no interest, since it corresponds to movement of the nucleus as a whole and not to internal motion.) The E1 state has been revealed by photon absorption studies in ~100 nuclei. Its energy falls from ~22 MeV in light nuclei to ~12 MeV in heavy nuclei. Its width is ~6 MeV. The integrated absorption cross section is proportional to $S_{EW}11$. When it is integrated in the energy range near the state, it is roughly equal to the theoretical value of $S_{EW}11$, thereby confirming that the observed state is collective.

E3 (T = 0?). In about 10 nuclei (e.g., O^{16}, Fe^{54}, Ni^{58}, Sr^{88}, Pb^{208}), the collective E3 character of a state has been established through measurement of its transition matrix element (usually by inelastic electron scattering[4,6]). Evidence of (pp′) scattering also strongly suggests the systematic occurrence[2] of an E3-pole state in nuclei (at least, in spherical nuclei; in deformed nuclei, the state is split into several components). The state falls in energy from ~6 MeV in light nuclei to ~$2\frac{1}{2}$ MeV in heavy nuclei. In light nuclei the transitions are definitely "T = 0" because the isotopic spins of both states are known to be T = 0. In heavier nuclei the assignment T = 0 is an assumption, partly based on extrapolation from light nuclei, partly on the theoretical belief that mass oscillations (T = 0) involve low energies, whereas T = 1 oscillations need more energy (e.g., E1).

E4 (T = 0?). Eight nuclei[4,6] are known to have strong E4 transitions. These occur near A = 60 and 208 and the energies are $3\frac{1}{2}$ (±1) MeV. It seems reasonable to assume that more will be found in time.

E0 pole (T = 0). There is no definite evidence for collective monopole effects. First, excited states of spin 0+ occur in even-even nuclei with some regularity near closed shells, which hints at collective excitation. On the other hand, matrix elements are usually only ~ 50 per cent of those for a single proton,[7,8] so that this may be due to chance. It may be relevant that the hydrodynamic model, assuming incompressible flow, does not allow collective monopole excitation.

E2 pole (T = 0). This is the most common case of collective excitation, and probably hundreds of collective states are known. It was originally discussed in the classic papers by Bohr and Mottleson[9] 10 years ago. Most of their discussion is still valid. In particular, there are two basic types of collective E2 motion. In some mass regions, especially in the rare earths, rotational spectra and large diagonal and nondiagonal E2 matrix elements are found. From this, one infers that the nuclei have a static spheroidal shape in their ground states. In other regions, vibrational spectra and large nondiagonal elements, and average diagonal ones, are found. The most commonly accepted interpretation is that these nuclei have a shape which is spherical on the average but has large R.M.S. values of the quadrupole moment. In fact, since the transition matrix elements are comparable for both kinds of E2 motion, one infers that the R.M.S. values are about the same in all nuclei, whether deformed or not. The transition strengths are usually of the order of 10 per cent of the EW sum rule. The energies for vibrational excitation are about 200 keV to 1 MeV, whereas those for rotation are usually ~100 keV, but larger (~1 MeV) in light nuclei (A ~ 25).

Theoretical Interpretation

The theory of nuclear collective motion has developed in a familiar way. Originally collective states were discussed from two extreme viewpoints—the shell model without interactions and the hydrodynamical model. Both models predict that the EW sum should be entirely taken by one energy state, which disagrees with the data. The former underestimates matrix elements, and fails to give the correct collective frequencies (it overestimates T = 0 frequencies, but underestimates others). The latter model can fit the data, but its parameters are not specified numerically.

At first sight, the two models appear irreconcilable. The shell model describes the collective state as single-particle excitations. The hydrodynamical model would appear to give a description that, in shell-model terms, involves a superposition of many hundreds of particle excitations, both single and multiple. Recent progress has stemmed from the realization that this latter statement is incorrect, at least in degree. Given the fact that nuclear intrinsic motion is essentially that of independent particles, collective states involve remarkably few particle excitations, often only ten or so. This is due to the action of the Pauli principle in forbidding a large fraction of particle excitations that would occur. For example, E1 excitation in Pb^{208}: if one analyzes the "collective state" $Q_{11M}\Phi_0$, where Φ_0 is the shell-model ground state, one finds that about 30 transitions are involved below 10 MeV. If the Pauli principle were ignored, there would probably be two or three times as many.

Attention was first drawn to this matter by Brink,[10] who pointed out that, for E1 excitation on O^{16}, the collective state $Q_{11M}\Phi_0$ was identical to one-particle excitation from the 1p-shell. Since then, a number of calculations have been done in which the collective state has been obtained by diagonalizing the interaction in a limited number of shell-model states of particle excitation (i.e., "particle-hole" states). It has become the custom to refer to such calculations as the "Tamm-Dancoff (TD) method." For E1 excitation in O^{16}, Elliott and Flowers[11] obtained excellent agreement with the data using this method. Later Brown and Bolsterli[12] pointed out that the approach could be systematized with the aid of some extra assumptions and that qualitative understanding of the E1 state could thereby be obtained.

This approach turns out to be inadequate to deal with T = 0 excitations, in particular E2. Although the TD states are more collective than any of the original particle-hole states, they are less collective than those observed. It is not unexpected that the particle-hole states are inadequate for the EL (L even) problem, since there occur two-particle–two-hole states of the same energy which are ignored (e.g., O^{16}; $1p^{-2}1d^2$ has the same energy as $1p^{-1}2p$). However it is not at all clear that the inclusion of such states will increase the collective effects (rather, if anything, the opposite, since they have no matrix elements with the ground state). Thus we must look to a different source of correction to the TD method. This source is suggested by the observation that, in the TD method, all of the "collectiveness" is attributed to the excited state. This asymmetry in approach is the main disadvantage of the TD method. One expects that the correct ground state has a "collective predisposition" that allows the collective excitation to occur from it. In the phenomenological collective model with a collective Hamiltonian (see Section 7), this feature is embodied in the zero-point motion in the ground state.

This trouble with the TD method has been rectified in the "random-phase approximation" (RPA) approach (developed in electron-gas studies), in which both states are treated symmetrically, and collective correlations thereby included in the ground state. Roughly speaking, whereas the TD method considers only one-particle + one-hole states $(j_1^{-1}\,j_1)_{\mathcal{L}}$, $(j_2^{-1}\,j_2)_{\mathcal{L}}$, . . . , etc., the extended method includes states of n particles and n holes of the type $(j_1^{-1}\,j_1)_{\mathcal{L}}^{\,n_1}$, $(j_2^{-1}\,j_2)_{\mathcal{L}}^{\,n_2}$, . . . , where $n(\equiv \Sigma_i\, n_i)$ is any number. (Actually only odd n occur for excited states and only even n for the ground state.) Since $\mathcal{L}$ can be coupled to $\mathcal{L}$ to give $J = 0+$, $T = 0$, some of these new states can (and do) mix with the ground state, thereby introducing correlations (i.e., collective effects) into it. Of course, the energies of these new states are high, and it is certainly an inconsistency that many other states of lower energy are ignored. As we saw above, this criticism also applies to the TD method for even-L modes. Thus neither method is perfect. Recently Vinh-Mau and Brown[13] have studied the $L = 0+$, $T = 0$ mode of O^{16} in an attempt to estimate the effect of the ignored states.

It turns out that the use of the RPA method results in considerable improvement for $T = 0$ modes. It is less important for the higher $(T = 1)$ modes, where it gives effects of the order of a few per cent. The formal quantum mechanics of the RPA method are given in Chaps. 8, 9, and 10. In Chap. 11 the applications to nuclei near closed shells is discussed.

The RPA method can be applied directly to nuclei near closed shells, where the configurations are fairly pure. For other nuclei, pairing-force effects are important and must be included. We have discussed these in Part I and have seen that they can be included by replacing particles and holes by "quasi-particles." The counter parts of particle-hole states for the closed shell case are states of two quasi-particles. In a paper remarkable for its clarity and the excellence of its presentation, Baranger[14] goes into the details of this and shows how collective effects emerge when these states are treated with the TD and the RPA approaches. When quasi-particles rather than real particles are involved, we shall distinguish the methods as TD(QP) and RPA(QP). These are discussed in Chap. 12. Of course, these methods can be no better than the quasi-particle approximation. In particular, they share its greatest shortcoming—the inability to treat the neutron-proton interactions properly.

These remarks do not apply to the case of the rotation of deformed nuclei, where the essential problem is to explain the observed moments of inertia. The observed values lie between the predictions of the extreme models (the shell model and hydrodynamic model). Recently Thouless and Valatin[68] and also Peierls and Thouless[15] have studied this problem, and it seems that a reliable theory, free of inconsistencies, may now be available. This is discussed in Chap. 13.

The chart below illustrates the development of the RPA theory of nuclear collective motion in terms of the basic publications that have appeared.

		No pairing forces included (closed shells)	Pairing forces included (quasi-particles)
Shell-model (Tamm-Dancoff) method: unperturbed ground state		Direct Tamm-Dancoff method for closed shells: Refs. 11, 12, 19, 45–47, 55–57 Hill-Wheeler-Griffin method: Refs. 17, 37	Tamm-Dancoff method applied to quasi-particle systems: Refs. 38, 54
Random-phase (linearized operator) method i.e., ground state correlations (backward-going graphs included)	Mathematics	Original paper on RPA method in electron-gas theory: Ref. 28	
	Mathematics	First applications to nuclear physics: Refs. 22, 29	
	Mathematics	Time-dependent formulation (extended Hartree-Fock theory): Refs. 24, 32–34	Time-independent formulation (linearized operator relations): Refs. 20–22, 27, 30, 31
	Mathematics	Extended RPA theory (HRPA): Refs. 25, 26, 61	
	Applications	Direct calculation of collective modes in closed-shell nuclei with RPA method: Refs. 13, 21–23, 36, 43, 44, 60	Calculation of collective modes of quasi-particle systems: Refs. 14, 40, 50–52
	Applications	Calculation of ground-state correlations: Refs. 48, 60, 61	Application to cross sections for (d,p), etc.: Refs. 53, 54
	Applications	Application of HRPA method: Ref. 25	Special case of low-frequency limit: the cranking model: Refs. 39, 41
	Applications	Special case of low-frequency limit: the cranking model: Refs. 35, 42	Use of HRPA method to derive anharmonic terms in collective model: Ref. 49

7

COLLECTIVE MODELS OF COLLECTIVE MOTION

In this section we survey the Hill-Wheeler-Griffin (HWG) and Bohr-Mottelson (BM) models of collective motion. These are an inevitable accompaniment to any general discussion of nuclear collective motion, but they do not in themselves give absolute numerical predictions easily. For this we must make recourse to the RPA method of later sections.

The HWG model[16,17] is more general and more satisfactory in some technical respects, but it is not easy to work with in its general form because of computational difficulties (overlap integrals). We begin with it and develop the BM model from it.

7-1 HWG WAVE FUNCTION

According to the HWG model,[16,17] nuclear wave functions have the following structure:

$$\Psi_n(x) = \int d\alpha \; f_n(\alpha)\psi_\alpha(x)$$

Here α is a collective deformation coordinate, undefined at present. $\psi_\alpha(x)$ is the "intrinsic nuclear wave function" for the value α, and $f_n(\alpha)$ are the "wave functions" of collective states $n = 0, 1, 2, \ldots$. To fix ideas, we could imagine that $\psi_\alpha(x)$ has the form

$$\psi_\alpha(x) = e^{\alpha D} \, \psi_0(x)$$

where D is the deformation generating function appropriate to coordinate α. For example, the volume-preserving deformation of multipole order LM is given by

$$D = \sum_i \nabla_i\left(r_i{}^L Y_{LM}(\Omega_i)\right) \cdot \nabla_i$$

Alternatively, we might understand $\psi_\alpha(x)$ to be the solution of

$$H_\alpha \psi_\alpha(x) = \epsilon_\alpha \psi_\alpha(x)$$

where H_α is an invented collective Hamiltonian that contains the parameter α (e.g., in the one-body potential, or in $H_\alpha = H - \lambda Q_{LM}$ with $\langle \psi_\alpha | Q_{LM} | \psi_\alpha \rangle = \alpha$).

One can, in principle, evaluate the expectation values of H and of the multipole operators in states $\Psi_n(x)$, but such results are numerical. In order to bring out such systematic physical effects as the uniformity of level spacing, we proceed to the BM, or "adiabatic," model.

7-2 BM WAVE FUNCTION[9]

We assume that, if $\bar{x}$ is a given set of coordinates x for which $\Psi_n(x)$ is not negligibly small, i.e., it is at least an appreciable fraction of its mean value, then $\psi_\alpha(\bar{x})$ is such that it is negligibly small except near a definite value, $\bar{\alpha}$ (say) of α. In other words, specification of a set $\bar{x}$ implies a value for α within narrow limits. We might take

$$\psi_\alpha(\bar{x}) = e^{-(\alpha-\bar{\alpha})^2/2a^2} \psi_{\bar{\alpha}}(\bar{x})$$

i.e.,

$$\int d\bar{x} \; \psi_{\bar{\alpha}}^*(\bar{x}) \psi_\alpha(\bar{x}) = e^{-(\alpha-\bar{\alpha})^2/2a^2}$$

then "a" measures the range of values of α about $\bar{\alpha}$. It follows that

$$\Psi_n(\bar{x}) = \psi_{\bar{\alpha}}(\bar{x}) \left[\int d\alpha \; f_n(\alpha) \, e^{-(\alpha-\bar{\alpha})^2/2a^2} \right]$$

If "a" is $\ll$ the range in which $f_n(\alpha)$ varies, then we have the BM wave function:

$$\Psi_n(\bar{x}) = f_n(\bar{\alpha}) \psi_{\bar{\alpha}}(\bar{x})$$

In this limiting case, it is implied that the set $\bar{x}$ specifies a definite value $\bar{\alpha}$ of α. In other words, $\bar{\alpha}$ is a function of $\bar{x}$: $\bar{\alpha} = \bar{\alpha}(\bar{x})$. Conversely, when $\bar{\alpha}$ is fixed, the coordinates $\bar{x}$ in $\psi_{\bar{\alpha}}(\bar{x})$ are not independent but are subject to the restraint $\bar{\alpha}(\bar{x}) = \bar{\alpha}$. This product form for $\Psi_n(\bar{x})$ implies that we may visualize the oscillation as an adiabatic readjustment of the particle motion to the oscillating coordinate α.

Collective Hamiltonian

It is plausible to assume that the energy associated with the α-oscillation is of the form

$$H_{\text{coll}} = \frac{1}{2}\left(\frac{\pi^2}{B} + C\alpha^2\right) + \text{higher-order terms}$$

Here π is the momentum conjugate† of α; this is $B\dot{\alpha}$ and $-i\hbar(\partial/\partial\alpha)$ in classical and quantum mechanics. Ignoring terms $0(\alpha^3)$,

$$H_{\text{coll}} = \frac{1}{2}\left(\frac{-\hbar^2}{B}\frac{\partial^2}{\partial\alpha^2} + C\alpha^2\right)$$

The wave functions $f_n(\alpha)$ are the eigenfunctions of the oscillator Hamiltonian:

$$f_0(\alpha) = (\sqrt{\pi}\,A)^{-\frac{1}{2}}\,e^{-\frac{1}{2}(\alpha/A)^2}$$

$$f_1(\alpha) = \sqrt{2}\,(\alpha/A)\,f_0(\alpha)$$

$$\ldots \text{ etc.}$$

---

† For simplicity, we have ignored here the fact that α_{LM}, as usually defined, is complex. We have (dropping subscript L):

$$\alpha_M = (-)^M \alpha_{-M}{}^*$$

$$H_{\text{coll}} = \frac{1}{2}\sum_M \left[\frac{-\hbar^2}{B}\frac{\partial}{\partial\alpha_M}\frac{\partial}{\partial\alpha_M{}^*} + C\alpha_M\alpha_M{}^*\right]$$

If we now write $\alpha_M = a_M + ib_M$ (a_M, b_M real):

$$H_{\text{coll}} = \frac{1}{2}\left\{\frac{-\hbar^2}{B}\frac{\partial^2}{\partial a_0{}^2} + Ca_0{}^2 + \sum_{M>0}\left[\frac{-\hbar^2}{2B}\left(\frac{\partial^2}{\partial a_M{}^2} + \frac{\partial^2}{\partial b_M{}^2}\right) + 2C\left(a_M{}^2 + b_M{}^2\right)\right]\right\}$$

The eigenfunctions are

$$f_0 = (\sqrt{\pi}\,A)^{-(2L+1)/2}\exp\left[-\frac{1}{2}\left(\sum_M |\alpha_M|^2/A^2\right)\right]$$

$$f_1 = \sqrt{2}\,(\alpha_M/A)f_0, \ldots$$

with $A = (\hbar^2/BC)^{1/4}$; the energies are $(n + \frac{1}{2})\hbar\omega$ with $\hbar\omega = \hbar(C/B)^{1/2}$, and $n = 0, 1, 2, \ldots$.

The above form of H_{coll} may actually be derived from the HWG approach. The energies of the HWG states are

$$E_n = \frac{\int d\alpha\, d\beta\, f_n^*(\alpha) f_n(\beta)\left[\int dx\, \psi_\alpha^*(x) H \psi_\beta(x)\right]}{\int d\alpha\, d\beta\, f_n^*(\alpha) f_n(\beta)\left[\int dx\, \psi_\alpha^*(x) \psi_\beta(x)\right]}$$

If ψ_β is approximated as $\psi_\alpha + \frac{1}{2}(\beta - \alpha)^2 (\partial^2\psi_\alpha/\partial\alpha^2)$ and the integrals $\int dx$ expanded in powers of α, we find

$$E_n = \epsilon_0 + \frac{\int d\alpha\, f_n^*(\alpha)\frac{1}{2}\left[\frac{-\hbar^2}{\tilde{B}}\frac{\partial^2}{\partial\alpha^2} + \tilde{C}\alpha^2\right] f_n(\alpha)}{\int |f_n(\alpha)|^2\, d\alpha}$$

where $\tilde{B}$ and $\tilde{C}$ are certain constants that can be computed. These can be identified with B and C above, thereby making the two theories identical.

If the eigenfunctions $f_n(\alpha)$ of H_{coll} are put into the HWG wave function with $\psi_\alpha(x) = e^{\alpha D}\psi_0(x)$, we get

$$\Psi_0(x) = N_0 e^{\frac{1}{2}(DA)^2}\psi_0(x)$$

$$\Psi_1(x) = N_1 DAe^{\frac{1}{2}(DA)^2}\psi_0(x)$$

$$\ldots \text{ etc.}$$

where the N's are normalizing factors. We see that we recover the BM results $\Psi_1 \propto \alpha\Psi_0$ if we replace iD by the collective coordinate α in the BM wave function. [For the realistic case when α,D are complex, the exponent should actually be $\Sigma_M A^2/4\,(D_M D_M^* + D_M^* D_M) = \Sigma_M A^2/4\,(-)^M(D_M D_{-M} + D_{-M}D_M)$. This is spherically symmetric, so that $\Psi_0(x)$ has the same angular momentum as $\psi_0(x)$.]

7–3 EVALUATION OF B,C FROM DATA

In practice, we want to evaluate B and C from the experimental data. This data consists of the vibration frequency $\hbar\omega$ and the multipole matrix element M. The former gives us the combination $\hbar\omega = \hbar\sqrt{C/B}$. In order to derive a corresponding relation involving B and C from M, we first replace dx by $d\alpha\, dx'$, where x′ are the set of independent internal coordinates occurring in $\psi_{\bar{\alpha}}$ such that $\int dx' |\psi_{\bar{\alpha}}|^2 = 1$. Let us denote ground-state expectation value by $\langle \cdots \rangle$, and use BM wave functions. We have

$$M \equiv \int dx\, \Psi_1{}^* Q \Psi_0 = \langle \alpha Q \rangle / \langle \alpha^2 \rangle^{1/2} = \langle \alpha^2 \rangle^{1/2} X$$

The factor $\langle \alpha^2 \rangle^{1/2}$ is given by

$$\langle \alpha^2 \rangle = \int d\alpha\ dx'\ \Psi_0{}^* \alpha^2 \Psi_0 = \int d\alpha\ f_0 \alpha^2 f_0{}^* = \frac{A^2}{2} = \tfrac{1}{2}\left(\frac{\hbar^2}{BC}\right)^{1/2}$$

and X is defined as

$$X \equiv \frac{\langle \alpha Q \rangle}{\langle \alpha^2 \rangle}$$

Under the scale change ($\alpha' = \lambda\alpha$, $B = B'\lambda^2$, $C = C'\lambda^2$), H_{coll} is invariant:

$$H_{coll} = \tfrac{1}{2}\left(\frac{\pi^2}{B} + C\alpha^2\right) = \tfrac{1}{2}\left(\frac{\pi'^2}{B'} + C'\alpha'^2\right)$$

Thus we may always choose the scale of α to give X any prescribed value. Usually one chooses α to be dimensionless, while Q has dimensions r^L. The deformation of a classical uniform-density sphere $|r| = R$ into the shape

$$r = R\left(1 + \alpha_{LM} Y_{LM}\right)$$

corresponds to the value for Q_{LM}:

$$Q_{LM} = \alpha_{LM} X_0$$

where $X_0 \equiv (3A/4\pi) R^L$. More generally, for nonuniform radial density,† we have

†This choice is dictated by the following consideration. Consider the deformation of a spherical density distribution $\rho_0(\mathbf{r})$ into an ellipsoidal one:

$$\rho(\mathbf{r}) = \sum_{LM} e^{\alpha_{LM} D_{LM}} \rho_0(\mathbf{r}) \qquad D_{LM} = \left(1/LR^{L-2}\right) \nabla\left(r^L Y_{LM}\right) \cdot \nabla$$

This transforms the sphere $r = r_0$ into $r = r_0(1 + \Sigma_{LM} \alpha_{LM} \times (r_0/R)^{L-2} Y_{LM})$ in first order. The mass multipole moment of $\rho(\mathbf{r})$ is

$$\int Q_{LM}\, \rho(\mathbf{r})\, d\mathbf{r} = \frac{A\alpha_{LM}}{4\pi} (2L+1) \langle r^{2L-2} \rangle / R^{L-2}$$

$$X_0 \equiv \frac{A(2L+1)}{4\pi} \frac{\langle r^{2L-2} \rangle}{R^{L-2}}$$

and this is the value we adopt for X.

The condition imposed on the scale of operator α is now

$$\frac{\langle \alpha Q \rangle}{\langle \alpha^2 \rangle} = X_0$$

This condition is satisfied by the hydrodynamic model, which is equivalent to having $\alpha \propto Q$, if we choose the constant of proportionality to be X_0^{-1}:

$$\alpha = \left(\frac{1}{X_0}\right) Q$$

However this does not at all demonstrate that the model is valid, since the condition can be satisfied for any functional form of α by making the right choice of scale. In fact, the hydrodynamic model cannot be correct, since it conflicts with the data; if $\alpha \propto Q$, then $\Psi_1 \propto Q\Psi_0$ and Ψ_1 exhausts all sum rules. Experimentally for E2 transitions Ψ_1 accounts for only ~ 10 per cent of the energy-weighted sum-rule limit S_{EW}. There is another way to see that the hydrodynamic model implies that Ψ_1 exhaust this sum; from the above equations,

$$(E_1 - E_0) |\langle 1 | Q | 0 \rangle|^2 \equiv \hbar\omega \, |M|^2$$

$$= \frac{\hbar^2}{2B} X_0$$

and from Chap. 1,

$$\sum_n (E_n - E_0) |\langle n | Q | 0 \rangle|^2 = \frac{\hbar^2}{2B_{hyd}} X_0$$

where

$$B_{hyd} \equiv \frac{2L+1}{L} \frac{AM}{4\pi} \frac{\langle r^{2L-2} \rangle}{R^{2L-4}}$$

This latter quantity is the value of B implied by the hydrodynamic model. It is clear that the sum is exhausted by Ψ_1, if $B = B_{hyd}$.

(It is of passing interest to note that the EW sum is exhausted by one state on any model that happens to imply that $Q\Psi_0$ is an eigenstate. The shell model with oscillator potential is in this category for $L = 1$ in all nuclei, and $L = 2$ at closed shells.)

7–4 FAILURE OF THE HYDRODYNAMIC MODEL

Now that we have seen that the hydrodynamic model is not correct, it is of great important to determine to what degree it fails. The model is equivalent to the condition $\alpha \propto Q$, and as a measure of the degree of validity of this, we can use the fraction

$$f \equiv |\langle 1|Q|0^2\rangle| / \sum_n |\langle n|Q|0\rangle|^2$$

We see that f is unchanged by a scale change in α (since $f = \langle \alpha Q\rangle^2/\langle\alpha^2\rangle\langle Q^2\rangle$). Introducing the mean excitation energy of the states n,

$$\overline{E}_n = \sum_n E_n |\langle n|Q|0\rangle|^2 / \sum_n |\langle n|Q|0\rangle|^2$$

we may write f as

$$f = \left(\frac{B_{hyd}}{B}\right)\left(\frac{\overline{E}_n - E_0}{E_1 - E_0}\right)$$

Since the second factor is > 1, the departure of α from Q as measured by f is less radical than is suggested by the small value (~ 0.1) of B_{hyd}/B. For example, for f to be 0.8, the mean energy of the other 20 per cent of strength $\Sigma_n |\langle n|Q|0\rangle|^2$ must be at $(E_n - E_0) \sim 40(E_1 - E_0)$. If $(E_1 - E_0) \sim 0.4$ MeV, this is 16 MeV, which seems an acceptable possibility. Unfortunately this is only speculation. The way to settle the matter is to estimate $\langle Q^2\rangle$ reliably. This has not been done, either by experiment or theory. The RPA method of following sections could be used for this purpose. As we shall see, it also gives the functional form of α.

Before concluding, we briefly check on two assumptions underlying the above discussion, viz., (1) the neglect of anharmonic terms $0(\alpha^3)$ in H_{coll}, and (2) the use of the BM wave function.

It is conceivable that the hydrodynamic formula $\alpha \propto Q$ is correct, but that Ψ_1 fails to exhaust the EW sum because of a failure in these assumptions.

1. Assumption $H_{coll} = \frac{1}{2}(B\dot{\alpha}^2 + C\alpha^2)$. The first corrections to this will be cubic terms like $D\alpha\dot{\alpha}^2$ and $E\alpha^3$. Recently the role of such terms has been studied.[18] They imply that the first excited state is no longer $\sim \alpha\Psi_0$, so it does not in general exhaust the sum rules. $E\alpha^3$ does not contribute to $[H_{coll}, Q]$ so this does not affect the EWS. The term in D changes the EW sum from $(\hbar^2/2B)$ to

$$(\hbar^2/2B)\langle 0|\frac{1}{1 + (2D\alpha/B)}|0\rangle$$

For reasonable values of D/B, the fractional change in the sum is small, so that small corrections to H_{coll} cannot explain the factor-of -10 discrepancy in the sum.

2. Assumption of BM wave function. If the BM wave functions are replaced by the HWG wave functions, Ψ_1 is not simply $\alpha\Psi_0$, so Ψ_1 does not exhaust the sum rules. However one does expect that the HWG functions are close approximations to the BM ones. (If they are very different, it is hard to see how such collective effects as uniform spacing of spectra can arise.) Thus we expect that the NEWS is mostly exhausted by Ψ_1. On the other hand, the EWS may not be. In contrast to the BM wave functions, states involving intrinsic excitation [i.e., excited states $\psi_\alpha^*(x)$] have nonzero matrix elements of Q with the ground state. If these states are at sufficient energy, they may take a major fraction of the EWS, leaving only a minor part for Ψ_1 (thereby implicitly increasing by B/B_{hyd} by a large factor). This surmise has not been checked because of the overlap problems involved in working with HWG functions. However, one may guess that this effect will probably *not* be important, because one believes that the essential physical cause of the large value of B/B_{hyd} is the short-range correlation between particles due to interactions. The above effect exists for pure shell-model wave functions, so it is likely that it is not responsible.

Thus we conclude that the failure of Ψ_1 to exhaust the EW sum rule is not due to failure of assumptions (1) and (2) but must be due to the fact that the collective coordinate α is not exactly $\propto$ Q.

8

FORMAL DESCRIPTION OF THE "LINEARIZATION METHOD" (OR "RANDOM PHASE APPROXIMATION")

8-1 DEFINITION OF LINEAR OPERATOR RELATION AND ITS IMPORTANCE

If H is the Hamiltonian and O^+ any operator satisfying the linear operator relation

$$[H,O^+] = \omega O^+$$

where ω is a positive number, then, given any eigenstate Ψ of energy E there is another state Ψ' of energy E' such that

(a) $\Psi' = O^+\Psi$

(b) $(E' - E) = \omega$

Also, since $[H,O] = -\omega O$ there is, in general, a third state Ψ'' of energy E'' such that

(a) $\Psi'' = O\Psi$

(b) $(E'' - E) = -\omega$

If Ψ is the ground state Ψ_0, then $\Psi'' = 0$. More generally, if O_r are a set of operators such that

$$[H,O_r] = \sum_s O_{rs} O_s$$

then we can find a set of operators, $O_\alpha{}^+$ (say) which satisfy a relation like that above:

$$[H, O_\alpha^+] = \omega_\alpha O_\alpha^+$$

These operators are linear in the O_r,

$$O_\alpha^+ = \sum_r x_{\alpha r} O_r$$

The vectors $\mathbf{x}_\alpha$ and energies ω_α can easily be seen to be the eigenvectors and values of

$$\widetilde{\mathbf{O}}\mathbf{x}_\alpha = \omega_\alpha \mathbf{x}_\alpha$$

If Ψ_0 is the actual ground state, then $O_\alpha^+ \Psi_0$ are excited states of energies $E_\alpha = E_0 + \omega_\alpha$; also $O_\alpha \Psi_0 = 0$. We sometimes write $|0\rangle'$ for Ψ_0.

8-2 SUCCESSIVE APPROXIMATIONS

We have a set of operators, A_i^+ (say) which are independent creation operators in the sense that state $A_i^+ |0\rangle \equiv |i\rangle$ are orthogonal, $|0\rangle \equiv \Phi_0$ being the unperturbed ground state. Further $A_i |0\rangle \equiv 0$ and

$$\left[A_i^+, A_j^+\right] = 0 = \left[A_i, A_j\right]$$

$$\left[A_i^+, A_j\right] \neq 0$$

and in general is an operator.

In the nuclear physics problem, A_i^+ destroys a particle in a state below the Fermi surface, and creates one in a state above. We assume here, and in the rest of this section, that all particle states are above or below the Fermi surface. In other words, there are no partly filled shells, so that we are considering closed-shell systems. Generalization to other nuclei will be considered in Chap. 10.

The method of 3-1 is applied at several levels of approximation, depending on how large the set of operators (O_r) is taken.

We discuss three possibilities:

(a) set $[O_r] \equiv$ set $[A_i^+]$

(b) set $[O_r] \equiv$ set $[A_i^+]$ + set $[A_i]$

(c) set $[O_r] \equiv$ set $[A_i^+]$ + set $[A_i]$
+ set of all quadratic terms in A, A^+

A. First Approximation: Tamm-Dancoff (TD); Set $[O_r]$ = Set $[A_i^+]$; No Ground-State Correlations

In this case,[11,12,19] the linearized relation above is

$$[H,A_i^+] = \sum_j O_{ij} A_j^+$$

If we assume that the A_j^+ are defined so that the state $|j\rangle \equiv A_j^+ |0\rangle$ is normalized thus:

$$\langle 0| A_i A_j^+ |0\rangle = \delta_{ij}$$

then taking the matrix element of this relation between $\langle j|$ and $|0\rangle$ gives

$$O_{ij} = \langle j| H |i\rangle - \langle 0| H |0\rangle \, \delta_{ij}$$

$$- \sum_{n \neq o} \langle 0| A_j A_i^+ |n\rangle \langle n| H |0\rangle$$

where n labels the complete set of unperturbed states. There are no states $|n\rangle$ for which $\langle 0| A_j A_i^+ |n\rangle \neq 0$ if $i \neq j$. When $i = j$, $A_i A_i^+ |0\rangle$ cannot differ from $|0\rangle$ in configuration, but only in coupling. When $|0\rangle$ is a closed shell, this means that no states n contribute to the last term in O_{ij}, so it can be dropped. We restrict our attention to this case.

We see that **O** is symmetric, so its eigenvectors $\mathbf{x}_\alpha$ are orthogonal: $\tilde{\mathbf{x}}_\alpha \mathbf{x}_\beta = 0$ for $\alpha \neq \beta$. The condition $O_\alpha \Psi_0 = 0$ with $O_\alpha = \Sigma_i x_{\alpha i} A_i$ is satisfied by $\Psi_0 = \Phi_0$, so the present approximation leaves the ground state undisturbed. This means that it is equivalent to the Tamm-Dancoff treatment of closed-shell nuclei, in which the ground state is taken as a pure shell state, and excited states are obtained by diagonalizing the interaction H in particle-hole states.

B. Second Approximation: Random Phase Approximation (RPA)[14,20–22]

Set $[O_r]$ = set $[A_j^+]$ + set $[A_j]$

In this case, the operators A_j as well as A_j^+ are included in the set of operators in the linearized relations:

$$[H,A_i^+] = \sum_j \left(O_{ij}' A_j^+ + O_{ij}'' A_j\right)$$

The conjugate relations are:

$$[H, A_i] = -\sum_j \left(O_{ij}' A_j + O_{ij}'' A_j^+ \right)$$

It follows that $\mathbf{O}$ is the nonsymmetric matrix:

$$\mathbf{O} = \begin{pmatrix} \mathbf{O}' & \mathbf{O}'' \\ -\mathbf{O}'' & -\mathbf{O}' \end{pmatrix}$$

By taking matrix elements between $\langle j|$ and $|0\rangle$ we get for O_{ij}' the same expression as given in 8-2A, and for O_{ij}'':

$$O_{ij}'' = \sum_n \langle j | A_i | n \rangle \langle n | H | 0 \rangle = \langle ij | H | 0 \rangle$$

Here we have used the fact that the only contributing term of the complete set is $|n\rangle = |ij\rangle$. Thus we see that $\mathbf{O}'$ and $\mathbf{O}''$ are symmetric, whereas $\mathbf{O}$ itself is not (so its eigenvectors are not orthogonal).

In terms of diagrams, we may take a line to represent a particle-hole state like $|i\rangle$ or $|j\rangle$ and a dot for the interaction. In the first approximation (A), only matrix elements like $\langle j | H | j \rangle$ occur, so that the only diagrams considered are of the type

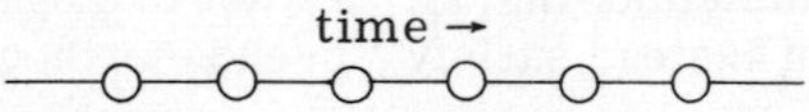

In the second approximation (i.e., the present one) the occurrence of matrix elements $\langle ij | H | 0 \rangle$ means that doubling back is allowed, so that diagrams considered are all those like

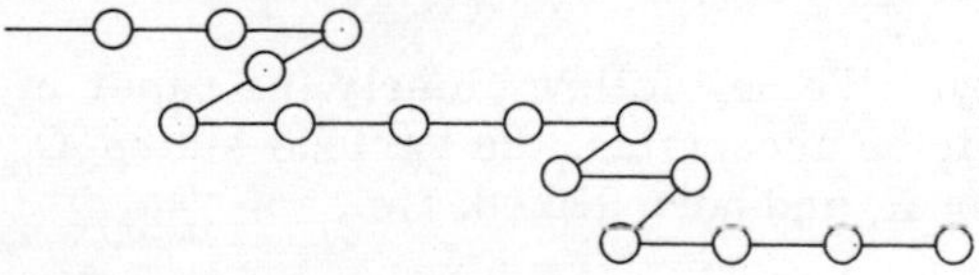

for the excited state, and

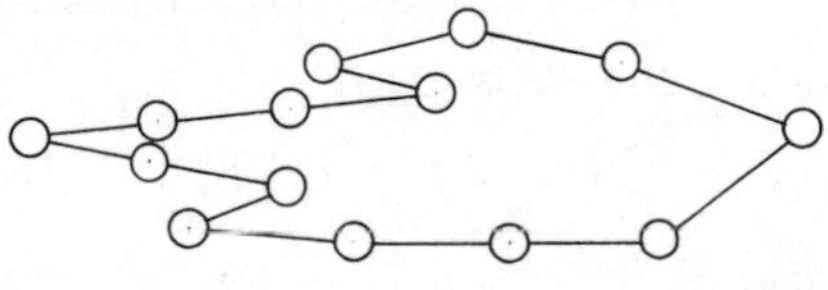

for the ground state. In higher approximations (see 8-2C below) one meets matrix elements like $\langle ij | H | k \rangle$ that correspond to splitting:

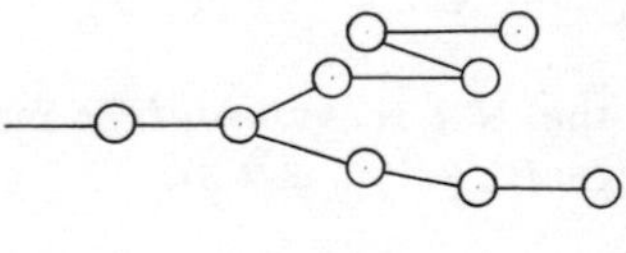

and ones like $\langle ij|H|k\ell\rangle$ that correspond to

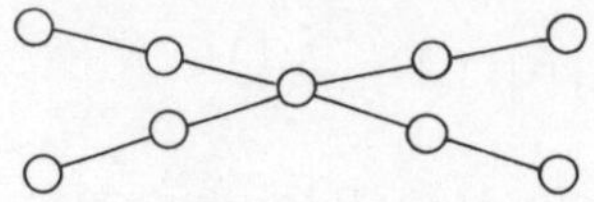

The virtual excitation energies involved in any diagram can be obtained by drawing verticle lines (i.e., for given time) and adding the number of states present.

If there are N states j, the $\mathbf{O}'$ and $\mathbf{O}''$ are $N \times N$ while $\mathbf{O}$ is $2N \times 2N$. If $\tilde{\mathbf{O}}$ has an eigenvector $\mathbf{x}_\alpha = \begin{pmatrix} \mathbf{y}_\alpha \\ \mathbf{z}_\alpha \end{pmatrix}$ with $\mathbf{y}_\alpha, \mathbf{z}_\alpha$ both $I \times N$, and if the eigenvalue is ω_α,

$$\mathbf{O}'\mathbf{y}_\alpha - \mathbf{O}''\mathbf{z}_\alpha = \omega_\alpha \mathbf{y}_\alpha$$

$$\mathbf{O}''\mathbf{y}_\alpha - \mathbf{O}'\mathbf{z}_\alpha = \omega_\alpha \mathbf{z}_\alpha$$

We see that these equations† guarantee that there also exists a second eigensolution, viz., $\mathbf{x}_\alpha{}' = \begin{pmatrix} \mathbf{z}_\alpha \\ \mathbf{y}_\alpha \end{pmatrix}$ with eigenvalue $\omega_\alpha{}' = -\omega_\alpha$. Thus the 2N eigensolutions occur in pairs $(\mathbf{x}_\alpha, \mathbf{x}_\alpha{}')$ with energies $\pm\omega_\alpha$. Physically only the positive energy solutions are significant. Since the matrix $\mathbf{O}$ is not symmetric, the $\mathbf{x}_\alpha$ are not orthogonal in the usual sense $\tilde{\mathbf{x}}_\alpha \mathbf{x}_\beta = 0$, but instead satisfy "pseudo-orthogonality relations":

$$\tilde{\mathbf{y}}_\alpha \mathbf{y}_\beta - \tilde{\mathbf{z}}_\alpha \mathbf{z}_\beta = 0$$

$$\tilde{\mathbf{y}}_\alpha \mathbf{z}_\beta - \tilde{\mathbf{z}}_\alpha \mathbf{y}_\beta = 0$$

Orthogonality. (We now follow closely the paper of Baranger.[14]) For the theory to be acceptable, the various states $O_\alpha{}^+\Psi_0, O_\beta{}^+\Psi_0$ must be orthogonal, and normalized, i.e.,

$$\langle \Psi_0 | O_\alpha O_\beta{}^+ | \Psi_0 \rangle = \delta_{\alpha\beta}$$

To test this, first we use the facts that:

$$O_\alpha \Psi_0 = 0 \qquad O_\alpha{}^+ = \sum_i \left(y_{\alpha i} A_i^+ + z_{\alpha i} A_{\alpha i} \right) \qquad [A_i, A_j] = 0 = [A_i^+, A_j^+]$$

---

† We can rearrange the equations thus:

$$\mathbf{O}_+ \mathbf{x}_{\alpha-} = \omega_\alpha \mathbf{x}_{\alpha+} \qquad \mathbf{O}_- \mathbf{x}_{\alpha+} = \omega_\alpha \mathbf{x}_{\alpha-}$$

where $\mathbf{O}_+$ and $\mathbf{O}_-$ are the $N \times N$ *symmetric* matrices $\mathbf{O}_\pm = \mathbf{O}' \pm \mathbf{O}''$ and $\mathbf{x}_{\alpha\pm}$ are the $I \times N$ vectors $(\mathbf{y}_\alpha \pm \mathbf{z}_\alpha)$.

Thus we have

$$\begin{aligned}\langle\Psi_0|\, O_\alpha O_\beta^+ \,|\Psi_0\rangle &= \langle\Psi_0|\left[O_\alpha, O_\beta^+\right]|\Psi_0\rangle \\ &= \sum_{ij}\Big\{y_{\alpha i}\, y_{\beta j}\,\langle\Psi_0|\left[A_i, A_j^+\right]|\Psi_0\rangle \\ &\qquad - z_{\alpha i} z_{\beta j}\,\langle\Psi_0|\left[A_j, A_i^+\right]|\Psi_0\rangle\Big\}\end{aligned}$$

For problems met in nuclear physics, if we assume that principal quantum number excitation is not allowed, and that Ψ_0 has spin 0^+, it follows† that

$$\langle\Psi_0|\left[A_i, A_j^+\right]|\Psi_0\rangle = 0 \qquad \text{for } i \neq j$$

If we write $\langle\Psi_0|\,[A_i, A_i^+]\,|\Psi_0\rangle \equiv c_i$, then

$$\langle\Psi_0|\, O_\alpha O_\beta^+ \,|\Psi_0\rangle = \sum_i c_i\left(y_{\alpha i} y_{\beta i} - z_{\alpha i} z_{\beta i}\right)$$

At this point, we have to make an assumption in order to proceed: We assume that the c_i are independent of i. (This would be correct if we replaced Ψ_0 by Φ_0, since $\langle\Phi_0|\,[A_i, A_i^+]\,|\Phi_0\rangle$ is independent of i; see below.) It then follows from the relation $\tilde{\mathbf{y}}_\alpha \mathbf{y}_\beta - \tilde{\mathbf{z}}_\alpha \mathbf{z}_\beta = 0$ that $\langle\Psi_0|\, O_\alpha O_\beta^+ \,|\Psi_0\rangle = 0$ for $\alpha \neq \beta$. For $\alpha = \beta$ the normalization condition implies:

---

† A_i^+ has the form of creation operators for orbit p_i coupled to destruction operators for orbit h_i to give multipole $\mathcal{L}$, i.e., $A_i^+ \sim \left(a_{p_i}^+ a_{h_i}\right)_\mathcal{L}$. It follows that

$$[A_i, A_j^+] = \sum_{\mathcal{L}'}\left[c_{\mathcal{L}'}\,\delta_{p_i p_j}\left(a_{h_i}^+ a_{h_j}\right)_{\mathcal{L}'} + d_{\mathcal{L}'}\,\delta_{h_i h_j}\left(a_{p_j}^+ a_{p_i}\right)_{\mathcal{L}'}\right]$$

Taking the expectation value in a state of spin 0^+ eliminates terms $\mathcal{L}' \neq 0$. The term $\mathcal{L}' = 0$ arises only if h_i and h_j (or if p_i and p_j) have the same spin. If we neglect the possibility of change in principal quantum number, this means that the states h_i and h_j must be the same. Thus

$$\langle\Psi_0|\left[A_i, A_j^+\right]|\Psi_0\rangle = 0 \qquad \text{for } i \neq j$$

$$\sum_i \left(y_{\alpha i}^2 - z_{\alpha i}^2\right) = 1$$

where we assume that the A_i are normalized to make $c_i = 1$, i.e., $\langle \Phi_0 | [A_i, A_i^+] | \Phi_0 \rangle = 1$.

Quasi-Boson Approximation. In order to justify assuming that c_i is independent of i, we have supposed that $\langle \Psi_0 | [A_i, A_i^+] | \Psi_0 \rangle$ is approximately equal to $\langle \Phi_0 | [A_i, A_i^+] | \Phi_0 \rangle$. This follows if the number of particles (or holes) in any given shell in Φ_0 is much the same in Ψ_0. This does not mean that we assume $\Psi_0 \approx \Phi_0$ in the sense of first-order perturbation theory, since Ψ_0 can contain large components of states in which a few particles are excited; what it does mean is that the number of excited particles (or holes) in any given shell is only a small fraction of the states in that shell. We expect that, if this property holds for Ψ_0, it is true for all low-lying states. Also, to the same approximation for $i \neq j$, we expect $\langle \Psi | [A_i, A_j^+] | \Psi \rangle \approx 0$ for any low-lying state Ψ; further, all nondiagonal elements $\langle \Psi | [A_i, A_j^+] | \Psi' \rangle = 0$ for $i = j$ and $i \neq j$. All of these expectations can be summarized in the relation

$$\left[A_i, A_j^+\right] = \langle \Phi_0 | \left[A_i, A_j^+\right] | \Phi_0 \rangle = \delta_{ij}$$

which is valid whenever it is used in connection with low-lying states. Taken in conjunction with the exact relations

$$\left[A_i^+, A_j^+\right] = 0 = \left[A_i, A_j\right]$$

we see that the operators A_i are exactly like boson operators. Furthermore, using the pseudo-orthogonality relations, it follows that

$$\left[O_\alpha^+, O_\beta\right] = \delta_{\alpha\beta}$$

$$\left[O_\alpha^+, O_\beta^+\right] = 0 = \left[O_\alpha, O_\beta\right]$$

so that the "step-up" and "step-down" operators O_α^+ and O_α are also like boson operators. This is why the approximation above is called the "quasi-boson approximation." As we shall see in 8-3, the same approximation has to be used in order to derive the linearized relations, so that it is not peculiar to the present discussion, but underlies the entire random phase method. Physically we expect a particle-hole pair to behave like a boson except when conflict arises with the exclusion principle for the component particle (or hole). This will happen only if there is a chance of finding another particle (or hole) in the same state. Provided this chance is small, the correction to the quasi-boson approach is small.

Effective Collective Hamiltonian. Assuming the boson commutation rules for the A operators, we easily see that the linear relations would follow if H has the form

$$H' = \sum_{ij} \left\{O_{ij}' A_i A_j^+ + \tfrac{1}{2} O_{ij}'' \left(A_i A_j + A_i^+ A_j^+\right)\right\} + \text{constant}$$

This is the boson Hamiltonian for a one-body potential. Either by transforming this form, or from the relations

$$[H, O_\alpha^+] = \omega_\alpha O_\alpha^+$$

$$[H, O_\alpha] = -\omega_\alpha O_\alpha$$

$$[O_\alpha, O_\beta^+] = \delta_{\alpha\beta} \qquad [O_\alpha, O_\beta] = 0 = [O_\alpha^+, O_\beta^+]$$

we may deduce the equivalent form:

$$H' = \sum_\alpha \omega_\alpha O_\alpha^+ O_\alpha + \text{constant}$$

This is the Hamiltonian for boson particles which may occur in any members of a set of different oscillator potentials α. In practice, one frequency ω_α is quite different to the others. This corresponds to the collective state. We distinguish it as $\alpha = 0$. The collective Hamiltonian may thus be taken as

$$H_{coll} = \omega_0 O_0^+ O_0$$

where

$$O_0^+ = \sum_i \left(y_{oi} A_i^+ + z_{oi} A_i\right)$$

This form may be identified with the phenomenological form of H_{coll} in Section 7, with a view to finding the effective collective coordinate. Unfortunately this is hampered by the fact that H_{coll} is invariant to phase change in O_0: $O_0 \to e^{i\gamma} O_0$. Thus we can deduce only that

$$\left(e^{i\gamma} O_0^+ \equiv\right) \frac{e^{i\gamma}}{2}(O_0' + iO_0'') \text{ ``=''} \left(\frac{BC}{4\hbar^2}\right)^{1/4} \left[\frac{\hbar\pi}{(BC)^{1/2}} + i\alpha\right]$$

Here O_0' and O_0'' are the Hermitian operators:

$$O_0' \equiv O_0^+ + O_0$$

$$O_0'' \equiv i(O_0 - O_0^+)$$

Thus

$$2\alpha\left(\frac{BC}{4\hbar^2}\right)^{1/4} \text{ ``='' } O_0' \sin\gamma + O_0'' \cos\gamma$$

This equation gives α in operator form:

$$\alpha = \sum_{pq} \langle p|\alpha|q\rangle a_p^+ a_q$$

Its equivalent coordinate form is obtained from the equation

$$\alpha = \sum_{pq} \psi_p(\mathbf{r}')\psi_q^*(\mathbf{r}'')\langle p|\alpha|q\rangle$$

In general, α will be nonlocal, i.e.,

$$\alpha = \alpha(\mathbf{r}',\mathbf{r}'')$$

implying that

$$\langle p|\alpha|q\rangle = \int d\mathbf{r}'\, \psi_p^*(\mathbf{r}') \int d\mathbf{r}''\, \alpha(\mathbf{r}',\mathbf{r}'')\psi_q(\mathbf{r}'')$$

It is an important feature that α is a one-particle operator†; this is guaranteed by its operator form (linear in A_i's). This fact enbodies the strongest and most uncertain assumption of RPA theory, viz., $\Psi_1 \propto \alpha\Psi_0$, where α is a one-particle operator.

Finally we consider the structure of the various states $\Psi_0, O_\alpha^+\Psi_0$. If Φ_0 is the unperturbed ground (vacuum) state, then

$$\Psi_0 = \left[\chi_0 + \sum_{ij} \chi_{ij} A_i^+ A_j^+ + \sum_{ijk\ell} \chi_{ijk\ell} A_i^+ A_j^+ A_k^+ A_\ell^+ + \cdots\right]\Phi_0$$

$$O_\alpha^+\Psi_0 = \left[\sum_i \chi_i^\alpha A_i^+ + \sum_{ijk} \chi_{ijk}^\alpha A_i^+ A_j^+ A_k^+ + \cdots\right]\Phi_0$$

Once the O_α are determined, then the χ's can be found using $O_\alpha\Psi_0 = 0$:

$$\left[\chi_0 \sum_i z_{\alpha i} A_i^+ + \sum_{ijk} \chi_{ij}\left(y_{\alpha k} A_k A_i^+ A_j^+ + z_{\alpha k} A_k^+ A_i^+ A_j^+\right) + \cdots\right]\Phi_0 = 0$$

---

†This suggests that the RPA results could be derived from a different viewpoint, viz., assume that $\Psi_1 \propto \alpha\Psi_0$, where α is a one-particle operator $\alpha = \Sigma_k \alpha_k$; now determine the "best" choice of the (nonlocal) function of coordinates, $\alpha_k(\mathbf{r}',\mathbf{r}'')$.

We have set $A_j\Phi_0 = 0$. If we take the matrix element with $\langle \Phi_0 | A_i$ then,

$$\chi_0 z_{\alpha i} + 4\sum_j \chi_{ij}\, y_{\alpha j} = 0$$

This determines the χ_{ij} in terms of χ_0. Successive application of this method gives $\chi_{ijk\ell}$. It should be noted that, in view of the "quasi-boson" approximation, terms after a certain stage in the above expansion of Ψ_0 are meaningless. In any case, for consistency, coefficients χ should become small when this stage is reached.

In some problems the χ_{ij} are already small (i.e., $\ll \chi_0$); this happens if $z_{\alpha i}$ are small, which occurs if $\mathbf{O}''$ is $\ll \mathbf{O}'$. For such cases, the solution is given to a good approximation by $\mathbf{O}'\mathbf{x}_\alpha = \epsilon_\alpha \mathbf{x}_\alpha$, and so we recover the TD (8-2A).

C. Higher Random Phase Approximation(s) (HRPA)[23–26]

Set $[O_i]$ = set $[A_i^+]$ + set $[A_i]$ + set of quadratic terms in A_i, A_i^+

In this case

$$[H, A_i^+] = \sum_j \left(O_{ij}' A_j^+ + O_{ij}'' A_j\right) + \sum_{jk} O_{i,jk} A_j^+ A_k^+$$

$$+ \text{ similar terms in } A_j^+ A_k,\ A_j A_k^+ \text{ and } A_j A_k$$

$$\left[H, A_j^+ A_k^+\right] = \sum_i \left(O_{jk,i}' A_i^+ + O_{jk,i}'' A_i\right)$$

$$+ \text{ similar terms in } A_j^+ A_k,\ A_j A_k^+ \text{ and } A_j A_k$$

The coefficients O_{ij}', O_{ij}'' are the same as those obtained in 8-2B. The other coefficients can be obtained by taking appropriate matrix elements. For example,

$$O_{i,jk} = \langle jk | H | i \rangle - \langle jk | A_i^+ H | 0 \rangle$$

The matrix $\mathbf{O}$ is now much larger than in 8-2B and its diagonalization in practice may often be impossible. Even so, we see that, in principle, the linearization method may be applied in better and better approximation by extending the set $[O_i]$.

It is important to note that, when the set of operators A_i consists of all subsets of operators $A_i^{(\mathcal{L})}$ for different multipoles $\mathcal{L}$, they are completely uncoupled in approximation 8-2B, but not in the present one; e.g., the quadratic term in L = 1, T = 1 operators can have the over-all character L = 2+, T = 0. This method has been applied by Sawicki[24] to the L = 0+, T = 0 state in O^{16}.

There is a more restricted method of taking the quadratic terms in $[H, A_i^+]$ into account, and it is more feasible computationally. This is to treat the quadratic terms by perturbation theory. Suppose that the collective operators from approximation 8-2B are O_α^+ and O_α. These are linear in the A_i and A_i^+. These operators can be expressed in terms of the O_α^+ and O_α, and the quadratic terms can be written in terms of the O_α^+ and O_α. Since $[O_\alpha, O_\beta]$ is linear in O's, we can bring the quadratic term to the form

$$\sum_\alpha \eta_\alpha O_\alpha^+ + \text{terms in } O, O^+O, OO, O^+O^+$$

If we now take the matrix element of $[H, A_i^{(\mathcal{L})+}]$ between the ground and collective state α, then a perturbation theory treatment leads to the retention of the term $\Sigma_\alpha \eta^{(\mathcal{L})} O_\alpha^{(\mathcal{L})+}$ only. It is important to note that, in applying this method, solution 8-2B must be obtained for all multipoles, since these are introduced in the quadratic term as treated above (i.e., the $\eta_\alpha^{(\mathcal{L})}$ depend on other multipoles $\mathcal{L}' \neq \mathcal{L}$). This method has been applied by Sawicki and Soda[23] to the $L = 1^-$, L = 1 state of O^{16}.

9

DERIVATION OF THE LINEAR OPERATOR RELATIONS: ASSUMPTIONS AND APPROXIMATIONS

9–1 TIME-INDEPENDENT DERIVATION[20,21,27–31]

The Hamiltonian H contains creation and destruction operators in the form

$$H \sim a_\alpha^+ a_\alpha + a_\alpha^+ a_\beta^+ a_\gamma a_\delta$$

where the first and second terms are kinetic energy and potential energy, respectively. We may re-order the second term if we include an appropriate one-body potential in the first:

$$H \sim a_\alpha^+ a_\alpha + a_\alpha^+ a_\gamma a_\beta^+ a_\delta$$

The operator A^+ has the form

$$A^+ \sim a_p^+ a_h$$

Using the theorem $[BC,A] = B[C,A] + [B,A]C$, we find

$$[H,A^+] \sim a_\alpha^+ a_h \delta_{p\alpha} - a_p^+ a_\alpha \delta_{h\alpha} + a_\alpha^+ a_\gamma \left[a_\beta^+ a_\delta , a_p^+ a_h\right] + \left[a_\alpha^+ a_\gamma , a_p^+ a_h\right] a_\beta^+ a_\delta$$

The basic approximation of the derivation is to replace commutators like $[a_\beta^+ a_\delta , a_p^+ a_h]$ by their vacuum (i.e., unperturbed ground state) expectation values:

$$\left[a_\beta^+ a_\delta , a_p^+ a_h\right] \approx \langle \Phi_0 | \left[a_\beta^+ a_\delta , a_p^+ a_h\right] | \Phi_0 \rangle = \delta_{\beta\delta,hp}$$

where we are considering a closed-shell system. This approximation can be restated in four other equivalent ways:

1. We have exactly

$$\left[a_\beta^+ a_\delta, a_p^+ a_h\right] = \delta_{\beta h}\, a_\delta a_p^+ + \delta_{\delta p}\, a_\beta^+ a_h$$

Thus

$$[H, A^+] \sim a_\alpha^+ a_\gamma a_\delta a_p^+ \; \delta_{\beta h} + \text{three similar terms}$$

The approximation is to replace one pair of the four a's by its vacuum expectation value. Since $\langle \Phi_0 | a_\alpha^+ a_\beta^+ | \Phi_0 \rangle = 0 = \langle \Phi_0 | a_\alpha a_\beta | \Phi_0 \rangle$, only pairs $a_\alpha^+ a_\beta$ contribute. For closed shells, $\langle \Phi_0 | a_\alpha^+ a_\beta | \Phi_0 \rangle = \delta_{\alpha\beta}$, and we achieve the previous result.

2. In the last-quoted (exact) form of $[H, A^+]$, retain only terms with two indices equal. Since $a_\alpha^2 = 0$, this prescription leads to $[H, A^+] \sim a_\alpha^+ a_\alpha a_\delta a_p^+$. Now replace all number operators $n_\alpha \equiv a_\alpha^+ a_\alpha$ by vacuum expectation values.

3. Write $[H, A^+]$ in terms of a's written in normal form (i.e., with all destruction to right of all creation operators). Now drop all terms with four operators. (This is mentioned in Sec. 10-3.)

4. The statement

$$\left[a_\beta^+ a_\delta, a_p^+ a_h\right] \approx \delta_{\beta\delta, hp}$$

is equivalent to

$$\left[A_i^{(\mathcal{L})}, A_j^{(\mathcal{L}')+}\right] = \delta_{i\mathcal{L}, j\mathcal{L}'}$$

This follows on expanding the A's in terms of $a_p^+ a_h$ and using the properties of the vector coupling coefficients. In the last section we met the quasi-boson approximation $[A_i^{(\mathcal{L})}, A_j^{(\mathcal{L})+}] = \delta_{ij}$. The present approximation is a generalization of this to include the case $\mathcal{L} \neq \mathcal{L}'$.

Whichever viewpoint is adopted, the result is the same, and the desired linearization of $[H, A^+]$ is achieved:

$$[H, A^+] \sim a_\alpha^+ a_\gamma \sim A^+$$

The justification of these procedures is difficult. The neglected four-particle terms are associated with energies of the order of 4ϵ, where ϵ is the mean particle (or hole) excitation energy. Since the correlations in Ψ_0 correspond to energies of 2ϵ, 4ϵ, 6ϵ, ..., we cannot justify their neglect on energetic grounds.

One can consider

$$\langle \Psi_\alpha | a_\alpha^+ a_\beta a_\gamma^+ a_\delta | \Psi_0 \rangle = \sum_{n=0,\alpha} \langle \Psi_\alpha | a_\alpha^+ a_\beta | \Psi_n \rangle \langle \Psi_n | a_\gamma^+ a_\delta | \Psi_0 \rangle + \sum_{n \neq 0,\alpha} \langle \Psi_\alpha | a_\alpha^+ a_\beta | n \rangle \langle n | a_\gamma^+ a_\delta | \Psi_0 \rangle$$

and argue that the sum can be dropped because the terms tend to cancel through random phases. This is not convincing.

A more plausible justification is probably that based on a derivation of the basic linearization method from an entirely different standpoint. This is time-dependent Hartree-Fock theory.

9-2 TIME-DEPENDENT DERIVATION[23-26, 32-35]

We might have suspected that the RPA method fits rather naturally into a time-dependent description, since, taken into the Heisenberg representation, the basic linear equations have the simple form in $\dot{O}_r = \Sigma\, O_{rs}\, O_s$.

Theorem: First we quote a result[33] valid for any closed system acted on by an external time-dependent perturbation. If the exact eigenstates and energies of the isolated system are Ψ_a, E_a with ground state Ψ_0, E_0, and if the perturbation is

$$\mathcal{W} = W e^{-i\omega t/\hbar} + W^+ e^{i\omega t/\hbar}$$

then, to first order in $\mathcal{W}$, the perturbed ground state is

$$\Psi_0'(\omega,t) = \Psi_0 e^{-iE_0 t/\hbar} + \sum_{a \neq 0} c_a(\omega,t)\Psi_a$$

where

$$c_a(\omega,t) = \frac{W_{a0}\, e^{-it(E_0+\omega)/\hbar}}{\omega + (E_0 - E_a) + i\epsilon} - \frac{(W^+)_{a0}\, e^{-it(E_0-\omega)/\hbar}}{\omega - (E_0 - E_a)}$$

This follows on inserting the expression for Ψ_0' in $(H + \mathcal{W})\Psi_0' = i\hbar(\partial\Psi_0'/\partial t)$. The important feature of this result is that $\Psi_0'(\omega,t)$ has a pole when $\hbar\omega$ falls on an eigenfrequency $(E_a - E_0)$. Thus variation of the frequency of the external perturbation makes the system reveal its natural frequencies.

Hartree-Fock Theory

The usual Hartree-Fock theory may be stated

$$(T + V[\phi] - \epsilon_n)\phi_n = 0$$

and

$$V[\phi]\phi_n(r) = \sum_m [\langle m|v|m\rangle \phi_n(r) - \phi_m(r)\langle m|v|n\rangle]$$

in self-evident notation. The sum over m is over occupied states only. If the external perturbation $\mathcal{W}$ is added, then ϕ_n becomes

$$\Phi_n(t) = \phi_n e^{-i\epsilon_n t/\hbar} + \sum_N \beta_{nN}(t)\phi_N$$

where

$$\left(T + V[\Phi] + \mathcal{W} - i\hbar\frac{\partial}{\partial t}\right)\Phi_n = 0$$

$V[\Phi]$ depends on time and ω through the occurrence of set $[\Phi]$ in place of set $[\phi]$:

$$\begin{aligned} V[\Phi]\Phi_n &= \sum_m [\langle\Phi_m|v|\Phi_m\rangle\Phi_n - \Phi_m\langle\Phi_m|v|\Phi_n\rangle] \\ &= V[\phi]\phi_n e^{-i\epsilon_n t/\hbar} + \sum_N \beta_{nN} V[\phi]\phi_N \\ &\quad + \sum_{mN} \Big\{ \beta_{mN}\Big[\langle m|v|N\rangle\phi_n \\ &\quad - \langle m|v|n\rangle\phi_N\Big] e^{-it(\epsilon_n-\epsilon_m)/\hbar} \\ &\quad + \beta_{mN}{}^*\Big[\langle N|v|m\rangle\phi_n \\ &\quad - \langle N|v|n\rangle\phi_m\Big] e^{-it(\epsilon_n+\epsilon_m)/\hbar}\Big\} \end{aligned}$$

to first order in $\mathcal{W}$. Inserting this expression in the last equation, taking the matrix element with $\langle N'|$, we have, to first order,

$$\begin{aligned} & e^{i\epsilon_n t/\hbar}\left(\epsilon_{N'} - i\hbar\frac{\partial}{\partial t}\right)\beta_{nN'} \\ &\quad + \sum_{mN} \Big\{\langle mN'|v|Nn\rangle_{\text{A.S.}}\, \beta_{mN} e^{it\epsilon_m/\hbar} \\ &\quad + \langle NN'|v|mn\rangle_{\text{A.S.}}\, \beta_{mN}{}^* e^{-it\epsilon_m/\hbar}\Big\} = -\mathcal{W}_{N'n} \end{aligned}$$

where "A.S." means antisymmetrized.

Trying the solution

$$\beta_{nN} = \left(y_{nN}\, e^{-i\omega t/\hbar} - z_{nN}{}^{*}\, e^{i\omega t/\hbar}\right) e^{-i\epsilon_n t/\hbar}$$

with y, z independent of t, gives, on separating terms in $e^{\pm i\omega t/\hbar}$,

$$\left(\epsilon_{N'} - \epsilon_n - \omega\right) y_{nN'} + \sum_{mN} \Big[\langle mN' \,|v|\, Nn\rangle_{A.S.}\, y_{mN}$$

$$- \langle NN' \,|v|\, mn\rangle_{A.S.}\, z_{mN}\Big] = -W_{N'n}$$

$$\left(\epsilon_{N'} - \epsilon_n + \omega\right) z_{nN'} + \sum_{mN} \Big[\langle mN' \,|v|\, Nn\rangle_{A.S.}\, z_{mN}$$

$$- \langle NN' \,|v|\, mn\rangle_{A.S.}\, y_{mN}\Big] = W^{+}{}_{N'n}{}^{*}$$

In the matrix notation

$$(\mathbf{\Delta} - \omega\mathbf{I})\,\mathbf{y} + \mathbf{V}\mathbf{y} - \mathbf{V}'\mathbf{z} = -\mathbf{W}$$

$$(\mathbf{\Delta} + \omega\mathbf{I})\,\mathbf{z} + \mathbf{V}\mathbf{z} - \mathbf{V}'\mathbf{y} = +\mathbf{W}^{+*}$$

where y, z, W are column vectors, and Δ, I, V, V′ are square matrices. **I** is the diagonal unit matrix, **Δ** is the matrix

$$\Delta_{nN',mN} = \left(\epsilon_{N'} - \epsilon_n\right)\delta_{nN',mN}$$

and **V**, **V′** are

$$V_{nN',mN} = \langle mN' \,|v|\, Nn\rangle_{A.S.}$$

$$V'_{nN',mN} = \langle NN' \,|v|\, mn\rangle_{A.S.}$$

We can now introduce the square matrix

$$D \equiv \begin{pmatrix} (\mathbf{\Delta} + \mathbf{V}) & -\ \mathbf{V}' \\ +\ \mathbf{V}' & -(\mathbf{\Delta} + \mathbf{V}) \end{pmatrix}$$

and the column vectors

$$\mathbf{x} = \begin{pmatrix} \mathbf{y} \\ \mathbf{z} \end{pmatrix}$$

Then our equations read

$$(\mathbf{D} - \omega\mathbf{I})\,\mathbf{x} = -\begin{pmatrix}\mathbf{W}\\ \mathbf{W}^{+*}\end{pmatrix}$$

The solution of this is

$$\mathrm{x} = -(\mathrm{D} - \omega\mathrm{I})^{-1}\begin{pmatrix}\mathbf{W}\\ \mathbf{W}^{+*}\end{pmatrix}$$

If $\mathbf{D}$ is diagonalized by χ: $\chi^{-1}\mathbf{D}\chi = \mathbf{d}$ (where $\mathbf{d}$ is diagonal with elements $\omega_1, \omega_2, \ldots$) then

$$\mathbf{x} = -(\mathbf{D} - \omega\mathbf{I})^{-1}\begin{pmatrix}\mathbf{W}\\ \mathbf{W}^{+*}\end{pmatrix}$$

$$= -[\chi(\mathbf{d} - \omega\mathbf{I})\chi^{-1}]^{-1}\begin{pmatrix}\mathbf{W}\\ \mathbf{W}^{+*}\end{pmatrix}$$

$$= -\chi(\mathbf{d} - \omega\mathbf{I})^{-1}\chi^{-1}\begin{pmatrix}\mathbf{W}\\ \mathbf{W}^{+*}\end{pmatrix}$$

The matrix $(\mathbf{d} - \omega\mathbf{I})^{-1}$ is diagonal with elements $(\omega_1 - \omega)^{-1}$, $(\omega_2 - \omega)^{-1}$, etc. It follows that $\mathbf{x}$ has a pole at each of the values $\omega = \omega_1, \omega_2, \ldots$, i.e., at the eigenvalues of D. Thus the equation for the excitation energies $\omega = \omega_\alpha$ of the system is

$$(\mathbf{D} - \omega_\alpha\mathbf{I})\,\mathbf{x}_\alpha = 0$$

This does not depend on W, so, in the limit when the external perturbation $W \to 0$, this equation continues to give the collective frequencies ω_α of the isolated system.

An interpretation of the eigenvectors $\mathbf{x}_\alpha$ is obtained by supposing that an excited state Ψ_α has the form $O_\alpha^{+}\Psi_0$. It follows that

$$[H, O_\alpha^{+}] = \omega_\alpha O_\alpha^{+}$$

Taking O_α^{+} in the representation of second quantization for states in the Hartree-Fock potential, *and assuming it to be linear in the particle-hole creation operators A* (i.e., to be a one-particle operator), we find (using the results earlier in this section) that

$$(D - \omega_\alpha I)O_\alpha^{+} = 0$$

Thus the x_α are the operators O_α^{+} creating the collective states Ψ_α from the ground state.

We have not separated different multipoles here, but this is easily done; assuming that W has a certain multipole order isolates that multipole. Thus the equation $(\mathbf{D} - \omega_\alpha \mathbf{I})\mathbf{x}_\alpha = 0$ can be decomposed into independent parts, one for each multipole.

We see that the eigenfrequencies are obtained by inserting the form of $\Phi_n(t)$ into

$$\left(T + V[\Phi] - i\hbar \frac{\partial}{\partial t}\right)\Phi_n = 0$$

and linearizing (i.e., keeping only linear terms) in β. To obtain improved results, one can retain quadratic terms in β. However, this does not appear to be a satisfactory procedure. It does not lead to an eigenvalue problem and it is not equivalent to the higher random phase approximation.[23-26]

Evaluation of Matrix Elements

To evaluate matrix elements like W_{ao}, one first notices from the general theorem above that

$$\langle \Psi_0' | W e^{-i\omega t/\hbar} | \Psi_0' \rangle$$
$$= W_{00} e^{-i\omega t/\hbar} + \sum_a \frac{|W_{a0}|^2}{\omega - (E_a - E_0)} \left(1 + e^{-2i\omega t/\hbar}\right)$$
$$+ \text{terms in } (\omega + E_a - E_0)^{-1} \text{ and terms } 0(W^3)$$

(The exponential terms disappear on taking the time average.) This quantity is essentially the "response function." We see that

$$|W_{a0}|^2 = \underset{\omega \to \omega_{a0}}{L} (\omega - \omega_{a0}) \overline{\langle \Psi_0' | W e^{-i\omega t/\hbar} | \Psi_0' \rangle}$$

where $\omega_{a0} \equiv (E_a - E_0)$ and the bar means time average. We may evaluate Ψ_0' using the results above:

$$\Psi_0'(\omega, t) = e^{-iE_{00}t/\hbar} \left[\Phi_0 + \sum_i \left(y_i e^{-i\omega t/\hbar} - z_i^* e^{i\omega t/\hbar}\right)\Phi_i\right]$$

where we combine subscripts n, N into the label i, and where Φ_i is the hole-particle state (hole state n, particle state N). Φ_0 is the usual Hartree-Fock ground state and E_{00} the sum of its single-particle energies.

To determine y_i and z_i, we must first specify χ and χ^{-1}. Since $(\mathbf{D} - \omega_\alpha \mathbf{I})\mathbf{x}_\alpha = 0$, it follows that

$$\chi = (\mathbf{x}_1 \mathbf{x}_2 \cdots \mathbf{x}_1' \mathbf{x}_2' \cdots)$$

where x_α' is the solution with $\omega = -\omega_\alpha$, viz., $\begin{pmatrix} z_\alpha \\ y_\alpha \end{pmatrix}$. We also have $\tilde{\mathbf{y}}_\alpha \mathbf{y}_\beta - \tilde{\mathbf{z}}_\alpha \mathbf{z}_\beta = 0$, from which it follows that

$$\chi^{-1} = \begin{pmatrix} \mathbf{y}_1 & -\mathbf{z}_1 \\ \mathbf{y}_2 & -\mathbf{z}_2 \\ & \vdots \end{pmatrix}$$

where we have used the normalization

$$\tilde{\mathbf{y}}_\alpha \mathbf{y}_\alpha - \tilde{\mathbf{z}}_\alpha \mathbf{z}_\alpha = 1$$

Thus

$$\mathbf{x} = -\chi(\mathbf{d} - \omega I)^{-1} \chi^{-1} \begin{pmatrix} \mathbf{W} \\ \mathbf{W}^{+*} \end{pmatrix}$$

becomes, writing W_i for $\langle N | W | n \rangle = \langle \Phi_i | W | \Phi_0 \rangle$,

$$y_i = \sum_{j\alpha} \frac{y_{\alpha i}\left(y_{\alpha j} W_j - z_{\alpha j} W^{+}{}_j{}^{*}\right)}{\omega - \omega_\alpha} + \text{terms in } (\omega + \omega_\alpha)^{-1}$$

$$z_i = \sum_{j\alpha} \frac{z_{\alpha i}\left(y_{\alpha j} W_j - z_{\alpha j} W^{+}{}_j{}^{*}\right)}{\omega - \omega_\alpha} + \text{terms in } (\omega + \omega_\alpha)^{-1}$$

Substitution in $\Psi_0'(\omega,t)$ leads to

$$|W_{a0}|^2 = \sum_i \underset{\omega \to \omega_\alpha}{L} (\omega - \omega_\alpha)(-z_i^* W^{+}{}_i{}^* + y_i^* W_i)$$

$$= |\sum_i (y_{\alpha i} W_i^* - z_{\alpha i} W^{+}{}_i)|^2$$

Hence, apart from a phase,

$$W_{a0} = \sum_i (y_{\alpha i} W_i^* - z_{\alpha i} W^{+}{}_i)$$

Since W is any arbitrary perturbation, while $y_{\alpha i}$ and $z_{\alpha i}$ are independent of W, this is consistent with giving the excited state Ψ_α the form $\Sigma_i (y_{\alpha i} A_i^+ + z_{\alpha i} A_i)\Psi_0$, where A_i^+ creates the particle-hole state i.

Transcription to Density Matrix Language

The above results can be stated compactly using the Dirac density-matrix formalism.

Formalism: The usual density matrix ρ for an n-particle system in a pure state $\Psi(t)$ is

$$\rho = |\Psi(t)\rangle\langle\Psi(t)|$$

This is a function of coordinates $\mathbf{r}_1 \cdots \mathbf{r}_n$ in $|\Psi(t)\rangle$ and $\mathbf{r}_1' \cdots \mathbf{r}_n'$ in $\langle\Psi(t)|$. The Dirac single-particle density matrix $\overline{\rho}$ is defined by

$$\overline{\rho}(\mathbf{r}_1,\mathbf{r}_1') \equiv \mathrm{Tr}_{(\mathbf{r}_2,\mathbf{r}_3\cdots\mathbf{r}_n)}\,\rho$$

$$= \int \delta(\mathbf{r}_2 - \mathbf{r}_2')\, d\mathbf{r}_2\, d\mathbf{r}_2' \int \delta(\mathbf{r}_3 - \mathbf{r}_3')\, d\mathbf{r}_3\, d\mathbf{r}_3' \int \cdots \rho$$

(Spin sums can be included if appropriate.)

From this definition, $\overline{\rho}$ is a function of r_1, r_1', t; since Ψ is antisymmetric, the form of $\overline{\rho}(r_i, r_i')$ is the same for all particles i, so we drop the particle label i.

If $K^{(1)}$ is a one-particle operator, we have

$$\mathrm{Tr}\,(K^{(1)}\rho) = n\,\mathrm{Tr}\,(K_1^{(1)}\rho)$$

$$= n\,\mathrm{Tr}_{(\mathbf{r}_1)}\left(K_1^{(1)}\,\mathrm{Tr}_{(\mathbf{r}_2,\mathbf{r}_2\cdots\mathbf{r}_n)}\,\rho\right)$$

$$= n\,\mathrm{Tr}_{(\mathbf{r}_1)}\,(K_1^{(1)}\,\overline{\rho})$$

Thus matrix elements of one-particle operators in many-particle states can be written in terms of $\overline{\rho}$. Clearly we may define the two-particle density matrix $\overline{\overline{\rho}}$:

$$\overline{\overline{\rho}} = \mathrm{Tr}_{(\mathbf{r}_3,\mathbf{r}_4,\ldots\mathbf{r}_n)}\,\rho$$

and then a similar result holds for two-particle operators $K^{(2)}$:

$$\mathrm{Tr}\,(K^{(2)}\rho) = \tfrac{1}{2}n(n-1)\,\mathrm{Tr}_{(r_1,r_2)}\,(K_{12}^{(2)}\,\overline{\overline{\rho}})$$

Time-Dependent Hartree-Fock Theory

The Hartree-Fock potential is

$$V[\overline{\rho}] = \mathrm{Tr}\,v\overline{\rho} = \sum_{NN'} \langle N|\,v\,|N'\rangle_{\mathrm{A.S.}}\,\langle N'|\,\overline{\rho}\,|N\rangle$$

In the unperturbed ground state, $\bar{\rho} = \Sigma_m |m\rangle\langle m| = \bar{\rho}_0$ (say), and

$$V[\bar{\rho}_0] = \sum_m \langle m|v|m\rangle_{A.S.}\,\theta(m)$$

where $\theta(m) = 1,0$ for m occupied, unoccupied.

The generalized (time-dependent) Hartree-Fock equation is

$$i\hbar\frac{\partial\bar{\rho}}{\partial t} = [H[\bar{\rho}],\rho]$$

$$= [T,\bar{\rho}] + [V[\bar{\rho}],\bar{\rho}]$$

Suppose that, in the presence of an external perturbation $\mathcal{W}$,

$$\bar{\rho} = \bar{\rho}_0 + \bar{\rho}_1$$

then, on insertion in this last equation, and keeping linear terms,

$$\left[i\hbar\frac{\partial}{\partial t} - (\epsilon_N - \epsilon_{N'})\right]\langle N|\bar{\rho}_1|N'\rangle$$

$$= [\theta(N') - \theta(N)]\left\{\sum_{MM'}\langle NM|v|N'M'\rangle_{A.S.}\langle M'|\bar{\rho}_1|M\rangle + \langle N|\mathcal{W}|N'\rangle\right\}$$

This has just the form of the previous equation if $\bar{\rho}_1$ is written in terms of β's. The appropriate relation is easily derived from

$$\bar{\rho} = \sum_n |\Phi_n\rangle\langle\Phi_n|\,\theta(n)$$

It is

$$\bar{\rho}_1 = \sum_{nM}\beta_{nM}|M\rangle\langle n|\,\theta(n)e^{i\epsilon_n t/\hbar} + \beta_{nM}{}^*|n\rangle\langle M|\,\theta(n)e^{-i\epsilon_n t/\hbar}$$

whence

$$\langle N|\bar{\rho}_1|N'\rangle = \theta(N')\beta_{N'N}e^{i\epsilon_{N'}t/\hbar} + \theta(N)\beta_{NN'}{}^*e^{-i\epsilon_N t/\hbar}$$

Consideration of the "response" $\mathrm{Tr}(W^+\bar{\rho}_1)$ leads to evaluation of the matrix elements W_{a0}, as before.

To conclude, in the sense that it appears as a natural extension of the familiar Hartree-Fock procedure, the RPA method is probably made most plausible by the present time-dependent approach. Even so, we are far from having a satisfactory justification of the method. It appears that this is not possible formally; the best we can do is to use the method and check its results against experiment. As an added check, it should be shown that corrections from the HRPA are small.

10

APPLICATION OF THE RPA METHOD TO NUCLEAR OSCILLATIONS: CASE OF SPHERICAL EQUILIBRIUM AND NO PAIRING FORCES

In those nuclei where pairing force effects are not well developed (i.e., there is little configuration mixing, such as in light nuclei, near closed shells, etc.) we may discuss collective vibrations in terms of real particles rather than quasi-particles. This has the advantage that we may treat neutrons and protons together in a proper fashion, using the isotopic spin formalism if convenient. [Since the pairing force theories have difficulty in coping with the presence of two (interacting) kinds of particle, this is not possible when working with quasi-particles.]

The results already derived in Chaps. 8 and 9 are nearly sufficient to enable one to set up an actual numerical calculation of a nuclear oscillation. It only remains to set up phase conventions and to express the matrix elements between states of the particle-hole type in terms of these between states of the particle-particle type.

We first do this, then we derive these same results by three somewhat different procedures. Each of these gives a certain special insight into the RPA method.

10-1 USE OF RESULTS OF CHAPTER 8

From Chap. 8 we have

$$[H, A_i^+] = \sum_j \left(o_{ij}' A_j^+ + o_{ij}'' A_j \right)$$

with

$$o_{ij}' = \langle i \,|\, H \,|\, j \rangle - \langle 0 \,|\, H \,|\, 0 \rangle \, \delta_{ij}$$

$$o_{ij}'' = \langle ij \,|\, H \,|\, 0 \rangle$$

We first set up a scheme of notation. The two-body potential-energy part of H, $\frac{1}{2}\Sigma_{i\neq j}\, v_{ij}$, may be written in the second quantization formalism as

$$V = -\tfrac{1}{2}\sum_{\alpha\text{'s}} \langle \alpha_1\alpha_2 | v | \alpha_3\alpha_4\rangle_{\text{N.A.S.}}\, a_{\alpha_1}{}^{+} a_{\alpha_2}{}^{+} a_{\alpha_3} a_{\alpha_4}$$

$$= -\tfrac{1}{4}\sum_{\alpha\text{'s}} \langle \alpha_1\alpha_2 | v | \alpha_3\alpha_4\rangle_{\text{A.S.}}\, a_{\alpha_1}{}^{+} a_{\alpha_2}{}^{+} a_{\alpha_3} a_{\alpha_4}$$

where $\alpha \equiv n\ell jmm_t$, the set of quantum numbers labeling particle states, and "A.S." and "N.A.S." mean "antisymmetrized" and "not antisymmetrized":

$$\langle \alpha_1\alpha_2 | v | \alpha_3\alpha_4\rangle_{\text{A.S.}}$$

$$= \langle \alpha_1\alpha_2 | v | \alpha_3\alpha_4\rangle_{\text{N.A.S.}} - \langle \alpha_1\alpha_2 | v | \alpha_4\alpha_3\rangle_{\text{N.A.S.}}$$

We assume, in N.A.S. matrix elements, that the first and third positions belong to one particle and the second and fourth to the other.

We introduce the operators

$$A^{+}(\bar{j}_1\,\bar{j}_2\,TM_T\,LM) \equiv \sum_{m\text{'s}} (j_1 m_1 j_2 - m_2 | LM)\left(\tfrac{1}{2} m_{t_1}\, \tfrac{1}{2} - m_{t_2} \,|\, TM_T\right)$$

$$a_{\alpha_1}{}^{+}\left[(-)^{j_2+\frac{1}{2}-m_2-m_{t_2}}\, a_{\alpha_2}\right]$$

where $\bar{j}$ is written for the set $(n\ell j)$ for brevity, and the phase is included because we use the phase conventions: $a_{jm}{}^{+}$ creates a particle state of rotation character jm; a_{jm} creates a hole state of character $j-m$, and multiplies by $(-)^{j-m}$. Extension to isotopic spin is immediate. It follows from the definition of A^{+} that

$$A^{+}(\bar{j}_1\,\bar{j}_2\,TM_T\,LM) = (-)^{j_2-j_1+M+M_T}\, A(\bar{j}_2\,\bar{j}_1\,T - M_T\,L - M)$$

We shall assume, unless stated otherwise, that $\bar{j}_1, \bar{j}_2$ are unoccupied, occupied in the unperturbed ground state. Also, except where confusion may result, we will drop the labels LT on the quantities A^{+}, o', etc., and assume that we are dealing specifically with one definite multipole $\mathcal{L} \equiv LT$. We have

$$[H, A^+(\bar{j}_1\,\bar{j}_2 M_T M)] = \sum_{\bar{j}_1{}'\bar{j}_2{}'} \Big[o'_{\bar{j}_1\bar{j}_2,\,\bar{j}_1{}'\bar{j}_2{}'}\; A^+(\bar{j}_1{}'\bar{j}_2{}' M_T M)$$

$$+\; o''_{\bar{j}_1\bar{j}_2,\,\bar{j}_1{}'\bar{j}_2{}'}\; A(\bar{j}_1{}'\bar{j}_2{}' - M_T - M)\Big]$$

with

$$o'_{\bar{j}_1\bar{j}_2,\,\bar{j}_1{}'\bar{j}_2{}'} = \langle \Phi_0 |\, A(\bar{j}_1{}'\bar{j}_2{}' M_T M)(T + V)\, A^+(\bar{j}_1\,\bar{j}_2 M_T M)\,|\Phi_0\rangle$$

$$= \delta_{\bar{j}_1\bar{j}_2,\,\bar{j}_1{}'\bar{j}_2{}'}\left(\epsilon_{\bar{j}_1} - \epsilon_{\bar{j}_2}\right)$$

$$+\; \frac{(-)^{L+T+j_1+j_2+1}}{\hat{L}\hat{T}}\; \langle \bar{j}_1{}'\,\bar{j}_2\,|v|\,\bar{j}_2{}'\,\bar{j}_1\rangle_{A.S.}$$

$$o''_{\bar{j}_1\bar{j}_2,\,\bar{j}_1{}'\bar{j}_2{}'} = \langle \Phi_0 |\, VA^+(\bar{j}_1{}'\bar{j}_2{}' - M_T - M)\, A^+(\bar{j}_1\,\bar{j}_2 M_T M)\,|\Phi_0\rangle$$

$$= \frac{(-)^{L+T-M-M_T}}{\hat{L}\hat{T}}\; \langle \bar{j}_1\,\bar{j}_1{}'\,|v|\,\bar{j}_2\,\bar{j}_2{}'\rangle_{A.S.}$$

where

$$\hat{P} \equiv \sqrt{2P+1}$$

$$\langle \bar{j}_1\,\bar{j}_2\,|v|\,\bar{j}_3\,\bar{j}_4\rangle_{N.A.S.}$$

$$= \sum_{m\text{'s},M\text{'s}} (LML - M\,|\,00)(TM_T T - M_T\,|\,00)$$

$$\times\, (j_1 - m_1 j_3 m_3\,|\,LM)(j_2 - m_2 j_4 m_4\,|\,L - M)$$

$$\times \left(\tfrac{1}{2} - m_{t_1} \tfrac{1}{2} m_{t_3}\,|\,TM_T\right)\left(\tfrac{1}{2} - m_{t_2} \tfrac{1}{2} m_{t_4}\,|\,T - M_T\right)$$

$$\times\, (-)^{j_1+j_2+1-m_1-m_2-m_{t_1}-m_{t_2}}\; \langle \alpha_1\alpha_2\,|v|\,\alpha_3\alpha_4\rangle_{N.A.S.}$$

and satisfies

$$\langle \bar{j}_1\,\bar{j}_2\,|v|\,\bar{j}_3\,\bar{j}_4\rangle_{N.A.S.} = \langle \bar{j}_2\,\bar{j}_1\,|v|\,\bar{j}_4\,\bar{j}_3\rangle_{N.A.S.}$$

$$= (-)^{j_1+j_2-j_3-j_4}\; \langle \bar{j}_3\,\bar{j}_4\,|v|\,\bar{j}_1\,\bar{j}_2\rangle_{N.A.S.}$$

The quantities $\epsilon_{\bar{j}}$ are single-particle energies:

$$\epsilon_{\bar{j}} = \langle \alpha | T | \alpha \rangle + \sum_{\alpha_2(\text{occ.})} \langle \alpha\alpha_2 | v | \alpha\alpha_2 \rangle_{A.S.}$$

To derive these results is a standard exercise in shell-model operator algebra. The diagonal terms $(\epsilon_{\bar{j}_1} - \epsilon_{\bar{j}_2})$ would have followed from the effective single-particle Hamiltonian:

$$H_p = T + V_p = \sum_\alpha \epsilon_{\bar{j}}\, a_\alpha^+ a_\alpha$$

Notice the reversal of magnetic quantum numbers in the terms in A.

10-2 DIRECT EVALUATION OF $[H,A_i^+]$ IN TERMS OF a_α

Consider the quantity $[V, a_{\alpha_1}^+ a_{\alpha_2}]$. Referring to Sec. 9-1, we can linearize thus with method (2). Retaining only terms in which a suffix on an **a** operator equals one on an **a**$^+$ operator,

$$\begin{aligned}\left[V, a_{\alpha_1}^+ a_{\alpha_2}\right] = -\sum_{1'2'} \Big\{ &\langle 1'\,2 | v | 12' \rangle_{A.S.}\, a_{1'}^+ (n_2 - n_1) a_{2'} \\ &+ \langle 1'2' | v | 12' \rangle_{A.S.}\, a_{1'}^+ n_{2'} a_2 \\ &- \langle 1'\,2 | v | 1'\,2' \rangle_{A.S.}\, a_1^+ n_{1'} a_{2'} \Big\}\end{aligned}$$

where we write, for brevity, 1,2,1′,2′ for $\alpha_1, \alpha_2, \alpha_{1'}, \alpha_{2'}$. If we now replace the number operators $n_\alpha \equiv a_\alpha^+ a_\alpha$ by their vacuum expectation values, this becomes

$$\begin{aligned}[V, a_1^+ a_2] = \pm &\sum_{1'2'} \langle 1'\,2 | v | 12' \rangle_{A.S.}\, a_{1'}^+ a_{2'} \\ &+ \sum_{1'} \langle 1' | V_p | 1 \rangle a_{1'}^+ a_2 - \sum_{2'} \langle 2 | V_p | 2' \rangle a_1^+ a_{2'}\end{aligned}$$

where + applies if α_1 is occupied, α_2 unoccupied, and − applies if the situation is reversed. If both α_1, α_2 are occupied or both unoccupied, the first term is zero. The single-particle potential V_p is such that

$$\langle 1 | V_p | 2 \rangle = \sum_{2'(\text{occ.})} \langle 12' | v | 22' \rangle_{A.S.}$$

is over occupied states only. For the kinetic energy T

$$= \sum_{1'} \langle 1' | T | 1 \rangle a_{1'}^{+} a_2 - \sum_{2'} \langle 2 | T | 2' \rangle a_1^{+} a_{2'}$$

...nce $(T + V_p)|\alpha\rangle = \epsilon_{\bar{j}} |\alpha\rangle$ it follows that

$$[H, a_1^{+} a_2] = \pm \sum_{1'2'} \langle 1' 2 | v | 12' \rangle_{A.S.}\, a_{1'}^{+} a_{2'} + \left(\epsilon_{\bar{j}_1} - \epsilon_{\bar{j}_2}\right) a_1^{+} a_2$$

When $\bar{j}_1, \bar{j}_2$ are unoccupied, occupied in the unperturbed ground state, we can directly couple $a_{\alpha_1}^{+}$ and a_{α_2} to give $A^{+}(\bar{j}_1 \bar{j}_2 M_T M)$. When the reverse is true, we first take the conjugate of the equation. In both cases, it is easy to see that we have exactly the equations quoted in 10-1 for $[H, A^{+}]$, o′, and o″.

When $\bar{j}_1, \bar{j}_2$ are both occupied or both unoccupied, $[H, a_{\alpha_1}^{+} a_{\alpha_2}] = 0$. This means that such combinations are uncoupled from the ones above, and so need not be considered.

10-3 DERIVATION WITH UNPERTURBED GROUND STATE AS VACUUM

It is instructive to re-derive the theory above in terms of new operators b instead of a, where the b's are such that the unperturbed ground state is the vacuum state. This also facilitates introduction to the more general problem, discussed in Chap. 12, of collective motion in the presence of pairing forces. We follow Reference 14. The transformation to the unperturbed ground state (assumed to be a closed shell) as vacuum may be written

$$b_\alpha = U_\alpha a_\alpha - V_\alpha a_{\bar{\alpha}}^{+}$$

$$b_{\bar{\alpha}} = U_\alpha a_{\bar{\alpha}} + V_\alpha a_\alpha^{+}$$

where $\bar{\alpha}$ is the time-reversed state of α, and where $(U_\alpha, V_\alpha) = (0,1)$ and $(1,0)$ for occupied and unoccupied states, respectively. Keeping general values of U_α, V_α for the moment, Wick's theorem gives

$$\begin{aligned} a_1^{+} a_2^{+} a_3 a_4 = {} & N(a_1^{+} a_2^{+} a_3 a_4) + \delta_{1,\bar{2}} U_1 V_1 N(a_3 a_4) + \delta_{4,\bar{3}} U_3 V_3 N(a_1^{+} a_2^{+}) \\ & + V_1^2 [\delta_{14} N(a_2^{+} a_3) - \delta_{13} N(a_2^{+} a_4)] \\ & + V_2^2 [\delta_{23} N(a_1^{+} a_4) - \delta_{24} N(a_1^{+} a_3)] \\ & - \delta_{1,\bar{2}} \delta_{2,\bar{3}} U_1 V_1 U_4 V_4 + (\delta_{14}\delta_{23} - \delta_{13}\delta_{24}) V_1^2 V_2^2 \end{aligned}$$

where N( ) means normal product with respect to the b operators, e.g.,

$$N(a_1^+ a_3) = U_1 U_3 b_1^+ b_3 - V_1 V_3 b_{\bar{3}}^+ b_{\bar{1}} + V_1 U_3 b_{\bar{1}} b_3 + U_1 V_3 b_1^+ b_{\bar{3}}^+$$

With the above choice of U_α, V_α, we have

$$V = V^{(0)} + V^{(2)} + V^{(4)}$$

$$V^{(0)} = \tfrac{1}{2} \sum_{12} \langle 12 | v | 12 \rangle_{A.S.} \; \theta(1)\theta(2)$$

$$V^{(2)} = \sum_{123} \langle 12 | v | 13 \rangle_{A.S.} \; N(a_2^+ a_3)\, \theta(1)$$

$$V^{(4)} = \tfrac{1}{2} \sum_{1234} \langle 12 | v | 43 \rangle_{A.S.} \; N(a_1^+ a_2^+ a_3 a_4)$$

In the expression for $V, V^{(0)}$ is the vacuum (ground state) energy. $V^{(2)}$ represents single-particle excitation energy. If we consider only one principal quantum number for given j, then only terms with $\alpha_2 = \alpha_3$ can occur (since V is scalar), so

$$V^{(2)} = \sum_{2} \langle 2 | V_p | 2 \rangle \; N(a_2^+ a_2)$$

$$= \sum_{2} \langle 2 | V_p | 2 \rangle \; b_2^+ b_2 (1 - \theta(2)) - \sum_{2} \langle 2 | V_p | 2 \rangle \; b_{\bar{2}}^+ b_{\bar{2}}\, \theta(2)$$

where V_p is the one-body potential defined above.

As before, we may cast $V^{(4)}$ in a form with pairs (1,3) and (2,4), each coupled to (L, T) which are coupled to (0,0). We may introduce

$$B^+(\overline{j_1}\,\overline{j_3}\; TM_T LM)$$

$$= \sum_{m's} (j_1 m_1 j_3 m_3 | LM) \left(\tfrac{1}{2} m_{t_1} \tfrac{1}{2} m_{t_3} | TM_T \right) b_{\alpha_1}^+ b_{\alpha_3}^+$$

$$B(\overline{j_1}\,\overline{j_3}\; TM_T LM)$$

$$= \sum_{m's} (j_1 m_1 j_3 m_3 | LM) \left(\tfrac{1}{2} m_{t_1} \tfrac{1}{2} m_{t_3} | TM_T \right) b_{\alpha_3} b_{\alpha_1}$$

and evaluate the commutators of these with $V^{(4)}$. This term contains parts which are zero, first, . . . , fourth order in b's (i.e., $b^+ b^+ b^+ b^+$, $b^+ b^+ b^+ b$, . . . , bbbb) and we write these $V_0 \cdots V_4$. These have the following commutation properties with B:

$$[V_0^{(4)} B^+] = 0$$

$$[V_1^{(4)}, B^+] \sim b^+ b^+ b^+ b^+$$

$$[V_2^{(4)}, B^+] \sim b^+ b^+ b b^+ + b^+ b^+ b^+ b$$

$$[V_3^{(4)}, B^+] \sim b^+ b b^+ b + b^+ b^+ b b$$

$$[V_4^{(4)}, B^+] \sim b b^+ b b + b^+ b b b$$

When these quantities are reduced to normal form, second-order terms are introduced, viz., $b^+ b^+$, $b^+ b$, and bb from V_2, V_3, V_4, respectively.

In Sec. 9-1 (paragraph 2) we saw that the RPA method consists in taking the fourth-order terms, contracting them to second order by putting indices equal where possible, then dropping the uncontracted terms and replacing number operators by ground-state expectation values in the contracted ones. This means that we entirely drop the fourth-order terms in normal form, since the expectation values arising from such terms are zero.

When this procedure is applied to $[V, b^+ b]$, this quantity vanishes, since all terms are in normal form without any second-order terms. This means that terms in $b^+ b$ in $[V, B]$ and $[V, B^+]$ can be dropped, since operators $b^+ b$ are "uncoupled" from the others.

The final result for the commutator is

$$\begin{aligned}[H, B^+(\overline{j_1}\,\overline{j_2})] &= \left(e_{\overline{j_1}} + e_{\overline{j_2}}\right) B^+(\overline{j_1}\,\overline{j_2}) \\ &\quad + \sum_{\overline{j_3}\,\overline{j_4}} \{P(\overline{j_1}\,\overline{j_2}\,\overline{j_3}\,\overline{j_4}\ TL)\, B^+(\overline{j_3}\,\overline{j_4}) \\ &\quad + R(\overline{j_1}\,\overline{j_2}\,\overline{j_3}\,\overline{j_4}\ TL)(-)^X B(\overline{j_3}\,\overline{j_4})\}\end{aligned}$$

In this equation $\overline{e}_j$ is quasi-particle energy, X is $(L + T + M_L + M_T)$, and

$$\begin{aligned}P(1234) &= -(U_1 U_2 U_3 U_4 + V_1 V_2 V_3 V_4)\, G(1234) \\ &\quad - (U_1 V_2 U_3 V_4 + V_1 U_2 V_3 U_4) F(1234) \\ &\quad + (U_1 V_2 V_3 U_4 + V_1 U_2 U_3 V_4)\, \theta(34TL)\, F(1243)\end{aligned}$$

$$\begin{aligned}R(1234) &= (U_1 U_2 V_3 V_4 + V_1 V_2 U_3 U_4)\, G(1234) \\ &\quad - (U_1 V_2 V_3 U_4 + V_1 U_2 U_3 V_4) F(1234) \\ &\quad + (U_1 V_2 U_3 V_4 + V_1 U_2 V_3 U_4)\, \theta(34TL)\, F(1243)\end{aligned}$$

Here we replace $\bar{j}$'s by subscripts for brevity and drop TL as understood. G, F are the matrix elements:

$$G(1234) = -\tfrac{1}{2}\langle \underbrace{12}{} | v | \underbrace{34}{} \rangle_{A.S.}$$

$$F(1234) = -\tfrac{1}{2}\theta(34TL)\langle 14 | v | 23 \rangle_{A.S.} / \hat{L}\hat{T}$$

and

$$\theta(34TL) = \theta(j_3 j_4 TL) \doteq (-)^{j_3+j_4+T+L+1}$$

The matrix elements with links are like those used before; in particular,

$$\langle \underbrace{12}{} | v | \underbrace{34}{} \rangle_{A.S.} = \sum_{\substack{m's \\ (M's\ \text{fixed})}} (j_1 m_1 j_2 m_2 | JM)(j_3 m_3 j_4 m_4 | JM)$$
$$\times \left(\tfrac{1}{2} m_{t_1} \tfrac{1}{2} m_{t_2} | TM_T\right)\left(\tfrac{1}{2} m_{t_3} \tfrac{1}{2} m_{t_4} | TM_T\right)$$
$$\times \langle \alpha_1 \alpha_2 | v | \alpha_3 \alpha_4 \rangle_{A.S.}$$

If we now make the special transformation to the Fermi sea as vacuum (no pairing forces), and if orbit $\bar{j}_1$ is above the sea and $\bar{j}_2$ below (i.e., $V_1 = U_2 = 0$), then terms in G drop out and

$$P(1234) = -U_3 V_4 F(1234) + V_3 U_4 \theta(34TL) F(1243)$$

$$R(1234) = -V_3 U_4 F(1234) + U_3 V_4 \theta(34TL) F(1243)$$

Inserting these expressions in the commutator:

$$[H, B^+(12)] = (e_1 + e_2) B^+(1,2) + \sum_{34} [U_3 V_4 C_{12}^+(34) + (-)^X U_4 V_3 C_{12}(34)]$$

where

$$C_{12}(34) = -F(1234) B(34) + \theta(34TL) F(1243)(-)^X B^+(34)$$

U_3V_4 and U_4V_3 are zero except for particle-hole pairs, so only these need be considered. If $\bar{j}_3$ is above the Fermi sea and $\bar{j}_4$ below, the pair $(\bar{j}_3, \bar{j}_4)$ contributes to the sum on the right:

$$C_{12}^+(3,4) + (-)^X C_{12}(4,3)$$
$$= 2[-F(1234) B^+(34) + \theta(34TL) F(1243)(-)^X B(34)]$$

where we use the fact that

$$B(43) = -\theta(34TL)B(34)$$

This linearized operator relation for $[H, B^+(12)]$ can be seen, on inspection, to be identical to that obtained in 10-1 and 10-2.

10–4 DERIVATION IN TERMS OF MULTIPOLE FORCES

Definition of Multipole Force

The multipole force of order TL is that force which converts a pair of nucleons in orbits $\bar{j}_1, \bar{j}_2$ into a pair in orbits $\bar{j}_1', \bar{j}_2'$, where pairs $(\bar{j}_1, \bar{j}_1')$, $(\bar{j}_2, \bar{j}_2')$ are each coupled to TL. Because of exchange, we must not demand that the particle in $\bar{j}_1'$ is the same as that in $\bar{j}_1$. If the actual force is v, we may define the corresponding multipole force of order TL, v_{TL} (say), as that force with matrix elements

$$\underbrace{\overbrace{\langle \bar{j}_1' \bar{j}_2' | v_{TL} | \bar{j}_1 \bar{j}_2 \rangle}^{(T'L')}}_{(T'L')}{}_{A.S.} = \begin{cases} \underbrace{\overbrace{\langle \bar{j}_1' \bar{j}_2' | v | \bar{j}_1 \bar{j}_2 \rangle}^{(TL)}}_{(TL)}{}_{A.S.} & \text{if } T'L' = TL \\ 0 & \text{if } T'L' \neq TL \end{cases}$$

Multipole Force in Coordinate Representation

We now try to extract an explicit coordinate form for v_{TL}. It is well known that we can expand the force v(ij) between nucleons i,j thus:

$$v(ij) = \sum_{TL} u_{TL}(i,j)$$

$$u_{TL}(i,j) = \sum_{\gamma} f_{TL\gamma}(i,j) \left[\bar{\chi}_{TL\gamma}(i) \cdot \chi_{TL\gamma}(j) \right]$$

where $\chi_{TL\gamma}(j)$ is an operator for particle j of rotation properties given by TL. It is combined in scalar product with the conjugate function for particle i. γ labels other features of the expansion, e.g., the coupling of intrinsic and orbital spin operators. f is scalar in particles i and j, i.e., depends on radial positions only. It is straightforward algebra to show

$$\langle \overbrace{\underbrace{\overline{j}_1'\,\overline{j}_2'\,|v|\,\overline{j}_1\,\overline{j}_2}_{TL}}^{TL} \rangle_{N.A.S.} = \sum_{\gamma} \frac{1}{\hat{L}^2\hat{T}^2} \left(\overline{j}_1'|\chi_{TL\gamma}|\overline{j}_1\right)\left(\overline{j}_2'|\chi_{TL\gamma}|\overline{j}_2\right)$$

$$\times \langle u_{\overline{j}_1'}(i)\,u_{\overline{j}_2'}(j)\,|\,f_{TL\gamma}(ij)\,|\,u_{\overline{j}_1}(i)\,u_{\overline{j}_2}(j)\rangle_{N.A.S.}$$

$$= \langle \overbrace{\underbrace{\overline{j}_1'\,\overline{j}_2'\,|\,u_{TL}\,|\,\overline{j}_1\,\overline{j}_2}_{TL}}^{TL} \rangle_{N.A.S.}$$

$$\langle \overbrace{\underbrace{\overline{j}_1'\,\overline{j}_2'\,|v|\,\overline{j}_2\,\overline{j}_1}_{TL}}^{TL} \rangle_{N.A.S.} = \sum_{T'L'} (-)^{j_1+j_2+j_1'+j_2'}\ U(j_1'j_2j_1j_2',L'L)$$

$$\times\ U(\tfrac{1}{2}\tfrac{1}{2}\tfrac{1}{2}\tfrac{1}{2},T'T)\ \langle \overbrace{\underbrace{\overline{j}_1'\,\overline{j}_2'\,|\,u_{T'L'}\,|\,\overline{j}_2\,\overline{j}_1}_{T'L'}}^{T'L'} \rangle_{N.A.S.}$$

Thus we see that, because of the presence of the exchange term, the multipole force is *NOT* simply the appropriate term u_{LT} in the above expansion. Rather the direct terms are given by U_{LT}, while the exchange ones are given by $v(i,j)P_{ij}$, where P_{ij} is the operator exchanging i and j. It is not possible to combine these two results into an explicit coordinate form for the multipole force. It is clear that it is also not possible to write v as a sum of independent multipole forces, $v = \Sigma_{TL} v_{TL}$, since the occurrence of a (direct) matrix element $\langle \overline{j}_1'\,\overline{j}_2'\,|\,u_{TL}\,|\,\overline{j}_1\overline{j}_2\rangle_{N.A.S.}$ of multipole order TL implies the occurrence of (exchange) matrix elements $\langle \overline{j}_1'\,\overline{j}_2'\,|\,u_{TL}\,|\,\overline{j}_1\,\overline{j}_2\rangle$ for other multipole orders T′L′.

In some published papers[14,30] calculations for a multipole oscillation have been done assuming that the only part of the force that need be considered is the "direct" one U_{TL}, e.g., TL = 0,2+:

$$u_{TL}(i,j) = r_i^2 r_j^2 P_2(\cos\theta_{ij})$$

(Furthermore, the exchange terms from u_{TL} are ignored.) This assumption has been made in almost all papers in which pairing force effects are included, i.e., RPA (QP) approximation (see Chap. 12

and Reference 14). From our discussion above it follows that such calculations must be regarded as schematic, and are not reliable for detailed numerical results. In fact, in some problems[36] it is found that the exchange terms from terms $U_{\mathcal{L}'}(\mathcal{L}' \neq \mathcal{L})$ are more important than the term $u_{\mathcal{L}}$ in determining the collective features of oscillations of multipole order $\mathcal{L}$.

Multipole Force in Second Quantization Formalism

On commuting $a_{\alpha_2}^+$ and a_{α_3}, and performing some vector coupling, it can be shown that V may be written in the following two ways:

$$V = \frac{1}{2} \sum_{TLj's} \langle \overline{j_1}\, \overline{j_2} | v | \overline{j_3}\, \overline{j_4} \rangle_{N.A.S.} [\tilde{A}^+(\overline{j_1}\, \overline{j_3}\, TL)\, \tilde{A}^+(\overline{j_2}\, \overline{j_4}\, TL)]_{00} + \text{one-body term} \qquad (A)$$

$$= \frac{1}{4} \sum_{TLj's} \langle \overline{j_1}\, \overline{j_2} | v | \overline{j_3}\, \overline{j_4} \rangle_{A.S.} [\tilde{A}^+(\overline{j_1}\, \overline{j_3}\, TL)\, \tilde{A}^+(\overline{j_2}\, \overline{j_4}\, TL)]_{00} + \text{one-body term} \qquad (B)$$

The one-body terms arise from the commuting of $a_{\alpha_2}^+$ and a_{α_3}, and are of no immediate interest. The notation $[\ \ ]_{00}$ means that the A^+ operators are coupled to T = 0, L = 0. The $\tilde{A}^+$ are the same as the earlier A^+ operators, except that no restriction is placed on the particle states being occupied or unoccupied in Φ_0.

At first sight it appears that the multipole force V is simply the term of appropriate TL in the above expansions (A) or (B) of V. Closer inspection shows that this is not so; for instance, the term from (A) is not antisymmetric; also the terms from (A) and (B) differ by a factor 2. Thus we must conclude that a term of given TL in (A) or (B) can contribute to multipole forces of order $T'L' \neq TL$ besides that of order TL. This is confirmed by the easily proved relations

$$[\tilde{A}^+(\overline{j_1}\, \overline{j_3}\, TL)\, \tilde{A}^+(\overline{j_2}\, \overline{j_4}\, TL)]_{00}$$

$$= - \sum_{T'L'} (-)^{j_1+j_2+j_3+j_4}\, U(j_1 j_3 j_4 j_2, LL')\, U(\tfrac{1}{2}\tfrac{1}{2}\tfrac{1}{2}\tfrac{1}{2}, TT')$$

$$\times [\tilde{A}^+(\overline{j_1}\, \overline{j_4}\, TL)\, \tilde{A}^+(\overline{j_2}\, \overline{j_3}\, TL)]_{00}$$

$$+ \text{ terms containing } \delta_{j_2 j_3},\ \delta_{j_2 j_4}$$

$$\underbrace{\overbrace{\langle \bar{j}_1 \bar{j}_2 | v | \bar{j}_3 \bar{j}_4 \rangle}^{TL}}_{TL}{}_{N.A.S.} = \sum_{T'L'} (-)^{j_1+j_2+j_3+j_4}\, U(j_1 j_3 j_4 j_2, LL')$$

$$\times\, U(\tfrac{1}{2}\tfrac{1}{2}\tfrac{1}{2}\tfrac{1}{2}, TT')\, \langle \bar{j}_1 \bar{j}_2 | v | \bar{j}_3 \bar{j}_4 \rangle_{N.A.S.}$$

The δ-function terms are similar to those in expression (A) for V and correspond to spherically symmetric one-body terms which are of no interest to us.

It follows from these relations that, for any given set of j's:

$$\sum_{TL} \underbrace{\overbrace{\langle \bar{j}_1 \bar{j}_2 | v | \bar{j}_3 \bar{j}_4 \rangle}^{TL}}_{TL}{}_{N.A.S.}\, [\tilde{A}^+(\bar{j}_1 \bar{j}_3\; TL)\, \tilde{A}^+(\bar{j}_2 \bar{j}_4\; TL)]_{00}$$

$$= -\sum_{T'L'} \underbrace{\overbrace{\langle \bar{j}_1 \bar{j}_2 | v | \bar{j}_3 \bar{j}_4 \rangle}^{T'L'}}_{T'L'}{}_{N.A.S.}\, [\tilde{A}^+(\bar{j}_1 \bar{j}_4\; T'L')\, \tilde{A}^+(\bar{j}_2 \bar{j}_3\; T'L')]_{00}$$

On summing over the j's we can see that we have found the missing exchange terms corresponding to the direct terms in (A), and have thus shown (A) and (B) to be identical. It can be seen that V may be written

$$V = \sum_{\substack{(\bar{j}_1 \bar{j}_2)\\(\bar{j}_3 \bar{j}_4)\\TL}} \langle \bar{j}_1 \bar{j}_2 | v | \bar{j}_3 \bar{j}_4 \rangle_{A.S.}\, [\tilde{A}^+(\bar{j}_1 \bar{j}_3\; TL)\, \tilde{A}^+(\bar{j}_2 \bar{j}_4\; TL)]_{00} + \text{one-body terms}$$

where a sum like that over $(\bar{j}_3 \bar{j}_4)$ means over each pair once only.

What we wish to do is to pick out from V the part V_{TL} corresponding to multipole order TL. This may be found by picking out those terms which can convert a pair of orbits $\bar{j}_3, \bar{j}_4$ into the pair $\bar{j}_1, \bar{j}_2$ by operators $\tilde{A}^+(\ldots TL)$. Clearly the part of V that makes $\bar{j}_3 \to \bar{j}_1$, $\bar{j}_4 \to \bar{j}_2$ is the TL term in the above:

$$V_{TL}(\bar{j}_3 \to \bar{j}_1, \bar{j}_4 \to \bar{j}_2)$$

$$= \langle \bar{j}_1 \bar{j}_2 | v | \bar{j}_3 \bar{j}_4 \rangle_{A.S.}\, [\tilde{A}^+(\bar{j}_1 \bar{j}_3\; TL)\, \tilde{A}^+(\bar{j}_2 \bar{j}_4\; TL)]_{00}$$

The part of V making $\overline{j_3} \to \overline{j_2}$, $\overline{j_4} \to \overline{j_1}$ is obtained from summing over terms T′L′ after rearranging using the relations above. This gives

$$V_{TL}(\overline{j_3} \to \overline{j_2}, \overline{j_4} \to \overline{j_1})$$

$$= -\langle \overline{j_1}\,\overline{j_2} | v | \overline{j_3}\,\overline{j_4} \rangle_{A.S.} \, [\widetilde{A}^+(\overline{j_1}\,\overline{j_4}\,TL)\,\widetilde{A}^+(\overline{j_2}\,\overline{j_3}\,TL)]_{00}$$

It is important to realize that these two terms do not contribute additively to V because there is a part of V that occurs in both terms. This is related to the fact that one can extract from $V(\overline{j_3} \to \overline{j_1}, \overline{j_4} \to \overline{j_2})$ a part that is capable of making $\overline{j_3} \to \overline{j_2}$ and $j_4 \to j_1$ (and vice versa). The common part is less than either term separately by the factor

$$U(j_1 j_3 j_4 j_2 LL)\,U(\tfrac{1}{2}\tfrac{1}{2}\tfrac{1}{2}\tfrac{1}{2}TT)$$

If this factor is considered small, and the presence of the common part ignored, then

$$V_{TL} = \sum_{\overline{j}\text{'s}} V_{TL}(\overline{j_3} \to \overline{j_1}, \overline{j_4} \to \overline{j_2}) + V_{TL}(\overline{j_3} \to \overline{j_2}, \overline{j_4} \to \overline{j_1})$$

$$= \tfrac{1}{2} \sum_{\overline{j}\text{'s}} \langle j_1 j_2 | v | j_3 j_4 \rangle_{A.S.} \, [\widetilde{A}^+(\overline{j_1}\,\overline{j_3}\,TL)\,\widetilde{A}^+(\overline{j_2}\,\overline{j_4}\,TL)]_{00}$$

It is important to realize that the extraction of an explicit form for the multipole force of given order TL is not at all necessary for the theory of collective vibrations. This theory can be carried through for any given vibration order TL in terms of V without any reference to V_{TL}. Our only motive in the present discussion was to see if we could pick out from V a part V_{TL} that is an effective multipole force in the sense that it gives the same results as V using the RPA method.

Application of the RPA Method to Multipole Force V_{TL}

The general commutation rule for the A's is

$$[\widetilde{A}^+(\overline{j_1}\,\overline{j_2}\,TM_T\,LM), \widetilde{A}^+(\overline{j_1}'\,\overline{j_2}'\,T'M_T'\,L'M')]$$

$$= \delta_{\overline{j_2}\,\overline{j_1}'} \frac{\hat{T}\hat{L}}{\sqrt{2}\,\hat{j}_2} (-)^{L+M+T+T_M} \sum_{L''T''} U(Lj_1L'j_2', j_2L'')$$

$$\times U(T\tfrac{1}{2}T'\tfrac{1}{2}, \tfrac{1}{2}T'')(L - ML''M'' | L'M')$$

$$\times (T - M_T T''M_T'' | T'M')\,\widetilde{A}^+(\overline{j_1}\,\overline{j_2}'\,T''M_T''\,L''M'')$$

—(same expression with primed and unprimed quantities reversed)

The expectation value of this taken in a closed-shell ground state is

$$(-)^{M+T_M+j_1-j_2}\,\delta(\overline{j_1}\,\overline{j_2}\,TM_T\,LM,\,\overline{j_2}'\,\overline{j_1}'\,T' - M_T'\,L' - M')$$
$$\times\,(\theta(\overline{j_1}) - \theta(\overline{j_2}))$$

Here we have used the fact that the expectation value of $\sqrt{2}\,\hat{j}\,\tilde{A}^+(\overline{j}\,\overline{j}0000)$ is $\theta(j)$.

Following the linearization procedure by replacing commutators by their ground-state expectation values, i.e., using the quasi-boson approximation as expressed in the commutation relation in 9-1,

$$[V_{TL},\tilde{A}^+(\overline{j_1}\,\overline{j_2}\,TM_T\,LM)]$$
$$= \frac{(-)^{L+T+j_2+j_1}}{\hat{L}\hat{T}}\,(\theta(\overline{j_2}) - \theta(\overline{j_1}))\sum_{j_1'j_2'}\langle\overline{j_1}'\,\overline{j_2}\,|\,v\,|\,\overline{j_1}\,\overline{j_2}'\rangle_{A.S.}$$
$$\times\,\tilde{A}^+(\overline{j_1}'\,\overline{j_2}'\,TM_T\,LM)$$

If the one-body part H_p of the Hamiltonian H is taken as

$$H_p = \sum_\alpha \epsilon_{\overline{j}}\,a_\alpha{}^+ a_\alpha$$
$$= \sum_{\overline{j}} \epsilon_{\overline{j}}\,\sqrt{2}\,\hat{j}\,\tilde{A}^+(\overline{j}\,\overline{j}\,0000)$$

then

$$[H_p,\tilde{A}^+(\overline{j_1}\,\overline{j_2}\,TM_T\,LM)] = \left(\epsilon_{\overline{j_1}} - \epsilon_{\overline{j_2}}\right)\tilde{A}^+(\overline{j_1}\,\overline{j_2}\,TM_T\,LM)$$

Thus the o-matrix satisfying $[\mathbf{H},\tilde{\mathbf{A}}] = \mathbf{o}\tilde{\mathbf{A}}$ is

$$o_{\overline{j_1}\,\overline{j_2},\overline{j_1}'\overline{j_2}'} = \left(\epsilon_{\overline{j_1}} - \epsilon_{\overline{j_2}}\right)\delta(\overline{j_1}\,\overline{j_2},\overline{j_1}'\overline{j_2}')$$
$$+\,\frac{(-)^{L+T+j_1+j_2}}{\hat{L}\hat{T}}\,(\theta(\overline{j_2}) - \theta(\overline{j_1}))$$
$$\times\,\langle\overline{j_1}'\overline{j_2}\,|\,v\,|\,\overline{j_1}\,\overline{j_2}'\rangle_{A.S.}$$

The presence of the factor $\theta(\overline{j_2}) - \theta(\overline{j_1})$ means that $[V_{TL},\tilde{A}_k{}^+]$ vanishes unless $\tilde{A}_k{}^+$ creates a hole-particle pair in the unperturbed ground state or destroys such a pair. This means that all operators $\widetilde{A}_k^+$ not of this class can be ignored. $[V,\widetilde{A}_k^+] = 0$ implies $\langle \Psi_{TL} | \widetilde{A}_k | \Psi_0 \rangle = 0$, where Ψ's are the actual ground and excited states; thus such A are uncoupled from other A's. If we restrict the $\widetilde{A}_k^+$ to be of the type that create a hole-particle pair ($\overline{j_1}$ = particle, $\overline{j_2}$ = hole), we have

$$[H, A^+(\overline{j_1}\,\overline{j_2}\, TM_T LM)]$$

$$= \sum_{j_1' j_2'} \left\{ o'_{\overline{j_1}\,\overline{j_2}, \overline{j_1'}\,\overline{j_2'}}\, A^+(\overline{j_1'}\,\overline{j_2'}\, TM_T LM) + o''_{\overline{j_1}\,\overline{j_2}, \overline{j_1'}\,\overline{j_2'}}\, A(j_1' j_2'\, T - M_T L - M) \right\}$$

with

$$o'_{\overline{j_1}\,\overline{j_2}, \overline{j_1'}\,\overline{j_2'}} = \left(\epsilon_{\overline{j_1}} - \epsilon_{\overline{j_2}}\right) \delta_{\overline{j_1}\,\overline{j_2}, \overline{j_1'}\,\overline{j_2'}} + \frac{(-)^{L+T+j_1+j_2}}{\hat{L}\hat{T}} \langle \overline{j_1'}\,\overline{j_2} | v | \overline{j_1}\,\overline{j_2'} \rangle_{A.S.}$$

$$o''_{\overline{j_1}\,\overline{j_2}, \overline{j_1'}\,\overline{j_2'}} = \frac{(-)^{L+T+M+M_T+j_1+j_2+j_1'+j_2'}}{\hat{L}\hat{T}} \langle j_2' j_2 | v | j_1' j_1 \rangle_{A.S.}$$

These expressions are identical to those found earlier in 10-1, 10-2, and 10-3. Thus we see that the results of the RPA method for multipole orders TL are unchanged if we replace V by the particular multipole force V_{TL}.

10-5 RELATION BETWEEN "PARTICLE-HOLE" AND "PARTICLE-PARTICLE" MATRIX ELEMENTS

The matrix elements of nuclear forces as usually given are particle-particle ones of the form

$$\langle \overline{j_1'}\,\overline{j_2} | v | \overline{j_1}\,\overline{j_2'} \rangle_{A.S.} = \sum_{\substack{m's \\ (M's\ \text{fixed})}} (j_1' m_1' j_2 m_2 | LM)(j_1 m_1 j_2' m_2' | LM) \times \left(\tfrac{1}{2} m_{t_1'}, \tfrac{1}{2} m_{t_2} | TM_T\right)\left(\tfrac{1}{2} m_{t_1}, \tfrac{1}{2} m_{t_2'} | TM_T\right) \times \langle \alpha_1' \alpha_2 | v | \alpha_1 \alpha_2' \rangle_{A.S.}$$

It is straightforward to write the matrix elements above in terms of these:

$$\langle \overline{j_1'}\,\overline{j_2}\,|v|\,\overline{j_1}\,\overline{j_2'}\rangle_{A.S.} = \sum_{T'L'} \hat{L}'\,\hat{T}'(-)^{L+T+L'+T'+j_1'+j_2'}$$
$$\times\, U(j_1'j_1j_2j_2',LL')$$
$$\times\, U(\tfrac{1}{2}\tfrac{1}{2}\tfrac{1}{2}\tfrac{1}{2},TT')\,\langle \overline{j_1'}\,\overline{j_2}\,|v|\,\overline{j_1}\,\overline{j_2'}\rangle_{A.S.}$$

10-6 EVALUATION OF TRANSITION MATRIX ELEMENTS

Given a one-particle operator

$$G = \sum_i g_i$$

we can write this in the second quantization formalism as

$$G = \sum_{\alpha\alpha'} \langle\alpha|g|\alpha'\rangle\, a_\alpha{}^{+} a_{\alpha'}$$

$$= \sum_{\substack{j\,j'\\ LTMM_T}} \langle \overline{j}\,|\,g\,|\,\overline{j'}\,\rangle_{LTM_TM}\; \widetilde{A}^{+}(\overline{j}\,\overline{j'} - M_T - M)(-)^{L+T-M-M_T}$$

where

$$\langle \overline{j}\,|\,g\,|\,\overline{j'}\,\rangle_{LTM_TM} = \sum_{m's} (j - mj'm'\,|\,LM)$$
$$\times\, (\tfrac{1}{2} - m_t\,\tfrac{1}{2}m_{t'}\,|\,TM_T)(-)^{j-m+\frac{1}{2}-m_t}$$
$$\times\, \langle\alpha|g|\alpha'\rangle$$

It follows that the transition matrix element is

$$\langle \Psi_{\alpha\overline{M}\overline{M}_T}|G|\Psi_0\rangle = \sum_{\substack{\overline{j}\,\overline{j'}\,LT\\ MM_T}} (-)^{L+T+M+M_T}\, \langle \overline{j}\,|\,g\,|\,\overline{j'}\,\rangle_{LTM_TM}$$
$$\times\, \langle \Psi_{\alpha\overline{M}\overline{M}_T}|\widetilde{A}^{+}(\overline{j}\,\overline{j'}\,M_TM)\,|\Psi_0\rangle$$

Thus it remains to specify the amplitudes $\langle \Psi_{\alpha\overline{M}\overline{M}_T}|\widetilde{A}^{+}(\overline{j}\overline{j'}M_TM)|\Psi_0\rangle$. From the discussion of the RPA method above (e.g., in 8-2), these are zero when $\overline{j},\overline{j'}$ are both occupied or both unoccupied. When $\overline{j}$ is unoccupied, $\overline{j'}$ occupied, $\widetilde{A}^{+}$ is our previous A^{+} and the only nonvanishing amplitude is that with $MM_T = \overline{M}\overline{M}_T$. $\widetilde{A}^{+}(\overline{j'}\,\overline{j}\,M_TM)$ is the previous $A(j\,j' - M_T - M)$, and only $MM_T = -\overline{M}, -\overline{M}_T$ need be considered. By taking matrix elements of the linear operator relation between Ψ_α and Ψ_0, it follows that these amplitudes are just the elements of the eigenvectors $\mathbf{x}_\alpha = \begin{pmatrix} \mathbf{y}_\alpha \\ \mathbf{z}_\alpha \end{pmatrix}$:

$$\langle \Psi_{\alpha \bar{M} \bar{M}_T} | A^+(\bar{j}\,\bar{j}'\,\bar{M}_T \bar{M}) | \Psi_0 \rangle = y_{\alpha, \bar{j}\,\bar{j}'} \qquad (\bar{j} \text{ unocc., } \bar{j}' \text{ occ.})$$

$$\langle \Psi_{\alpha \bar{M} \bar{M}_T} | A(\bar{j}\,\bar{j}' - \bar{M}_T - \bar{M}) | \Psi_0 \rangle = -z_{\alpha, \bar{j}\,\bar{j}'}$$

10-7 SCHEMATIC MODELS

Carrying out the TD or RPA programs for a general force v implies numerical diagonalization of matrices. It is instructive to consider schematic situations in which the appropriate diagonalization may be performed explicitly by algebra. In this way, one is lead to see the factors that are most responsible for the collective phenomena observed.

We first set up the schematic models entirely mathematically, by assigning matrix elements certain simple forms; then we enquire whether these forms have any physical justification.

Mathematical Model[12] 1

Let us designate particle-hole states by k, ℓ. We assume that matrix elements $\langle k | v | \ell \rangle$ have the product form $\xi D_k{}^1 D_\ell{}^2$, where ξ is a strength parameter. Since v is Hermitian and the elements are real, it follows that

$$\langle k | v | \ell \rangle = \langle \ell | v | k \rangle$$

Thus $D_k{}^1 \equiv D_k{}^2$; and so

$$\langle k | v | \ell \rangle = \xi D_k D_\ell$$

The elements $\langle k\ell \, | v | 0 \rangle$ will also have this same value.

Model 1 in TD Approximation. Writing the particle-hole energies as $\Delta\epsilon_k$, the complete energy matrix in the TD case has elements $\Delta\epsilon_k \, \delta_{k\ell} + \xi D_k D_\ell$. This matrix can be diagonalized, with the result that the eigenvalues are the roots of

$$\sum_k \frac{\xi D_k{}^2}{\omega - \Delta\epsilon_k} = 1$$

and the eigenvectors have components $c_k \propto D_k / (\omega - \Delta\epsilon_k)$. The solutions of the eigenvalue equation are such that one of the extreme states in energy is moved away. Whether it is the highest or lowest depends on the sign of ξ; if this is positive (i.e., repulsion) the highest state moves up; if negative (attraction), the lowest state comes down. The state which moves is the "collective state." The matrix element for any operator Q between an excited state and the ground state is

$$(\Phi_\alpha |Q| \Phi_0) = \sum_k c_k Q_k \Big/ \left(\sum_k c_k^2\right)^{1/2}$$

In the extreme case when all $\Delta\epsilon_k$ are the same ($\Delta\epsilon$, say) as in the oscillator, all states except the collective state are unchanged in energy. This state is moved in energy by $\xi \Sigma_k D_k^2$, and its structure is

$$\Phi_\alpha = N \sum_k D_k \Phi_k$$

N being the normalization constant.

The matrix element for operator Q between this state and the ground state is

$$(\Phi_\alpha |Q| \Phi_0) = \sum_k D_k Q_k \Big/ \left(\sum_k D_k^2\right)^{1/2}$$

Model 1 in RPA Approximation.[43] The relevant matrix equation is now:

$$\begin{pmatrix} \boldsymbol{\Delta\epsilon} + \mathbf{v} & -\mathbf{v} \\ \mathbf{v} & -(\boldsymbol{\Delta\epsilon} + \mathbf{v}) \end{pmatrix} \begin{pmatrix} \mathbf{y} \\ \mathbf{z} \end{pmatrix} = \omega \begin{pmatrix} \mathbf{y} \\ \mathbf{z} \end{pmatrix}$$

where

$$\Delta\epsilon_{k\ell} = \Delta\epsilon_k \, \delta_{k\ell}$$

$$v_{k\ell} = \xi D_k D_\ell$$

Thus

$$\sum_\ell \left(\Delta\epsilon_k \, \delta_{k\ell} + \xi D_k D_\ell\right) y_\ell - \xi D_k D_\ell z_\ell = \omega y_\ell$$

$$\sum_\ell \xi D_k D_\ell y_\ell - \left(\Delta\epsilon_k \, \delta_{k\ell} + \xi D_k D_\ell\right) z_\ell = \omega z_\ell$$

Writing $\Sigma_\ell D_\ell y_\ell = Y$, $\Sigma D_\ell z_\ell = Z$,

$$\Delta\epsilon_k y_k + \xi D_k(Y - Z) = \omega y_k$$

$$\xi D_k(Y - Z) - \Delta\epsilon_k z_k = \omega z_k$$

so

$$y_k = \frac{\xi D_k}{\omega - \Delta\epsilon_k}(Y - Z) \qquad z_k = \frac{\xi D_k}{\omega + \Delta\epsilon_k}(Y - Z)$$

The eigenvalue condition is

$$\sum_k \xi D_k^2 \left(\frac{1}{\omega - \Delta\epsilon_k} - \frac{1}{\omega + \Delta\epsilon_k} \right) = 1$$

In the extreme case when the $\Delta\epsilon_k$ are degenerate and equal $\Delta\epsilon$,

$$\omega = \pm \left((\Delta\epsilon)^2 + 2\Delta\epsilon\xi \sum_k D_k^2 \right)^{1/2}$$

$$= \pm \left(\omega_{TD}^2 - \left(\xi \sum_k D_k^2 \right)^2 \right)^{1/2}$$

where ω_{TD} is the frequency given by the TD approximation above. Thus we see that the frequency from the RPA method is less than ω_{TD} for both signs of ξ. Also we see that the fractional change in replacing the TD by the RPA method is $O(\Delta/\omega_{TD})^2$, where Δ is the TD energy shift $\xi \Sigma_k D_k^2$. The excited states are

$$\Psi_\alpha = O_\alpha^+ \Psi_0$$

where

$$O_\alpha^+ = \sum_k \left(y_{\alpha k} A_k^+ + z_{\alpha k} A_k \right)$$

The matrix element of a one-body operator Q between such a state and the ground state is

$$(\Psi_\alpha | Q | \Psi_0) = \sum_k y_{\alpha k} Q_k - z_{\alpha k} Q^+_k{}^* \Big/ \left[\sum_k \left(y_{\alpha k}^2 - z_{\alpha k}^2 \right) \right]^{1/2}$$

In the case of degeneracy, $y_{\alpha k} \propto D_k/(\omega - \Delta\epsilon)$ and $z_{\alpha k} \propto D_k/(\omega + \Delta\epsilon)$ and if $Q_k^* = Q^+_k$,

$$(\Psi_\alpha|Q|\Psi_0) = (\Delta\epsilon/\omega)^{1/2}\left(\sum_k D_k Q_k\right)\Big/\left(\sum_k D_k{}^2\right)^{1/2}$$

which differs from the above TD value by the factor $(\Delta\epsilon/\omega)^{1/2}$. In the case when we choose Q to equal D, we see that Ψ_α exhausts the energy-weighted sum†

$$\sum_n (E_n - E_0)\,|(\Psi_n|D|\Psi_0)|^2 = \langle\Psi_0|[[H,D],D]|\Psi_0\rangle$$

$$= \Delta\epsilon\left(\sum_k D_k{}^2\right)$$

(The commutator is a one-body operator, so we can use a shell model for Ψ_0 without error provided it gives the correct density distribution.) In contrast, the above TD results do not have this property, but lead in the case $\omega > \Delta\epsilon$ to the sum-rule limit being exceeded by the single transitions from Ψ_α.

Mathematical Model 2

The assumed form in this case[36] is

$$\left.\begin{array}{l}\langle k|v|\ell\rangle \\ \langle 0|v|k\ell\rangle\end{array}\right\} = \xi D_k D_\ell + \eta D_k{}' D_\ell{}'$$

Model 2 in TD Approximation.[36] Quite straightforwardly we find that the eigenvalues are the solutions of

$$\xi\eta(\Sigma\Sigma' - (\Sigma^x)^2) + (\xi\Sigma + \eta\Sigma') = -1$$

where

$$\Sigma \equiv \sum_k D_k{}^2/(\omega - \Delta\epsilon_k)$$

$$\Sigma^x \equiv \sum_k D_k D_k{}'/(\omega - \Delta\epsilon_k)$$

---

† This is a special case of an important result stated and proved by Thouless,[31] viz., that the values of $(E_n - E_0)$ and $(\Psi_n|D|\Psi_0)$ given by the RPA method are such that the energy-weighted sum formed from these has exactly the correct value (provided only that the particle states involved, taken without correlations, give the proper ground-state density): in contrast, the TD method contains no such guarantee that the sum rule will not be violated; to this extent it is deficient.

$$\Sigma' \equiv \sum_k D_k'^2/(\omega - \Delta\epsilon_k)$$

and the components of an eigenvector are

$$c_{\alpha k} = N\left(\frac{\xi D_\alpha D_k + \eta D_\alpha' D_k'}{\omega_\alpha - \Delta\epsilon_k}\right)$$

where

$$D_\alpha \equiv \sum_\ell c_{\alpha\ell}\, D_\ell \qquad D_\alpha' \equiv \sum_\ell c_{\alpha\ell}\, D_\ell'$$

N is the normalization constant fixed by

$$\sum_k c_{\alpha k}^2 = 1$$

In the degenerate case, the eigenvalue condition is a quadratic equation, so two states are moved by the interaction. If $\Sigma^x \ll \Sigma, \Sigma'$ the eigenvalues are $\omega = \Delta\epsilon_k - \xi(\Sigma_k D_k^2)$ and $\omega = \epsilon_k - \eta(\Sigma_k D_k'^2)$. Thus, in a sense, in this case, model 2 reduces to two separate instances of model 1.

Thus model 2 in general gives two collective states. Sometimes one is much stronger than the other; in other problems, both are comparable and split the collective state between them. This happens, e.g., in the E1 state of O^{16}, which is split by ~3 MeV.

Model 2 in RPA Approximation.[36] The eigenvalue condition is now

$$\xi\tilde{\Sigma} + \eta\tilde{\Sigma}' + \xi\eta(\tilde{\Sigma}\tilde{\Sigma}' - (\tilde{\Sigma}^x)^2) = -1$$

where

$$\tilde{\Sigma} = \sum_k \frac{2\Delta\epsilon_k D_k^2}{\omega^2 - (\Delta\epsilon_k)^2}$$

$$\tilde{\Sigma}^x = \sum_k \frac{2\Delta\epsilon_k D_k D_k'}{\omega^2 - (\Delta\epsilon_k)^2}$$

$$\tilde{\Sigma}' = \sum_k \frac{2\Delta\epsilon_k D_k'^2}{\omega^2 - (\Delta\epsilon_k)^2}$$

The excited states are

$$\Psi_\alpha = O_\alpha^+ \Psi_0$$

where

$$O_\alpha^{+} = \sum_k (y_{\alpha k} A_k^{+} + z_{\alpha k} A_k)$$

and

$$y_{\alpha k} = \frac{\xi D_k D_\alpha + \eta D_k' D_\alpha'}{\omega_\alpha - \Delta\epsilon_k}$$

$$z_{\alpha k} = \frac{\xi D_k D_\alpha + \eta D_k' D_\alpha'}{\omega_\alpha + \Delta\epsilon_k}$$

$$D_\alpha \equiv \sum_k D_k (y_{\alpha k} - z_{\alpha k}) \qquad D_\alpha' \equiv \sum D_k' (y_{\alpha k} - z_{\alpha k})$$

It is clear that this model 2 could easily be extended to include a term $\xi D_k'' D_\ell''$ and other similar terms. A special case where a total of four terms appears is met when dealing with collective states in heavy (non-self-conjugate) nuclei, as we see below. In that problem, however, D_ℓ and D_ℓ' vanish for about half the states ℓ and D_ℓ'' and D_ℓ''' vanish for the rest. Thus any given matrix element contains only two terms. In general such problems lead to a quartic eigenvalue equation when all $\Delta\epsilon_k$ are degenerate. Physically two of these correspond to T = 0 oscillations and two to T = 1.

Approximate Physical Situation Giving Model 1

The use of a schematic multipole force[12] in place of the actual force leads directly to model 1. Such a schematic force is

$$v_{TL}(i,j) = \xi \sum_{MM_T} (-)^{M+M_T} Q_{TLM_TM}(i)\, Q_{TL-M_T-M}(j)$$

$$\equiv \xi \mathbf{Q}_{TL}(i) \cdot \mathbf{Q}_{TL}(j)$$

Generally, the matrix element between particle-hole states $j_2^{-1} j_1$ and $j_2'^{-1} j_1'$ in a T = 0 nucleus is

$$\langle \overline{j_2'^{-1}\, j_1'} \,|v|\, \overline{j_2^{-1}\, j_1} \rangle_{A.S.} = \langle \Phi_0 | A(\bar{j}_1' \bar{j}_2')\, v A^{+}(\bar{j}_1 \bar{j}_2) | \Phi_0 \rangle$$

$$= \frac{(-)^{L+T+j_1+j_2+1}}{\hat{L}\hat{T}} \langle \bar{j}_1' \bar{j}_2 | v | \bar{j}_2' \bar{j}_1 \rangle_{A.S.}$$

Evaluating the last matrix element with v_{TL} and neglecting exchange gives us the required form:

$$\langle \underbrace{\overline{j}_2{}'^{-1}\,\overline{j}_1{}'}\, | v_{TL} |\, \underbrace{\overline{j}_2{}^{-1}\,\overline{j}_1} \rangle = \xi D(\overline{j}_1{}'\,\overline{j}_2{}')D(\overline{j}_1\,\overline{j}_2)$$

where

$$D(\overline{j}_1\,\overline{j}_2) = \langle \overline{j}_1 || Q_{TL} || \overline{j}_2 \rangle / \hat{L}\hat{T}$$

$$= (-)^{j_1 - j_2} \langle \overline{j}_2 || Q_{TL} || \overline{j}_1 \rangle / \hat{L}\hat{T}$$

Thus, if one can convince oneself that the above schematic force is an approximation to reality, model 1 is confirmed, and all the above-cited consequences about the collective state and sum rules follow.

Approximate Physical Situation Giving Model 2

Goswami and Pal[36] have pointed out that model 2 follows from a much more plausible situation than model 1. If we assume that v is a short-range force and that most radial integrals are roughly equal in value, then the required form for model 2 follows.

We may write the force v(i,j) between nucleus i and j as

$$v(i,j) = -|V|\,\delta(\mathbf{r}_{ij})\left(W + MP_M + BP_B + HP_H\right)$$

where the exchange mixture is written with the usual convention that the operators are +1 when acting on the deuteron ground state $^{13}S[2]$.

Quite generally, from the results in 10-5 we have

$$\langle \underbrace{\overline{j}_2{}'^{-1}\,\overline{j}_1{}'}_{LT}\, | v |\, \underbrace{\overline{j}_2{}^{-1}\,\overline{j}_1}_{LT} \rangle_{A.S.} = \frac{(-)^{L+T+j_1+j_2+1}}{\hat{L}\hat{T}} \langle \underbrace{\overline{j}_1{}'\,\overline{j}_2 | v | \overline{j}_2{}'\,\overline{j}_1}_{LT} \rangle_{A.S.}$$

$$= \sum_{L'T'} \hat{L}'\hat{T}'(-)^{L'+T'+j_1'+j_2+1}$$

$$\times\, U(j_1'j_2'j_2j_1, LL')U(\tfrac{1}{2}\tfrac{1}{2}\tfrac{1}{2}\tfrac{1}{2}, TT')$$

$$\times \langle \underbrace{\overline{j}_1{}'\,\overline{j}_2}_{L'T'} | v | \underbrace{\overline{j}_2{}'\,\overline{j}_1}_{L'T'} \rangle_{A.S.}$$

For δ-function forces, with antisymmetrized wave functions, interaction occurs only in states $S' = 0$, $T' = 1$ or $S' = 1$, $T' = 0$. Thus the terms $T' = 1,0$ in the last sum correspond to singlet ($S' = 0$) and triplet ($S' = 1$) forces. The two terms can be evaluated for the δ-function force above (using tricks first used by de Shalit[58]):

$$\langle \underbrace{\bar{j}_1'\,\bar{j}_2}_{L'1} | v | \underbrace{\bar{j}_2'\,\bar{j}_1}_{L'1} \rangle = -2[(W + M) - (B + H)](1 + (-)^X) \times (-)^{\ell_1' + \ell_2' + Y} M_{L'}(\bar{j}_1'\,\bar{j}_2) M_{L'}(\bar{j}_2'\,\bar{j}_1)$$

$$\langle \underbrace{\bar{j}_1'\,\bar{j}_2}_{L'0} | v | \underbrace{\bar{j}_2'\,\bar{j}_1}_{L'0} \rangle = -2[(W + M) + (B + H)](-)^{\ell_1' + \ell_2'} \times \Big\{ 2N_{L'}(\bar{j}_1'\,\bar{j}_2) N_{L'}(\bar{j}_2'\,\bar{j}_1) + (1 - (-)^X) M_{L'}(\bar{j}_1'\,\bar{j}_2) M_{L'}(\bar{j}_2'\,\bar{j}_1) \Big\}$$

where:

$$X \equiv \ell_2' + \ell_1 - L' \qquad Y = j_1 + j_2 + j_1' + j_2'$$

$$M_{L'}(j_a j_b) \equiv (-)^{\ell_a + \ell_b + j_b - 1/2} \frac{\hat{j}_a \hat{j}_b}{2\hat{L}'} C^{j_b j_a L'}_{\frac{1}{2}\, -\frac{1}{2}\, 0} \sqrt{I|V|/4\pi}$$

$$N_{L'}(j_a j_b) \equiv (-)^{\ell_b + j_a + j_b} \frac{\hat{j}_a \hat{j}_b}{2\hat{L}'} C^{j_b j_a L'}_{\frac{1}{2}\, \frac{1}{2}\, 1} \sqrt{I|V|/4\pi}$$

and I is the radial integral. The terms in M, N are non-spin-flip and spin-flip. Combining these expressions with the above formula and using some Racah algebra,

$$\langle \underbrace{\bar{j}_2'^{-1}\,\bar{j}_1'}_{TL} | v | \underbrace{\bar{j}_2^{-1}\,\bar{j}_1}_{TL} \rangle$$

$$= 2(-)^Y \Big\{ -(W + M)\big(2(-)^T + 1\big) + (B + H)\big(1 - (-)^T\big) \Big\} \times M_L(\bar{j}_1'\,\bar{j}_2') M_L(\bar{j}_1\,\bar{j}_2)$$

$$+ 2(-)^Y \Big\{ (W + M) - (B + H)\big(1 + (-)^T\big) \Big\} \times N_L(\bar{j}_1'\,\bar{j}_2') N_L(\bar{j}_1\,\bar{j}_2)$$

For $T = 0$, the combinations in square brackets are $-3(W + M)$ and

(W + M) − 2(B + H). For T = 1, they are W + M + 2(B + H) and (W + M). Only the combinations (W + M), (B + H) occur, because of the use of δ-function forces. If we normalize with the usual choice: W + M + B + H = 1, and take the ratio of interactions in S = 0 and S = 1 states to be 0.6, then (W + M) = 0.8, (B + H) = 0.2. Thus the diagonal matrix elements in T = 1 states are positive, i.e., the effective force in such states is repulsive. This is why such states are pushed up in energy. For T = 0, the combinations have the values −2.4 and +0.4. We may assume that the first term dominates in general, so that diagonal matrix elements are negative and the effective force attractive. This demonstrates the important result that in self-conjugate (i.e., T = 0) nuclei, the collective state is pushed up for T = 1 and down for T = 0 multipoles.

In nuclei which are not self-conjugate, but are closed-shell systems, the appropriate formulas are somewhat different. The natural classification of the states is that of neutron excitation or proton excitation. If, as occurs in practice, there is a neutron excess, then states of neutron excitation *from* the "excess orbitals" have pure isotopic spin,† viz., that of the ground state $T_0 \equiv \frac{1}{2}(N - Z)$; similarly for proton excitation *to* the "excess orbitals." Neutron excitation from states below the excess orbitals, or proton excitation to states above, results in states of isotopic spins T_0 and $(T_0 + 1)$. In heavier nuclei, these latter states have high excitations ($\gtrsim$ 20 MeV) and so need not be considered. Thus the states of neutron excitation or proton excitation that one takes into account all have isotopic spin as a quantum number, and all have the same isotopic spin, viz., T_0. This means that there is an essential difference between calculations in self-conjugate light nuclei and heavy nuclei. In the former, the two isotopic spin multipole orders T = 0,1 are quite independent; each has its own interaction matrix, and the diagonalization of these results in an elevated T = 1 collective state and a depressed T = 0 one.

In heavy nuclei there is only one interaction matrix to be diagonalized, viz., that for isotopic spin T_0. In general, both types of collective state will emerge from diagonalization of this one matrix. One identifies the collective state for a T = 0 multipole by evaluating matrix elements of the mass multipole operator Q_{0LM} between the eigenstates and the ground state, and finding which state has the largest; similarly one evaluates elements of Q_{1LM} to find the collective state for a T = 1 multipole. [Notice that, again unlike self-conjugate nuclei, the states of one T-type will have nonzero matrix elements for the operator of the other type; in general, the value will be reduced by $O((N - Z)/A)$ relative to the value for the operator of the same type.]

† Isotopic spin is pure as far as coupling of particles goes. Lack of equality of neutron and proton orbital states brings some impurity.

Interaction matrix elements between the basic particle-hole states in heavy nuclei can be found from the formulas

$$\langle \underbrace{\bar{j}_2'^{-1}\bar{j}_1'}_{L} | v | \underbrace{\bar{j}_2^{-1}\bar{j}_1}_{L} \rangle = \sum_{L'} \hat{L}'(-)^{L'+j_1'+j_2}\, U(j_1' j_2' j_2 j_1, LL') \times \langle \underbrace{\bar{j}_1' \bar{j}_2}_{L'} | v | \underbrace{\bar{j}_2' \bar{j}_1}_{L'} \rangle$$

$$\langle \underbrace{\bar{j}_1' \bar{j}_2}_{L'} | v | \underbrace{\bar{j}_2' \bar{j}_1}_{L'} \rangle = \sum_{T'} C^{\frac{1}{2}\,\frac{1}{2}\,T'}_{m_1' m_2 M_{T'}}\, C^{\frac{1}{2}\,\frac{1}{2}\,T'}_{m_2' m_1 M_{T'}} \times \langle \underbrace{\bar{j}_1' \bar{j}_2}_{L'T'} | v | \underbrace{\bar{j}_2' \bar{j}_1}_{L'T'} \rangle$$

and the expressions given above for the last particle-particle matrix elements. As mentioned above, the particle-hole states considered like $\bar{j}_2'^{-1}\bar{j}_1'$, $\bar{j}_2^{-1}\bar{j}_1$ automatically have pure isotopic spin $T = \frac{1}{2}(N - Z)$, so there is no need to couple isotopic spins to T, but only the j's to L. It is possible to reduce the final expressions for the matrix elements, again using the methods of de Shalit.[58] We have

$$\langle \underbrace{\bar{j}_2'^{-1}\bar{j}_1'}_{L} | v | \underbrace{\bar{j}_2^{-1}\bar{j}_1}_{L} \rangle = -2[(W + M) - (B + H)](-)^{Y} \times \left\{(-)^{L} M_{L}(\bar{j}_2' \bar{j}_1') M(\bar{j}_2 \bar{j}_1) + N(\bar{j}_2' \bar{j}_1') N(\bar{j}_2 \bar{j}_1)\right\}$$

where both states are of the same kind (i.e., both neutron or both proton excitation), and

$$\langle \underbrace{\bar{j}_2'^{-1}\bar{j}_1'}_{L} | v | \underbrace{\bar{j}_2^{-1}\bar{j}_1}_{L} \rangle = -2\left[(W + M)\left(1 - (-)^{L}\right) + (B + H)\right](-)^{Y} \times M(\bar{j}_2' \bar{j}_1') M(\bar{j}_2 \bar{j}_1) + 2(B + H) N(\bar{j}_2' \bar{j}_1') N(\bar{j}_2 \bar{j}_1)$$

where the two states are of opposite kinds.

As expected, the former matrix elements depend on the singlet mixture (W + M) − (B + H). The sign of the diagonal matrix elements is that of

$$(-)^L \left[C^{j_2 j_1 L}_{\frac{1}{2}\,-\frac{1}{2}\,0} \right]^2 + \left[C^{j_2 j_1 L}_{\frac{1}{2}\,\frac{1}{2}\,1} \right]^2$$

$$= \left[C^{j_2 j_1 L}_{\frac{1}{2}\,\frac{1}{2}\,0} \right]^2 \left\{ (-)^L + \frac{\left[(2j_1 + 1) + (-)^{j_1+j_2+L}(2j_2 + 1)\right]^2}{4L(L + 1)} \right\}$$

For $L = 1$, $|j_1 - j_2| = 0$ or 1; in the former case, the last expression is $\frac{1}{2}[(2j_1 + 1)^2 - 2]$, which is always ≥ 1; in the latter it is $-\frac{1}{2}$. Thus the sign of the trace of the matrix is uncertain but has a tendency to be positive (repulsive). Since the $T = 0$ and $T = 1$ collective states are expected to be moved in opposite directions by the interaction, there is no simple interpretation of the sign of the trace.

11

NUMERICAL RESULTS AND COMPARISON WITH EXPERIMENT FOR CLOSED-SHELL NUCLEI

The significance of specialization to closed-shell nuclei is that pairing force effects may be ignored. This is true of all calculations in the present section. A summary of the work discussed in this section is given in Table 11-1.

The first attempts to calculate detailed features of nuclear collective oscillations used the Hill-Wheeler-Griffin approach described in Chap. 7. Ferrell and Visscher[37] discussed the L = 0+, T = 0 states in O^{16} and the L = 1−,2+,3−; T = 0 states of C^{12} from this viewpoint. They assumed that the weight functions in the HWG integral have zero range. The calculations met with some success, but this was vitiated by parametric fitting. Griffin[17] made a more complete calculation of the collective L = 0+,2+; T = 0 states of O^{16}. Unfortunately there is no data on these states. The predicted collective 0+ state occurs at $>$ 11 MeV. Thus it cannot be the state observed at 6 MeV. In any case, the predicted matrix element for EO decay to the ground state is several times too large. Similarly there is no known collective 2+ state with which to make a comparison. Ferrell and Fallieros[37] also considered the L = 2+, T = 1 state of O^{16}; they managed to obtain some data on the state by considering E2 effects observed in O^{17}, N^{16} and then representing these nuclei as particles or holes coupled to the O^{16} core. They tentatively conclude that the collective state is at $\sim$ 20 MeV.

The first extensive application of the TD method to nuclear spectra was the study by Elliott and Flowers[11] of the negative parity states of O^{16}. Their study of the case L = 1−, T = 1 is especially interesting. There are five particle-hole states with zero-order energies between 12 and 22 MeV. In L-S coupling two are S = 0 and three are S = 1 (spin-flip). For both kinds of states in L-S coupling, it is found that the result of diagonalizing the interaction is to push one state up in

Table 11-1
Summary of Work Reported on
Collective Modes in Closed Shells with Parameters Used†

Ref.	Nuclei	Multipoles	Method(s)	Oscillator-size parameter b, mf	Interaction: Type and range	Interaction: Strength V	Interaction: Mixture (W,M,B,H)
11	O^{16}	{L=0,1,2,3,4−; T=0,1	TD	1.56	Yuk. 1.4 f	30-50 MeV	{−0.13,0.93,0.46,−0.26 (S=0, T=0 part varied)
21	O^{16}	L=0+,2+; T=0	TD and RPA	1.68	Gaus. 1.73 f	52 MeV	0.32,0.5,0,0.18
19	{O^{16}; Ca^{40}	L=1−, T=1	TD		zero range	$8.5(4\pi b^3)$; $14.4(4\pi b^3)(\frac{16}{40})$	1,0,0,0; 0.3,0.43,0.27,0
43	{O^{16}; Ca^{40}	L=3−, T=0	TD and RPA		as Ref. 19	$8.5(4\pi b^3)$; $8.5(4\pi b^3)(\frac{16}{40})$	
23	O^{16}	L=1−, T=1	RPA (HRPA)	1.68	(I) as Ref. 21; (II) as Ref. 11		
13	C^{12}	{L=0−,1−,2−,1+,2+; T=1	TD and RPA		as Ref. 19	$10.2(4\pi b^3)$	
48	O^{16}	{L=1−, T=1; L=3−, T=0	"HRPA"	1.75	Yuk. 1.46 f	41-54 MeV	−0.13,0.93,0.46,−0.26; 0.5,0.5,0,0
36	C^{12}	{L=2+, T=0; L=1−, T=1	TD and RPA		zero range	fitted to 3-state in O^{16}	(W + M) = 4(B + H)

47	O^{16}	L=0+, T=0	TD (with doubles)		zero range	$5.4(4\pi b^3)$	−0.13, 0.93, 0.46, −0.26(?)
44	C^{12}	1−, T=1 3−, T=0	TD			40 MeV	0.35, 0.35, −0.1, 0.4
	O^{16}	0−; T=0,1 1−, T=1 2−, T=1 3−, T=0,1	RPA		Gaus. b	40 MeV	0.4, 0.4, −0.2, 0.4
	Ca^{40}	1−, T=1 3−, 5−; T=0		0.86	55 MeV	0.17, 0.57, 0.25, 0	
45	Ca^{40}	L=1−, T=1	TD	1.96	Gaus. 1.73 f zero range	0–50 MeV 825 MeV (f^3)	1, 0, 0, 0 0.5, 0.5, 0, 0 −0.13, 0.93, 0.46, −0.26
60	C^{12}	L=1−, T=1 L=2+, 3−, T=0	RPA	1.64	Yuk. 1.36	37 MeV	0.3, 0.43, 0.27, 0
25	O^{16}	L=0+, T=0	HRPA	1.68	Gaus. 1.73	52 MeV	0.5, 0.5, 0, 0
56	Pb^{208}	L=1−, T=1	TD		zero range		0.3, 0.43, 0.27, 0 1, 0, 0, 0
57	Pb^{208}	L=1−, T=1	TD	(Saxon-Woods potential)	zero range		0.3, 0.43, 0.27, 0
55	Pb^{208}	L=1−, T=1	TD				

† *N.B.*: The strength V is defined differently for zero-range and finite-range forces.

excitation energy. This state accounts for almost all of the appropriate sum rules (for S = 0 and S = 1, respectively), so the states are collective. The E1 operator has matrix elements with the ground state for the S = 0 states only. When spin-orbit effects are introduced, the S = 0 and S = 1 collective states mix, and both have comparable E1 matrix elements. These states are at 22.6 and 25.2 MeV and have E1 widths equal to 12 and 6 eV, while other states are at 13, 17, and 20 MeV with widths < 0.2 eV. Experimentally dipole absorption in O^{16} appears to be mainly concentrated in two states near 22 and 25 MeV, in excellent accord with these results.

The calculation of the L = 3−, T = 0 mode predicted a state near the observed energy of ~ 6 MeV, but seriously underestimated its E3 transition, probably suggesting that a more adequate treatment of its collective nature was needed. This is provided by the RPA calculation (see below).

In this work, and other work cited below, the usual procedure is to take diagonal matrix elements (the particle energies) from data on single particle nuclei, but to compute the off-diagonal particle-hole matrix elements. Fallieros[46] has pointed out that the two quantities are closely related, and this imposes a consistency requirement on such an approach.

Although the TD calculation does provide a good general description of the E1 case, it cannot be entirely satisfactory in that it does not give the correct value for the exact sum rule (as explained in 10-7). If there were more precise data on the E1 widths of the states, this failure would probably be more apparent. Thus, even for the E1 mode, RPA calculations are desirable.

Brown, Castillejo, and Evans[19] repeated the above work on the E1 mode in O^{16}, and extended it to Ca^{40}. They used zero-range forces in order to try to bring out systematic features of the collective mode. They point out that accepted exchange mixtures have the property of being mainly repulsive (attractive) in particle-hole states of T = 1 (T = 0). Thus collective T = 1 (T = 0) states are moved upward (downward) in energy. In O^{16}, results were very similar to those found above. In Ca^{40} there are eight states. There is some experimental doubt about the particle energies needed to specify the diagonal particle-hole energies. Using reasonable values, one finds that 99 per cent of E1 absorption in Ca^{40} is concentrated in two states at 18.5 and 21.5 MeV.

Balashov, Shevchenko, and Yudin[45] also calculated the E1 features of Ca^{40}. Their calculation differed in details from the last one, but arrives at the same general conclusion, viz., that most absorption takes place to an energy region at about 19 MeV. They also compute the energy spectra of protons and neutrons. At present, the only data for comparison is some (γ,n) data, and agreement is good. The exchange mixture is varied between pure Wigner and pure Majorana without much effect on results. The same authors have also considered the E1 mode[56] in Pb^{208}. (This has also been considered by Gillet and Sanderson[55] and by Pal, Soper, and Stamp.[57]) There are 29 states in this case, 15 for neutron excitation, 14 for proton excitation, so the diagonalization effort is large. Zero-order energies range between 6 and 12 MeV. The only snag is that the spurious state of centroid motion is not now automatically excluded, but must be explicitly removed. A sharp difference was found between results using Wigner and Soper forces. The peak in the latter case is near the observed position, 13 MeV, and 5 MeV wide. In the former it is at 9 MeV and 8 MeV wide. Thus, in contrast with the situation in light nuclei, the development of strong collective E1 effects depends rather critically on the force mixture used.

The first applications of the RPA method to nuclear physics were made by Ferentz, Gell-Mann, and Pines,[29] and by Ferrell.[22] The former discussed the E1 giant resonance in terms of an infinite medium, and made some general observations on the effect of including ground-state correlations. More detailed results were promised for a subsequent paper which never appeared. The latter discussed the $L = 0+$, $T = 0$ mode in O^{16}. Since the observed 0+ state at 6 MeV exhausts only a few per cent of the exact sum rule this cannot be the predicted state, so this was not a very good case on which to try out the RPA method. Nevertheless Fallieros[21] in his unpublished thesis studied this case and that of the $L = 2+$, $T = 0$ mode in O^{16}. He also was the first to write down in detail all the formulas of the RPA method as applied to nuclear physics problems. He predicts that both collective modes should occur near 20 MeV and have strong transition matrix elements to the ground state. The effect of replacing the TD by the RPA method (i.e., including ground-state correlations) is to increase the matrix elements by ~ 20 per cent but the energies are only decreased by a few per cent.

Brown, Evans, and Thouless[43] studied $L = 3-$, $T = 0$ "octupole" vibrations in O^{16} and Ca^{40} using the TD and RPA methods with zero-range forces. The effects of replacing the TD by the RPA method is to lower the states by 1 MeV and to increase transition probabilities by a factor ~ 2. By adjustment of the interaction strength V, both energies and transition probabilities agree quite well with experiment. The difference between values of V needed for best fits to the dipole and octupole states is about 15 per cent. The authors quote also a result obtained by Sanderson[59] that the $L = 3-$, $T = 1$ mode of O^{16} occurs in two parts at 18 and 25 MeV.

The same authors point out that, with model 1 of Sec. 10-7, if we consider the RPA method in the limit $\Delta \gg \Delta\epsilon_R$ (i.e., the opposite limit to that where the TD method applies), we have the adiabatic situation $\omega \approx 0$. If we expand the eigenvalue condition in powers of ω, we have

$$\left(\frac{1}{2} - \sum_k \frac{\xi D_k^{\,2}}{\Delta\epsilon_k}\right) - \omega^2\left(\sum_k \frac{\xi D_k^{\,2}}{(\Delta\epsilon_k)^3}\right) = 0$$

This is similar to the formula $\hbar^2 C - B\omega^2 = 0$. This is derived from the collective model, which should be valid in this limit. In fact, the mass and potential parameters B and C have just the values given by this approach, the former being given by the "cranking" formula. Thus we have the important result that, in the low-frequency limit, the RPA method reproduces the cranking model.

Vinh-Mau and Brown[13] apply the TD and RPA methods to the $T = 1$ modes in C^{12} with $L = 0-$, $1-$, $2-$, $1+$, and $2+$. Of these, the modes $L = 0-$, $2-$, and $1+$ are "magnetic multipoles," which we have not previously mentioned, on the grounds that there is almost no evidence for strong collective effects in these modes. In order to treat C^{12}, one must regard the unperturbed ground state as a closed shell, which means that $j - j$ coupling must be assumed. One knows that this is not very accurate, so that anomalies must be expected when such a viewpoint is taken. One such is that the $1p_{3/2}^{\;-1}\, 1p_{1/2}$ energy is 13.7 MeV, which is much more than the accepted spin-orbit splitting of ~ 5 MeV for the 1p orbit. The effects of this assumption will be most severe in the $1+$, $2+$ modes, where the $1p_{3/2}^{\;-1}\, 1p_{1/2}$ excitation can occur.

The observed $1-$ state at 22 MeV is fitted quite well in energy and strength. A predicted $2-$ state at 19.2 MeV is identified with one observed at 19.5 MeV. Theoretically the state is strongly collective, taking 86 per cent of the M2 strength. A predicted $1+$ state at 16.1 MeV is identified with one observed at 15.1 MeV. Theoretically it has 100 per cent of the M1 strength. The $2+$ case is rather different. The E2 strength is predicted to be spread over several states from 16 to 40 MeV.

Comparison of the results of the TD and RPA calculations in the last two papers verifies the expected trend, viz., the differences are small for high excitations and large for low ones. This means in practice that the ground-state correlations in the RPA method are crucial for good fits to $T = 0$ modes, but give only slight improvement for $T = 1$ modes.

Another feature brought out in these papers is the fact that the "electric multipole" modes have two collective components, called "non-spin-flip" and "spin-flip." These are excited by the $S = 0$ and $S = 1$ multipole operators. In self-conjugate nuclei, in L-S coupling, the two modes occur as two distinct states of $S = 0, 1$, respectively. The addition of a spin-orbit potential mixes these so that either multipole operator excites both states. Thus one finds in calculations that the collective state is usually split into two parts, each part being a mixture of spin-flip and non-spin-flip (i.e., of $S = 1$ and $S = 0$).

The hole-particle matrix elements of the interaction in j-j coupling can be written as a sum of $S = 0$ and $S = 1$ parts, as shown in Sec. 10-7; in the notation used there, the term with M's is the $S = 0$ (non-spin-flip) part and that with N's is the $S = 1$ (spin-flip) part.

The model 2 of Sec. 10-7 in which these two terms appear has been used by Goswami and Pal[36] to study the $L = 2+$, $T = 0$ and $L = 1-$, $T = 1$ states of C^{12} with the TD and RPA methods. The energy of the 2+-state with the RPA method is quite well fitted with an interaction strength V that fits the $3-$, $T = 0$ state in O^{16}.

The TD method underestimates the transition probability by a factor of 4, but the RPA method fits the observed value to within a few per cent. This shows how vital the ground-state correlations are for low-frequency modes. The results on the $1-$ state of C^{12} are like those above.

The radial matrix elements of the interaction which are set equal in the schematic model 2 that is used are computed and found to have quite small dispersion about the mean value (7 out of 10 values lie in the range 0.26 to 0.35).

In a subsequent paper[60] the same authors have extended their work. They have dropped the schematic model 2 (which depends on the assumptions of zero-range forces and equal matrix elements), and have diagonalized the TD and RPA matrices numerically for a finite-range Soper force. They find that the corrections to the schematic model values of energies and multipole transition strengths for $L = 1-$, $T = 1$ and $L = 2+, 3-$, $T = 0$ are quite small. Presumably, more detailed reflections of the wave functions, such as reduced widths, might be more sensitive. They also evaluate in lowest order the ground-state correlations. They find that correlations from the three modes above contribute 54 per cent of the ground state, of which $1p_{3/2}^{-1}\,1p_{1/2}$ accounts for 18 per cent of the 40 per cent contribution of the 2+-mode. Leaving this special excitation aside, the correlations constitute 36 per cent of the ground state. If other modes (and other types of correlation) were included, this figure could well be $\gtrsim 50$ per cent. Such a large value is rather disturbing. Apart from the implied serious departure from the accepted shell-model approximation, it implies that interference between the various collective modes might well be appreciable, i.e., that higher RPA corrections should be evaluated. At the very least, the change in normalization of the ground state due to correlations from one multipole must change the transition probabilities in other modes.

Barker[48] has drawn similar conclusions about ground-state correlations on the basis of a standard shell-model perturbation calculation for the ground state of O^{16}. This is more complete in the sense that the admixed states are not restricted to combinations of particle-hole states of given multipole order. He finds that correlations typically account for ~ 50 per cent of the ground state. Another criticism of the RPA method as applied to light nuclei is implied by Barker. He suggests that the matrix element $\langle (j_1^{-1}j_2)_L (j_1^{-1}j_2)_L | Q_1 | (j_1^{-1}j_2)_L \rangle$ is implicitly taken equal to $\langle (j_1^{-1}j_2)_L | Q_L | 0 \rangle$ in the RPA method. [This appears to follow from the basic quasi-boson approximation which suggests that excitations $(j_1^{-1}j_2)_L$ are essentially independent of each other and unrestricted by the Pauli principle provided there are not too many of them.] In contrast, he finds that the former matrix element is always $\gtrsim$ 50 per cent of the latter for excitations in O^{16}. This appears to be a valid criticism unless the spin-statistical factor has not been properly taken into account.

Gillet and Vinh-Mau[44] have made the most exhaustive survey of collective states in light nuclei using the RPA method. They study known states of $L = 0,1,2,3-$, $T = 1$ and of $L = 0-, 3-$, $T = 0$ in O^{16}, states of $1-$, $1+$, $2+$, $T = 1$ and of $2+$, $3-$, $T = 0$ in C^{12}; and states of $L = 3-, 5-$, $T = 0$ and of $L = 1-$, $T = 1$ in Ca^{40}. They use a force whose finite range, mixture, and strength is obtained by fitting some of the known states. They take single-particle energies from the data. In O^{17}, they suppose the 4.6-MeV state to be the $1f_{7/2}$ state, but this is unlikely, since the state does not have single-particle properties, and this energy is much lower than expected from a reasonable shell-model potential.

In O^{16} they find $W = M = 0.35$, $B = -0.1$, $H = 0.4$. In C^{12}, $W = M = 0.4$, $B = -0.2$, $H = 0.4$. In both cases $V = -40$ MeV, and the range of the force is equal to the oscillator-size parameter. The above values are much the same if the TD method is used, except that V is changed, but generally the RPA method is more sensitive to parameters, especially to V and (W − M). Altogether eight states are fitted in O^{16} and six in C^{12}, so there are more states than parameters. Good agreement is found with all these states.

In O^{16} they predict a strong collective $2+$, $T = 0$ state at 13 MeV, but this depends critically on taking the $1f_{7/2}$ state in O^{17} to be at 4.6 MeV excitation. If it is raised to ~ 12 MeV, the collective state is raised by a similar amount to 20 MeV.

In Ca^{40}, Coulomb effects become significant. For instance, the $1f_{7/2} - 1d_{5/2}$ splitting differs by 0.7 MeV between neutron and proton levels. The parameters used are: $W = 0.17$, $M = 0.57$, $B = 0.25$, $H = 0$ with $V = -55$ MeV and force range = 0.8 of oscillator parameter b. The E1 state is spread among four main states at 17 (35 per cent), 19 (24 per cent), 21 (12 per cent), and 22 MeV (28 per cent), the figures in parentheses being strengths.

Sawicki and Soda[23] have studied the $L = 1-$, $T = 1$ mode of O^{16} using finite-range forces and two exchange mixtures. They find good agreement with the two observed levels near 23 MeV, and very little difference between the TD and RPA results. They find also that the effects of higher RPA terms, when treated as a perturbation, are very small.

Sawicki[25] has studied the effects of the HRPA terms, treated *not* as a perturbation, on the L = 0+, T = 0 mode of O^{16}. The complete matrix is 46 × 46. Just as the usual RPA matrix has a TD counterpart of half the dimension, so, in this case, the corresponding TD matrix is 23 × 23. The basic set of states now includes not only $1p^{-1}2p$ and $1s^{-1}2s$ but $1p^{-2}1d^2$, $1p^{-2}2s1d$, etc. The exclusion of these states in the usual RPA method has been the main source of criticism and error, so it is very satisfactory to find that they are now included. The calculational problem is severe, and Sawicki reduces the 23 × 23 matrix to a 7 × 7 one by various approximations. He indicates that there is some uncertainty in values to be used for the diagonal energies; normally one adds the particle-hole interaction matrix element to the observed energies of the particle and hole. Sawicki suggests that some of the former is included in the latter. A more correct statement would appear to be that both should be included, but that there is a consistency relation between them. In other words, the two-body potential used in the interaction matrix element should have the property of giving the one-body potential that is implied by the observed particle energies. Fallieros[46] has also stressed this point, and remarked that, in the case of L = 1−, if this consistency is not satisfied, then the spurious T = 0 state will not be separated out.

The result of the 7 × 7 TD calculation with a Serber force of finite range in L-S coupling is a weak monopole state at 7.55 MeV and a strong one at 12.4 MeV. The corresponding 14 × 14 HRPA calculation lowers these states to 6.6 and 8.5 MeV. The former may be identified with the observed state at 6.1 MeV. Although the reported calculation makes rather strong approximations, it shows that this HRPA approach is a promising one in those cases (e.g., L = 0+), where the RPA method is poor. An improved calculation would be very interesting.

Fano and Sawicki[61] have studied the effects of fluctuations in the Hartree-Fock potential of a system using the HRPA method. No reference is made to collective modes; they are entirely concerned with improving the ground-state wave function and energy by including correlation effects.

Vinh-Mau and Brown[47] have also studied the L = 0+, T = 0 states of O^{16}. They confine their study to the TD method, but use 12 states in L-S coupling with a common basic excitation energy of 34 MeV. The force is taken to be zero range with Rosenfeld mixture and of normal strength. They find a very weak state at 8.3 MeV with a strong (collective) state at 22 MeV. The state at 8.3 MeV contains very little single-particle excitation of the $1s^{-1}2s$ and $(1p^{-1}2p)_{L=0}$ types, but consists mainly of "Cooper pair" types of states, e.g., $(1p)_{L=0}^{-2}(1d)_{L=0}^{2}$, met in the pairing force model.

12

COLLECTIVE VIBRATIONS WITH PAIRING FORCES

12-1 APPLICATION OF THE RPA METHOD[14,83]

It is straightforward to extend the results of Sec. 10-3 to the case when the effects of pairing forces are included. Unfortunately only pairing forces for each type of particle (neutron or proton) separately can be allowed for,† and this severely restricts applications.

Pairing forces are taken into account by making a preliminary transformation from real particles to quasi-particles. The corresponding operator transformation is exactly that from the a's to the b's given in 10-3. The interaction becomes

$$V = V^{(0)} + V^{(2)} + V^{(4)}$$

and the total energy is

$$H = H^{(0)} + H^{(2)} + H^{(4)}$$

with

$$H^{(0)} \equiv T^{(0)} + V^{(0)} = \sum_{\alpha} [(\epsilon_\alpha - \lambda - \tfrac{1}{2}\mu_\alpha)V_\alpha^{\,2} - \tfrac{1}{2}U_\alpha V_\alpha \Delta_\alpha]$$

$$H^{(2)} \equiv T^{(2)} + V^{(2)} = \sum_{\alpha} e_\alpha b_\alpha^{\;+} b_\alpha$$

$$H^{(4)} \equiv V^{(4)} = \tfrac{1}{4} \sum_{\alpha\beta\gamma\delta} \langle \alpha\beta | v | \gamma\delta \rangle \, N\big(a_\alpha^{\;+} a_\beta^{\;+} a_\delta a_\gamma\big)$$

---

†A recent paper by Bremond and Valatin[62] attempts to extend the force theory to include the neutron-proton interaction (see Sec. 5-1).

and

$$e_\alpha = \sqrt{(\epsilon_\alpha - \lambda - \mu_\alpha)^2 + \Delta_\alpha{}^2} = e_j$$

$$\mu_\alpha = \mu_j = \frac{1}{\hat{j}} \sum_{j'} \hat{j}' V_{j'}{}^2 \langle \overbrace{j j' | v | j j'}^{0} \rangle_{0}$$

$$\Delta_\alpha = \Delta_j = -\frac{1}{2\hat{j}} \sum \hat{j}' U_{j'} V_{j'} \langle \underbrace{j\,j}_{0} | v | \underbrace{j' j'}_{0} \rangle$$

As before, we define operators B and take the commutators of V and B and retain only terms linear in B and B^+, and drop terms in $b^+ b$. The equations that result for $[B,H]$ and $[B^+,H]$ are those given in 10-3.

The values of U_α and V_α are (see Part I)

$$V_j{}^2 = \frac{1}{2}\left[1 - \frac{\epsilon_j - \lambda - \mu_j}{e_j}\right]$$

$$U_j{}^2 = \frac{1}{2}\left[1 + \frac{\epsilon_j - \lambda - \mu_j}{e_j}\right]$$

The chemical potential λ is fixed by the number of particles:

$$N = \langle n \rangle = \sum_j \hat{j}^2 V_j{}^2$$

It is now quite straightforward to apply the theory to practical cases of collective transitions in nuclei with pairing force effects. As in the case of problems with no pairing forces, it is instructive to consider schematic models in which diagonalization of matrices can be done algebraically. In such models one ascribes simple forms to matrix elements. For example, as in model 1 of 10-7, one may assume a separable product form. In the notation of 10-3, we see that there are two kinds of matrix element, F and G. We shall assume $G = 0$ and take

$$\begin{aligned} F(1234) &= -\theta(34L)F(1243) \\ &= \xi M(12)\, M(34) \end{aligned}$$

This gives for the commutator

$$[H, B^+(12)] = (e_1 + e_2)B^+(1,2) - \xi \sum_{34} M'(12)M'(34)(B^+(34) + B(34))$$

where

$$M'(12) \equiv (U_1V_2 + U_2V_1)M(12)$$

Mathematically this is exactly the same problem as model 1 in Sec. 10-7, and we can directly take over the secular equation for the eigenvalues:

$$\sum_{12} \frac{\xi [M'(12)]^2 (e_1 + e_2)}{(e_1 + e_2)^2 - \omega^2} = 1$$

Physically this schematic model would be reasonable if the effective force v was a multipole force (as discussed in Sec. 10-7). In that case, G is small (through recoupling), and F(1234) is related to F(1243) as above. The further assumption of equal radial integrals (or that the radial dependence of the force is a product $r_i^L r_j^L$) then leads to the above product form of F.

The transition matrix element is easily shown to be given by

$$\langle \Psi_{\alpha LM} | Q_{0LM} | \Psi_0 \rangle^2 = \frac{1}{\omega_\alpha \xi^2} \left\{ \sum_{12} \frac{[M'(12)]^2 (e_1 + e_2)}{[(e_1 + e_2)^2 - \omega_\alpha^2]^2} \right\}$$

where the multipole force is $-\xi \mathbf{Q}_{0L}(i) \cdot \mathbf{Q}_{0L}(j)$. If all energies $(e_1 + e_2)$ are degenerate (= 2e, say) then

$$\omega = \sqrt{4e^2 - 2\xi \Sigma_{12} [M'(12)]^2 e}$$

Clearly ω is > or < 2e, depending on the sign of ξ. If the multipole force is attractive (ξ positive) then the frequency falls with ξ until it vanishes. Beyond this point it is imaginary and one interprets this as meaning that the basic nuclear shape is unstable against deformation of the multipole order being considered.

The discussion of 8-2 about orthogonality of excited states and the conditions for validity of the RPA method can be taken over as it stands, except for replacing particles by quasi-particles. The basic quasi-boson condition ensuring that the Pauli principle is not badly violated is now satisfied if the number of quasi-particles is $\ll$ number of particle states available to them. Since one usually considers only one or two quasi-particles and many states, this condition should be adequately met.

One special feature of quasi-particle systems that needs to be discussed is[14,20] the occurrence of spurious states, especially one of J = 0+. If the ground state is $|\Psi_0\rangle$, this spurious state is $n|\Psi_0\rangle$, where n is the number operator. More accurately, noting that $n|\Psi_0\rangle$

contains components of no and two quasi-particles, it is the latter component that is spurious. Sometimes it may occur as one single two-quasi-particle state, but usually it is spread over several such states. A remarkable feature of the RPA method is that it automatically eliminates the effects of such spurious parts of the states. The equation for the collective operators is $[H, Q_\alpha^+] = \omega_\alpha Q_\alpha^+$. Since $[H, n] = 0$, one may regard n as one of the collective operators with eigenfrequency $\omega_\alpha = 0$. Thus one of the collective states from the RPA method is entirely spurious, whereas the others are not at all (within the usual accuracy of the RPA method as given in the orthogonality relation $\langle \Psi_0 | O_\alpha O_\beta^+ | \Psi_0 \rangle \approx 0$).

This discussion is valid for any type of spurious state that is shared among the basic set of states, and is generated by an operator that commutes with H. For instance, as stressed by Thouless,[34] the spurious dipole state $Q_{01M} | \Psi_0 \rangle$ is automatically isolated by the RPA calculation, since $[H, Q_{0LM}] = 1$.

12-2 LESS GENERAL METHODS: TD AND CRANKING MODEL METHODS

As we have seen in Chap. 10, for problems with no pairing forces the RPA method specializes to the TD method in the case of small collective energy shift, and to the adiabatic or cranking model in the case of large downward shift (i.e., of low frequency). The same is true when pairing forces are included. The derivation of the adiabatic-model results of Belyaev[39] from the RPA method has been explicitly made by Kobayasi and Marumori.[51]

The TD method is easily derived from the above equations. In particular, in the expression for $[H, B^+]$ it is obtained by dropping terms in B. There seems to be no significant merit in the TD method in the present context, so we say no more about it.

The adiabatic method[39] is of some interest because it has more direct physical interpretation. Generally it would give the collective potential energy in the form $E(q) = \langle \Psi_q | H | \Psi_q \rangle$, where q is the multipole moment, and Ψ_q is the lowest state of this moment. One evaluates E(q) by taking Ψ_q to be an eigenstate of $\widetilde{H} \equiv H + \mu Q$, where Q is the multipole moment operator, and determining the multiplier μ from

$$\langle \Psi_q | Q | \Psi_q \rangle = q$$

If we make some extra assumptions this can be done more explicitly. For instance, if we assume that the term μQ can be regarded as a perturbation, and we take the Rayleigh-Schrödinger series,

$$\Psi_q = \Psi_0 + \frac{P}{e}(\mu Q - \delta E)\Psi_0 + \frac{P}{e}(\mu Q - \delta E)\frac{P}{e}(\mu Q - \delta E)\Psi_0 + \cdots$$

where $e \equiv E_0 - H$, $E_0 \equiv \langle \Psi_0 | H | \Psi_0 \rangle$, and P excludes intermediate state Ψ_0, then it is easily shown that, to second order in μQ,

$$E(q) = \langle \Psi_q | H | \Psi_q \rangle = E_0 - \left\langle \mu Q \frac{1}{e} \mu Q \right\rangle$$

$$q = \langle \Psi_q | Q | \Psi_q \rangle = 2\left\langle Q \frac{1}{e} \mu Q \right\rangle$$

whence

$$E(q) = E_0 - \frac{q^2}{4\left\langle Q \frac{1}{e} Q \right\rangle}$$

The second term is always positive. Here we have considered the case of a spin 0 nucleus and supposed its wave function Ψ_0 to have spin 0+. It remains to evaluate $\langle Q(1/e)Q \rangle$. This is difficult in general since H is exact but we can get some guidance from an intuitive approach in which one separates out from H the multipole part $\xi \mathbf{Q} \cdot \mathbf{Q}$ and replaces it by the nonspherically symmetric one-body potential ξqQ. Thus, eigenstates of this new Hamiltonian $H' \equiv H_0 + \xi qQ$ are to be regarded as the "intrinsic states" which have nonspherical shape and no definite spin. Solving as before with the aid of a multiplier term added to H': $\tilde{H}' + \mu Q$ and treating $(\xi q + \mu)Q$ as a perturbation, one finds, to second order,

$$E(q) = E_0 - \frac{q^2}{4\left\langle Q \frac{1}{e_0} Q \right\rangle} - \xi q^2$$

where $e_0 \equiv (E_0 - H_0)$.

The third term ξq^2 is negative and acts against the second term to give a smaller value of C, the potential parameter in $E(q) = A + \frac{1}{2}Cq^2$. In the earlier formula, e occurs instead of e_0 in the second term, i.e., the effects of $\xi \mathbf{Q} \cdot \mathbf{Q}$ have not been explicitly taken out as in the present formula. There is no precise equivalence between the two formulas, but one can see that replacing e_0 by e in the last formula gives a smaller second term, i.e., gives effects in the same direction as those due to $-\xi q^2$. The first formula is more general but does not display the entire collective effects explicitly, since e contains $\xi Q \cdot Q$. If one assumes that most of $\langle Q(1/e)Q \rangle$ comes from one intermediate state, the last formula can be derived from the first one.

To complete the adiabatic picture, the mass parameter B must be calculated. This is defined by the collective Hamiltonian

$$H_{\text{coll}} = \tfrac{1}{2}B\dot{q}^2 + \tfrac{1}{2}Cq^2$$

which implies the collective frequency

$$\omega = \hbar\sqrt{C/B}$$

We have already discussed in Chap. 7 an objection to assuming that q is the collective parameter. Within the spirit of the adiabatic picture, B is given by the cranking model formula:

$$B = 2\left(\sum_{n\neq 0} \frac{\langle n(q)|\frac{\partial}{\partial q}|0(q)\rangle^2}{E_n(q) - E_0(q)}\right)_{q\to 0}$$

where $E_n(q)$ are the eigenvalues of H_0 for fixed moment q. As above, treating $(\xi q + \mu)Q$ as a perturbation,

$$|0(q)\rangle \equiv \Psi_q = \Psi_0 + (\xi q + \mu)\frac{1}{e_0}Q\Psi_0 + \cdots$$

Thus

$$\frac{\partial}{\partial q}\Psi_q = \frac{1}{e_0}Q\Psi_0\frac{\partial}{\partial q}(\xi q + \mu)$$

Using the condition

$$2(\xi q + \mu)\left\langle Q\frac{1}{e_0}Q\right\rangle = q$$

we find

$$B = \frac{\left\langle Q\frac{1}{e_0{}^3}Q\right\rangle}{2\left\langle Q\frac{1}{e_0}Q\right\rangle^2}$$

These formulas hold with or without pairing forces. When pairing forces are present, the energy denominators are energies of two quasi-particles. Since quasi-particle energies are > particle energies, pairing forces increase B and decrease C, thus reducing ω. In evaluating B or C completely with pairing forces, we need the result

$$\left(\Psi_{\nu\nu'}|Q|\Psi_0\right) = \langle\nu|Q|\nu'\rangle\left(U_\nu V_{\nu'} + U_{\nu'}V_\nu\right)$$

where ν, ν' are any particle states.

In the case of the degenerate pairing force model, all contributing two-quasi-particle intermediate states have the same energy $|G|\,\Omega$, so

$$B = \frac{1}{2|G|\,\Omega\,\langle Q^2\rangle}$$

$$C = \frac{|G|\,\Omega}{2\langle Q^2\rangle} - 2\xi$$

so the energy is

$$\omega = |G|\,\Omega\sqrt{1 - \frac{4\xi\langle Q^2\rangle}{|G|\,\Omega}}$$

The quantity $\langle Q^2\rangle$ is $\overline{(U_\nu V_{\nu'} + U_{\nu'}V_\nu)^2\,\langle\nu|Q|\nu'\rangle^2}$ which, in the degenerate model, is $(2N/\Omega)(1-(N/2\Omega))\overline{\langle\nu|Q|\nu'\rangle^2}$. ω will reach zero and become imaginary for values of N such that

$$\theta_0 \equiv \frac{|G|\,\Omega}{4\xi\langle\nu|Q|\nu'\rangle^2} < 1$$

In this case, the spherical shape is unstable and a permanent deformation sets in at this value.

In this case of the degenerate pairing force model, the RPA method is easily shown[61] to lead to exactly the same results, thereby giving the adiabatic method some strong backing. (In general, the adiabatic method results are valid only for low ω. In the same calculation, the collective coordinate turns out to be Q_{LM}.)

12-3 APPLICATIONS

Nearly all reported applications consider only quadrupole oscillations and all use the schematic multipole force. Since the practical advantage of this is only to give separable form for the matrix elements, such calculations can be extended to cover the case of zero-range forces with equal radial force integrals, which also gives the separable form for like particles.

Belyaev[39] used the cranking model to deduce that

$$\omega = |G|\,\Omega\sqrt{1 - \left[\frac{\frac{2N}{\Omega}\left(1 - \frac{N}{2\Omega}\right)}{\theta_0}\right]}$$

He allows for nondegenerate energies and the occurrence of a deformable nuclear core of closed shells. θ_0 may be $\gtrsim 1$ and depends on G, ξ, K, and $d\rho/d\epsilon$, where $\rho(\epsilon)$ is the single-particle-level density and K is the quadrupole polaris ability of the closed-shell core:

$$E(q_c) = E_0 + \frac{K}{2} q_c^2$$

In the absence of collective effects, ω is the usual two-quasi-particle energy $|G|\,\Omega$. Collective effects make $\omega < |G|\,\Omega$. If θ_0 is < 1, then $\omega \to 0$ as N increases from 0 to a critical value N_0 ($< \Omega$). Beyond this value, the ground state has a permanent quadrupole shape. For values of N just $< N_0$ (or just $> 2\Omega - N_0$), ω is very small, i.e., collective effects are very strong. This kind of discussion is very useful for showing qualitative trends, but it does not readily give numerical values for specific cases.

Kisslinger and Sorensen[38] first try perturbation theory, but find that the predicted transition rates are too low and the energies too high. Thus they also use the adiabatic method in their studies of single closed-shell systems. In fitting data on the isotopes of Pb, Sn, Zr, etc., they use ξ as a parameter as well as G, the pairing force strength. They find that the quantity $X \equiv (5/2\hbar)\,\xi\,\overline{\langle j\,|r^2|\,j'\rangle^2}$, where the latter factor is the mean radial matrix element, is $\sim 110/A$ in all mass regions. In the Pb isotopes, the multipole force has only a small effect on the 2+ energies, lowering them by ~ 10 per cent from ~ 1 MeV. In the Sn isotopes, the lowering is larger, from ~ 2 to ~ 1 MeV. The transition probabilities are typically ~ 12 times single particle in the Sn isotopes (4 times for Pb^{206}). These values are reproduced quite well by the above value of X (taking the effective charge for neutrons to be ~ 1). Sorensen[66] has extended this work to odd nuclei, describing their states in terms of phonons on the core interacting with the odd nucleon.

Bes[63] has used the adiabatic method to extend Belyaev's work to study the γ-dependence of the collective potential, i.e., the nonaxially symmetric part, especially the last term in $E(q,\gamma) = A + \frac{1}{2}Cq^2 + \frac{1}{2}Dq^3 \cos 3\gamma$.

Baranger[14] has repeated the calculation of Kisslinger and Sorensen for Sn^{118} using the RPA method with multipole force $\xi\,\mathbf{Q}\cdot\mathbf{Q}$ in place of the adiabatic method, and finds results differing by only ~ 1 per cent. Recently[81] an extensive application of the RPA method with realistic forces has been made to the Sn isotopes.

Tamura and Udagawa[50] extend the work of Kisslinger and Sorensen (K and S) by, first, using the RPA method and, second, treating non-closed-shell systems by including a multipole neutron-proton force (but not pairing force between neutrons and protons). They fit ~ 30 nuclei between Mo and Te, using about the same parameters of K and S, and with effective charge in most cases in the range 0.5 to 1.0.

In a later paper they apply the same methods to collective 3− and 4+ states found in Pb^{208}, $Ni^{58,60}$ by electron scattering.[4] Again satisfactory agreement is found when the effective charges are adjusted in the above range, and the strengths of the $\mathbf{Q}_3 \cdot \mathbf{Q}_3$ and $\mathbf{Q}_4 \cdot \mathbf{Q}_4$ forces are selected appropriately.

Mitra and Pal[49] have pointed out that, just as the RPA method can be used to derive a collective oscillator Hamiltonian, so the extra effects introduced by the HRPA method can be used to derive anharmonic correction terms in the collective Hamiltonian. The most general cubic terms allowed by time-reversal invariance are

$$G_1 H_1 + G_2 H_2$$

where

$$H_1 = \{\{Q_L, Q_L\}_L Q_L\}_0$$

$$H_2 = \{\{Q_L, P_L\}_L P_L\}_0$$

(The notation $\{A,B\}_L$ means that operators A,B are coupled to angular momentum L.) Making the usual schematic-model assumption of factorable matrix elements, and taking the two quasi-particle energies as degenerate and neglecting ground-state correlation terms, Pal and Mitra show that the above form emerges with $G_1 = G_2$. Some approximations are made in carrying out summations over particle states, but these appear reasonable. This result is especially interesting in that recently such anharmonic terms have been suggested[64] by analysis of the data, especially the splitting of the second excited (triplet) level. Belyaev and Zelevinsky[82] have also used the HRPA method to study anharmonic (cubic) terms.

Kisslinger[52] has examined the possibility that collective effects may arise from spin-dependent parts of the force. In particular, he considers the possibility that L = 2+ collective effects can arise from a force $\{\{\sigma_i, Y_2(i)\}_2, \{\sigma_j, Y_2(j)\}_2\}_0$ rather than the usual schematic force $\{Y_2(i), Y_2(j)\}_0$. Such a force can be extracted from the tensor interaction. In general the new force produces weaker effects than the usual one, and the tensor force would have to be much larger than is usually assumed if the data were to be fitted. For this reason, it is concluded that the tensor forces are responsible for only a small part of observed collective 2+ effects.

In two papers Yoshida[54,81] has studied the important question of the prediction by the TD and RPA methods of the nucleon reduced width of a collective 2+ state. In Part I we have given his formulas for reduced widths for transitions from excited states of two quasi-particles. For the TD method[54] it only remains to specify the linear combination of those states that constitute the collective 2+ state. Experimentally the cross section for (dp) or (dt) reactions in the Sn isotopes leading to the 2+ collective state (ln = 2) are ~ 20 per cent of that to the 0+ ground state (ln = 0). This factor is predicted by the theory for reasonable values of the parameter ξ in the schematic force.

In the second paper[81] Yoshida uses the RPA method and applies it to both 2+ and 3− states. He also considers the spectra of odd nuclei; he follows Sorensen,[66] representing their states as those of a single particle interacting with phonons in the even ("core") system. The interaction is diagonalized in these states for phonon numbers 0, 1, and, in some cases, 2. The effect of the RPA method is to add a second term to the TD expression for the reduced width amplitude. For transitions to the ground state of an even system, this new term is small, but for those to the excited collective state, it is comparable with the other term and must be included. Yoshida also considers transition probabilities and the related cross sections for inelastic scattering in the forward direction.

Kisslinger[53] has studied the question of inelastic scattering. He uses first- and second-order Born approximation, and takes the interaction to be the two-body ones rather than the phenomenological collective one considered by Lemmer, de Shalit, and Wall.[67] He applies the RPA method to the nuclear states and find that the cross section for one-phonon excitation can be simply related to that of the latter authors, but not that for two-phonon excitation.

The well-known empirical phase rule for angular distributions says that processes with odd (even) angular momentum transfer are in (out of) step with the elastic scattering. Kisslinger finds that this simple rule is implied by his results for one-phonon, but not for two-phonon excitations in general. He also considers 183-MeV electron scattering and finds that the angular distributions, even to the one-phonon states, are very sensitive to details of the nuclear wave functions.

13

PERMANENTLY DEFORMED NUCLEI AND THEIR MOMENTS OF INERTIA

Quite a large number of nuclei show spectra characteristic of rotation with $E_J = J(J+1)(\hbar^2/2\mathscr{I})$. Measurement of their electric quadrupole moments and transition probabilities yields values of the deformation parameter α. The prediction of α and the moment of inertia, $\mathscr{I}$, has been the subject of a large number of papers.

The observed moments lie between the predictions of the extreme models, viz., the shell model, which predicts $\mathscr{I} = \mathscr{I}_{rig}$, the rigid-body value ($\frac{2}{5}MAR^2$), and the hydrodynamic model, which predicts $\mathscr{I} = \mathscr{I}_{hyd}$, the hydrodynamic value ($\approx \mathscr{I}_{rig}\,\alpha^2$). More precisely the observed values are several times $\mathscr{I}_{hyd}$, and about half of $\mathscr{I}_{rig}$.

Theoretically, for any given nucleus, one has to show that there is is a minimum in the energy surface versus deformation, and that the minimum is sharp enough and the deformation sufficiently large to make the deformed shape permanent. The excited states of this system are then rotational states. The two essential parameters to be evaluated are $\mathscr{I}$ and α.

Most discussion has centered on the "cranking model."[70] This model assumes that nucleons move in their (deformed) self-consistent potential in the ground state, and that excited collective states can be simulated by supposing the potential to rotate with given angular velocity, Ω, say. Of course the second assumption means that the model is a classical one, and is unsatisfactory in that one never constructs proper excited quantum states with discrete angular momenta. However, in the limit when $\Omega \to 0$, one expects that quantum corrections are small, and that this cranking model is reliable.

Quite generally, for any system in which the potential $V(\phi)$ depends on a collective coordinate $\phi = \phi(t)$ which changes slowly with time, the energy can be expanded in powers of ϕ:

$$E(\phi,\dot{\phi}) = E(\phi,0) + \tfrac{1}{2}(\partial^2 E/\partial\dot{\phi}^2)_0\,\dot{\phi}^2 + \cdots$$

where

$$\frac{1}{2}\left(\frac{\partial^2 E}{\partial \dot{\phi}^2}\right)_0 = \hbar^2 \sum_n \frac{\langle \phi n | \frac{\partial}{\partial \phi} | \phi 0 \rangle^2}{E_{\phi,n} - E_{\phi,0}}$$

$$E(\phi,0) \equiv E_{\phi,0}$$

Here the states $|\phi,n\rangle$ and eigenvalues $E_{\phi,n}$ are solutions of $(T + V(\phi) - E_{\phi,n})|\phi n\rangle = 0$, with ϕ taken as a fixed parameter. This result follows from use of the time-dependent equation

$$\left(T + V(\phi) - i\hbar \frac{\partial}{\partial t}\right)\Psi = 0$$

with $\phi = \phi(t) \approx \phi(0) + t\dot{\phi}(0)$, treating $\dot{\phi}$ as small.

In the collective rotation problem, $\phi = \phi(0) + \Omega t$, where Ω is the angular velocity of rotation. Since the angular momentum operator ℓ is related to ϕ by $\ell = i(\partial/\partial\phi)$, the collective energy is $\frac{1}{2}\mathcal{J}\Omega^2$, with

$$\mathcal{J} = \hbar^2 \sum_n \frac{\langle n | \ell | 0 \rangle^2}{E_n - E_0}$$

where states $|n\rangle$ are intrinsic states which are not dependent on ϕ. The collective angular momentum is $\Omega\mathcal{J}$.

In addition to the classical "cranking" assumption, an extra undesirable feature of this derivation is that the self-consistent field in $V(\phi)$ is assumed independent of and uninfluenced by the rotation. This feature is removed by the derivation of Thouless and Valatin[68]:

Using the density matrix formulation for convenience,

$$i\frac{\partial \rho(x)}{\partial t} = [H[\rho], \rho(x)]$$

where $H[\rho]$ is the Hartree-Fock self-consistent Hamiltonian, dependent functionally on the Dirac (i.e., one-particle) density matrix ρ. Transforming this equation to a reference system rotating with angular velocity Ω at time t:

$$\rho(x) = e^{-i\Omega t \ell}\rho(\hat{x})e^{i\Omega t \ell}$$

where $\hat{x}$ are the coordinates in the rotating frame, whence

$$\frac{\partial \rho}{\partial t} = e^{-i\Omega t \ell}(\rho(\hat{x}) + [\Omega\ell, \rho(x)])e^{i\Omega t \ell}$$

So

$$i \frac{\partial \hat{\rho}}{\partial t} = [H[\hat{\rho}] - \Omega \ell, \hat{\rho}]$$

where we write $\hat{\rho} \equiv \rho(\hat{x})$. A stationary solution in the rotating frame means that $\partial \hat{\rho}/\partial t = 0$, so

$$[H[\hat{\rho}] - \Omega \ell, \hat{\rho}] = 0$$

ρ is now the time-dependent solution in the stationary frame that consists of the uniform rotation of the stationary solution $\hat{\rho}$. The usual Hartree-Fock stationary solution is $\hat{\rho}^{(0)}$:

$$[H[\hat{\rho}^{(0)}], \hat{\rho}^{(0)}] = 0$$

Treating $\Omega \ell$ as a perturbation, and working to first order:

$$\hat{\rho} = \hat{\rho}^{(0)} + \hat{\rho}^{(1)}$$

$$\begin{aligned} H[\hat{\rho}] &= H[\hat{\rho}^{(0)}] + H[\hat{\rho}^{(1)}] \\ &= \text{(say) } \hat{H}^{(0)} + \hat{H}^{(1)} \end{aligned}$$

$$[\hat{H}^{(0)}, \hat{\rho}^{(1)}] + [H^{(1)}, \hat{\rho}^{(0)}] = [\Omega \ell, \hat{\rho}^{(0)}]$$

where we use the fact that $H[\rho]$ is linear in ρ: $H[\rho] = T + \mathrm{Tr}\,(V\rho)$. Defining $\mathcal{I}$ by

$$\langle \ell \rangle - \langle \ell \rangle^{(0)} = \mathcal{I}\Omega$$

and using

$$\begin{aligned} \langle \ell \rangle &= \mathrm{Tr}\,(\ell \hat{\rho}) \\ &= \mathrm{Tr}\,(\ell \hat{\rho}^{(0)}) + \mathrm{Tr}\,(\ell \hat{\rho}^{(1)}) \\ &= \langle \ell \rangle^{(0)} + \langle \ell \rangle^{(1)} \end{aligned}$$

we have

$$\mathcal{I} = \frac{1}{\Omega} \mathrm{Tr}\,(\ell \hat{\rho}^{(1)})$$

If we drop the term $[H^{(1)}, \hat{\rho}^{(0)}]$ above,

$$\mathcal{I} = \sum_{\beta\gamma} \frac{\langle \beta | \ell | \gamma \rangle^2}{E_\beta - E_\gamma} \langle \gamma | \hat{\rho}^{(0)} | \gamma \rangle$$

which is the cranking model formula, with β and γ labeling particle states. Inclusion of the term $[H^{(1)}, \hat{\rho}^{(0)}]$ allows for the modification of the self-consistent field by the rotation.

The extension to the case when particles are replaced by quasi-particles through the action of pairing effects is straightforward.[68] Defining

$$\rho = \sum_{\beta} V_{\beta}^{2} |\beta\rangle\langle\beta|$$

$$\chi = \sum_{\beta} U_{\beta} V_{\beta} |\beta\rangle\langle\beta|$$

H now contains both self-consistent and pairing terms:

$$H = T + H_{sc} + H_{pair}$$
$$= T + \mathrm{Tr}\,(V\rho) + \mathrm{Tr}\,(V\chi)$$

The pairing force solution satisfies

$$[\widetilde{H}, \widetilde{\rho}] = 0$$

where

$$\widetilde{H} = \begin{bmatrix} H_{sc} & H_{pair} \\ -H_{pair}^{*} & -H_{sc}^{*} \end{bmatrix}$$

$$\widetilde{\rho} = \begin{bmatrix} \rho & \chi \\ -\chi^{*} & 1-\rho^{*} \end{bmatrix}$$

We may now directly apply all the above results to this more general case. Again, if the effects of the rotation on the self-consistent field are ignored, we get the craking formula—but with quasi-particles instead of real ones.

The fact that the intrinsic excitation energies of deformed even-even nuclei are not simply independent particle excitations but rather those of quasi-particles was first pointed out[71] in 1958. The most direct and impressive evidence comes from the occurrence of the "energy gap" in such nuclei. Free particle excitations would normally begin to occur at ~0.15 MeV, but the lowest excited states (of intrinsic excitation) are found at > 1 MeV. Using the cranking model formula (ignoring the effect of rotation on the self-consistent field), this large increase in excitation energy leads to a reduction in the moment of inertia below the value, $\mathcal{I}_{rig}$, expected for free particles. This reduction comes essentially from the increased energy denominator in the cranking formula and reduction of the numerator by the factor $(U_\alpha V_{\alpha'} - U_{\alpha'}V_\alpha)^2$, and is qualitatively just what is needed to explain the observed facts. Altogether the deformed nuclei provide an excellent demonstration of the validity of the ideas behind the pairing force model of intrinsic structure and the cranking model of collective motion.

Turning to detailed numerical fits to observed data, we recall that there are two quantities to be predicted, the equilibrium deformation and the moment of inertia.

Concerning the first, early success was obtained by Mottelson and Nilsson.[74] They used Nilsson's particle spectra[72] to find the energy minimum, and found good agreement with observed deformations in the rare earth nuclei. Pairing forces were not explicitly included, but only simulated by imposing the condition that nuclear volume be constant. Later Belyaev[39] showed how pairing force effects could be included properly. In Chap. 12 we have already quoted his essential result determining the mass number at which permanent deformation occurs. The same result also predicts the degree of deformation of deformed nuclei. Belyaev made no attempt to fit individual data, but set up schematic models to derive qualitative trends. He found, as expected, that the pairing force always reduces the equilibrium deformation. Also, the minimum and maximum deformations occurring in regions of deformed nuclei vary with the mass number of the region as

$$\alpha_{min} \sim A^{-2/3}$$
$$\alpha_{max} \sim A^{-1/3}$$

Bes and Szymanski[78] applied Belyaev's model in a quantitative way. They minimized the energy with respect to deformation in the presence of pairing forces. They also retained the condition of constant nuclear volume, used by Mottelson and Nilsson.[74] It would, of course, be better to drop this latter condition in favor of a full self-consistent treatment of nuclear forces, including the pairing force, but this is very difficult to do in practice. They found that the values of the equilibrium deformation agreed well with the data, but that the shape of the potential near the minimum was much flatter than found by Mottelson and Nilsson. This means that the Coulomb potential can be rather decisive in fixing the minimum for some nuclei.

Concerning the moment of inertia, Griffen and Rich[73] used the cranking formula for $\mathcal{I}$.

$$\mathcal{I} = \hbar^2 \sum_{\beta,\gamma} \frac{(\beta|\ell|\gamma)^2}{e_\beta + e_\gamma}$$

Here $|\beta\rangle$ and $|\gamma\rangle$ are quasi-particle states, and e_β, e_γ their energies. Essentially they regard $\mathcal{I}$ as a function of deformation α, gap parameter Δ, and the quasi-particle energies. They determine the former two items from the data, and predict $\mathcal{I}$. They find remarkably good agreement, and most values agreeing within 5 per cent and all within 15 per cent.

Nilsson and Prior[75] have carried out a similar program, but at a more fundamental level. They take empirical values of α, but evaluate Δ from theory, using pairing forces for neutrons and protons of strengths $|G_n|, |G_p|$:

$$|G_n| \approx 17 \text{ MeV/A}$$

$$|G_p| \approx 24 \text{ MeV/A}$$

They use the analysis of Mottelson and Nilsson[76] for the energies of the single-particle levels. One important feature of this work is that "blocking" effects are taken into account. As discussed in Sec. 9-2, such effects mean that excited state energies may be seriously reduced below $e_\beta + e_\gamma$. The predicted values for even nuclei are in quite good agreement with, although somewhat less than, the observed values. (In a separate paper, Prior[77] has discussed moments of odd nuclei.) The same authors also evaluate g_R, the collective gyromagnetic ratio and find values ~ 0.32, whereas observed ones are $\sim 0.2 \pm 0.1$.

Mottelson and Valatin[69] have pointed out that the tendency of rotation to decouple paired nucleons means that a rotational band spectrum will be cut off above a critical value of angular momentum. They estimate such value to be ~ 12 for A = 180 and ~ 18 for A = 238. Of course, the bands disappear anyway when the energies are comparable to intrinsic excitations, but this is expected to occur at higher values (~ 40).

Finally, although the validity of the cranking model has been reasonably well confirmed by the numerical accuracy of the predictions, there is still a need to give it a more quantum mechanical basis. This has been the subject of a number of papers[16,79,80] which use variational methods and wave functions:

$$\Psi_J(x) = \int d\theta \; f_J(\theta)\Psi_\theta(x)$$

$\Psi_\theta(x)$ are intrinsic states. The demand that $\Psi_J(x)$ have angular momentum J means that $f_J(\theta) \sim D^J(\theta)$, the rotation function. Peierls and Thouless[15] have pointed out that this method is not general enough, since it cannot reproduce known results in the translation problem.

They propose to use instead

$$\Psi_J(x) = \iint d\theta \; d\Omega \; D^J(\theta) g(\Omega) \psi_\theta(x,\Omega)$$

where $\psi_\theta(x,\Omega)$ is the intrinsic wave function for the prescribed expectation value of J_{op}. This is obtained by minimizing $H - \Omega J_{op}$. The previous form is achieved by the special choice $g(\Omega) = \delta(\Omega)$, i.e., fixing the angular velocity Ω to be zero. Although this method is formally satisfactory, it is clear that its practical usefulness is limited by fearful problems of computing overlap integrals.

References

1. V. L. Telegdi and M. Gell-Mann, *Phys. Rev.*, **99**, 169 (1953).
2. A. M. Lane and E. Pendlebury, *Nucl. Phys.*, **15**, 39 (1960).
3. H. A. Bethe and J. S. Levinger, *Phys. Rev.*, **78**, 115 (1950).
4. Crannell, Helm, Kendall, Oeser, and Yearian, *Phys. Rev.*, **123**, 923 (1961); R. H. Helm, *Phys. Rev.*, **104**, 1466 (1956).
5. M. Goldhaber and E. Teller, *Phys. Rev.*, **74**, 1046 (1948).
6. J. Bellicard and P. Barreau, *Nucl. Phys.*, **36**, 476 (1962).
7. A. S. Reiner, *Nucl. Phys.*, **27**, 115 (1961); *Physica*, **23**, 338 (1957).
8. Bayman, Reiner, and Sheline, *Phys. Rev.*, **115**, 1627 (1959).
9. A. Bohr, *Mat. Fys. Medd.*, **26**, No. 14 (1952); A. Bohr and B. R. Mottelson, *Mat. Fys. Medd.*, **27**, No. 16 (1953).
10. D. M. Brink, *Nucl. Phys.*, **4**, 215 (1957).
11. J. P. Elliott and B. H. Flowers, *Proc. Roy. Soc. (London)*, **24**, 2A, 57 (1957).
12. G. E. Brown and M. Bolsterli, *Phys. Rev. Letters*, **3**, 472 (1959).
13. N. Vinh-Mau and G. E. Brown, *Nucl. Phys.*, **29**, 89 (1962).
14. M. Baranger, *Phys. Rev.*, **120**, 957 (1960).
15. R. E. Peierls and D. J. Thouless, *Nucl. Phys.*, **38**, 154 (1962).
16. D. L. Hill and J. A. Wheeler, *Phys. Rev.*, **89**, 1106 (1953); J. J. Griffin and J. A. Wheeler, *Phys. Rev.*, **108**, 311 (1957).
17. J. J. Griffin, *Phys. Rev.*, **108**, 328 (1957).
18. A. K. Kerman and C. M. Shakin, *Phys. Letters*, **1**, 151 (1962).
19. Brown, Castillejo, and Evans, *Nucl. Phys.*, **22**, 1 (1961).
20. P. W. Anderson, *Phys. Rev.*, **112**, 1900 (1958).
21. S. Fallieros, Thesis, University of Maryland, 1959; Maryland Tech. Rept. No. 128, 1959.
22. R. A. Ferrell, *Phys. Rev.*, **107**, 1631 (1957).
23. Sawicki and Soda, *Nucl. Phys.*, **28**, 270 (1961).

24. J. Sawicki, *Nucl. Phys.*, **23**, 285 (1961).
25. J. Sawicki, *Phys. Rev.*, **126**, 2231 (1962).
26. H. Suhl and N. R. Wertheimer, *Phys. Rev.*, **122**, 359 (1961).
27. K. Sawada, *Phys. Rev.*, **106**, 372 (1957).
28. D. Bohm and D. Pines, *Phys. Rev.*, **92**, 609 (1953).
29. G. M. Ferentz, M. Gell-Mann, and D. Pines, *Phys. Rev.*, **92**, 836 (1953).
30. Ikeda, Kobayasi, Marumori, Shiozaki, and Takagi, *Progr. Theoret. Phys.*, **22**, 663 (1959).
31. S. Takagi, *Progr. Theoret. Phys.*, **21**, 174 (1959).
32. H. Ehrenreich and M. H. Cohen, *Phys. Rev.*, **115**, 786 (1959).
33. J. Goldstone and K. Gottfried, *Nuovo Cimento*, **13**, 849 (1959).
34. D. J. Thouless, *Nucl. Phys.*, **22**, 78 (1961).
35. J. M. Araujo, *Nucl. Phys.*, **1**, 259 (1956); *ibid.*, **13**, 360 (1959).
36. A. Goswami and M. K. Pal, *Nucl. Phys.*, **35**, 544 (1962); M. K. Pal and Y. C. Lee, *Bull. Am. Phys. Soc.*, II, **4**, 406 (1959).
37. R. A. Ferrell and W. M. Visscher, *Phys. Rev.*, **102**, 450 (1956); *ibid.*, **104**, 475 (1956). R. A. Ferrell and S. Fallieros, *ibid.*, **116**, 660 (1959).
38. Kisslinger and Sorensen, *Mat. Fys. Medd.*, **32**, No. 9 (1960).
39. S. T. Belyaev, *Mat. Fys. Medd.*, **31**, No. 11 (1959).
40. R. Arvieu and M. Veneroni, *Compt. Rend.*, **252**, 670 (1961).
41. D. R. Bes, *Mat. Fys. Medd.*, **33**, No. 2 (1961).
42. D. R. Inglis, *Phys. Rev.*, **97**, 701 (1955).
43. Brown, Evans, and Thouless, *Nucl. Phys.*, **24**, 1 (1961).
44. V. Gillet and N. Vinh-Mau, *Phys. Letters*, **1**, 25 (1962); V. Gillet, Thesis, University of Paris, 1962.
45. Balashov, Shevchenko, and Yukin, *Nucl. Phys.*, **27**, 323 (1961).
46. S. Fallieros, *Nucl. Phys.*, **26**, 594 (1961).
47. N. Vinh-Mau and G. E. Brown, *Phys. Letters*, **1**, 36 (1962).
48. F. C. Barker, *Nucl. Phys.*, **31**, 535 (1962).
49. D. Mitra and M. K. Pal, *Phys. Letters*, **1**, 153 (1962).
50. T. Tamura and T. Udagawa, *Progr. Theoret. Phys.*, **26**, 947 (1961); *ibid.* (to be published).
51. M. Kobayasi and T. Marumori, *Progr. Theoret. Phys.*, **23**, 387 (1960). T. Marumori, *Progr. Theoret. Phys.*, **24**, 331 (1960).
52. L. S. Kisslinger, *Nucl. Phys.*, **25**, 114 (1962).
53. L. S. Kisslinger, *Phys. Rev.*, **129**, 1316 (1963).
54. S. Yoshida, *Phys. Rev.*, **123**, 2122 (1961).
55. Gillet and Sanderson (to be published).
56. Balashov, Shevchenko, and Yudin, *JETP*, **14**, 1371 (1962).
57. Pal, Soper, and Stamp (to be published).
58. A. de Shalit, *Phys. Rev.*, **91**, 1479 (1953).
59. E. Sanderson (unpublished).
60. A. Goswami and M. K. Pal, *Nucl. Phys.*, **44**, 294 (1963).
61. A. Fano and J. Sawicki, *Nuovo Cimento*, **25**, 586 (1962).

62. B. Bremond and J. G. Valatin, *Nucl. Phys.*, **41**, 640 (1963).
63. D. R. Bes, *Mat. Fys. Medd.*, **33**, No. 2 (1961).
64. A. K Kerman and C. M. Shakin, *Phys. Letters*, **1**, 151 (1962).
65. Cohen, Lawson, and Soga (to be published).
66. R. A. Sorensen, *Nucl. Phys.*, **25**, 674 (1961).
67. Lemmer, de Shalit, and Wall, *Phys. Rev.*, **124**, 155 (1961).
68. D. J. Thouless and J. G. Valatin, *Phys. Rev. Letters*, **5**, 512 (1960); *Nucl. Phys.*, **31**, 211 (1962).
69. B. R. Mottelson and J. G. Valatin, *Phys. Rev. Letters*, **5**, 520 (1960).
70. D. R. Inglis, *Phys. Rev.*, **96**, 1059 (1954).
71. Bohr, Mottelson, and Pines, *Phys. Rev.*, **110**, 936 (1958).
72. S. A. Nilsson, *Mat. Fys. Medd.*, **29**, No. 16 (1955).
73. J. J. Griffin and M. Rich, *Phys. Rev. Letters*, **3**, 342 (1959).
74. B. R. Mottelson and S. G. Nilsson, *Phys. Rev.*, **99**, 1615 (1955).
75. S. G. Nilsson and O. Prior, *Mat. Fys. Medd.*, **32**, No. 16 (1961).
76. B. R. Mottelson and S. G. Nilsson, *Mat. Fys. Medd.*, **1**, No. 8 (1959).
77. O. Prior, *Ark. Fys.*, **14**, 451 (1958).
78. Bes and Szymanski, *Nucl. Phys.*, **28**, 42 (1961).
79. R. E. Peierls and J. Yoccoz, *Proc. Phys. Soc. (London)*, **A70**, 381 (1957); J. Yoccoz, *ibid.*, **A70**, 388 (1957).
80. T. H. R. Skyrme, *Proc. Phys. Soc. (London)*, **A70**, 433 (1957).
81. S. Yoshida, *Nucl. Phys.*, **38**, 380 (1962).
82. S. T. Belyaev and V. G. Zelevinsky, *Nucl. Phys.*, **39**, 582 (1962).
83. Arvieu, Baranger, Veneroni, Baranger, and Gillet, *Phys. Letters*, **4**, 119 (1963).

Reprinted from THE PHYSICAL REVIEW, Vol. 110, No. 4, 936–938, May 15, 1958
Printed in U. S. A.

Possible Analogy between the Excitation Spectra of Nuclei and Those of the Superconducting Metallic State

A. BOHR, B. R. MOTTELSON, AND D. PINES*
Institute for Theoretical Physics, University of Copenhagen, Copenhagen, Denmark, and Nordisk Institut for Teoretisk Atomfysik, Copenhagen, Denmark

(Received January 7, 1958)

The evidence for an energy gap in the intrinsic excitation spectrum of nuclei is reviewed. A possible analogy between this effect and the energy gap observed in the electronic excitation of a superconducting metal is suggested.

THE nuclear structure exhibits many similarities with the electron structure of metals. In both cases, we are dealing with systems of fermions which may be characterized in first approximation in terms of independent particle motion. For instance, the statistical level density, at not too low excitation energies, is expected to resemble that of a Fermi gas. Still, in both systems, important correlations in the particle motion arise from the action of the forces between the particles and, in the metallic case, from the interaction with the lattice vibrations. These correlations decisively influence various specific properties of the system. We here wish to suggest a possible analogy between the correlation effects responsible for the energy gaps found in the excitation spectra of certain types of nuclei and those responsible for the observed energy gaps in superconducting metals.

We first briefly recall the evidence for an energy gap in the spectra of nuclei, and shall especially consider nuclei of spheroidal type. The single-particle level spectra for such nuclei exhibit a particularly close similarity to that of a Fermi gas, since the degeneracies characterizing the particle motion in a spherical potential are largely removed by the distortion in the shape of the nuclear field. The levels remain doubly degenerate, and their average spacing may be most directly obtained from the observed spectra of odd-A nuclei. These exhibit intrinsic states which may be associated with the different orbits of the last particle, and the observed single-particle level spacing is approximately[1]

$$\delta \approx 50A^{-1}\ \text{Mev}, \qquad (1)$$

where A is the number of particles in the nucleus.

If the intrinsic structure could be adequately described in terms of independent particle motion, we would expect, for even-even nuclei, the first intrinsic excitation to have on the average an energy $\frac{1}{2}\delta$, when we take into account the possibility of exciting neutrons as well as protons. Empirically, however, the first intrinsic excitation in heavy nuclei of the even-even type is usually observed at an energy of about 1 Mev (see Fig. 1). The only known examples of intrinsic excitations with appreciably smaller energy are the $K=0-$ bands which occur in special regions of nuclei, and which may possibly represent collective octupole vibrations.[2]

Such an energy gap between the ground-state and first intrinsic excitation indicates an important departure from independent-particle motion, a departure arising from the residual forces between the particles. In lowest order, such forces give rise to a pairing effect, since the attractive interaction is expected to be especially strong for a pair of particles in degenerate orbits. This effect implies a shift upwards, relative to the ground state, of states involving the breaking of a pair. However, to this order, one still expects that levels corresponding to the simultaneous excitation of two particles remaining as a pair will have an average energy spacing of about δ. Such low-lying $K=0$ bands

* National Science Foundation Senior Post-Doctoral Fellow on leave of absence from Princeton University, Princeton, New Jersey, 1957–1958.

[1] B. R. Mottelson and S. G. Nilsson (to be published); F. Bakke (to be published).

[2] See, e.g., K. Alder *et al.*, Revs. Modern Phys. 28, 432 (1956).

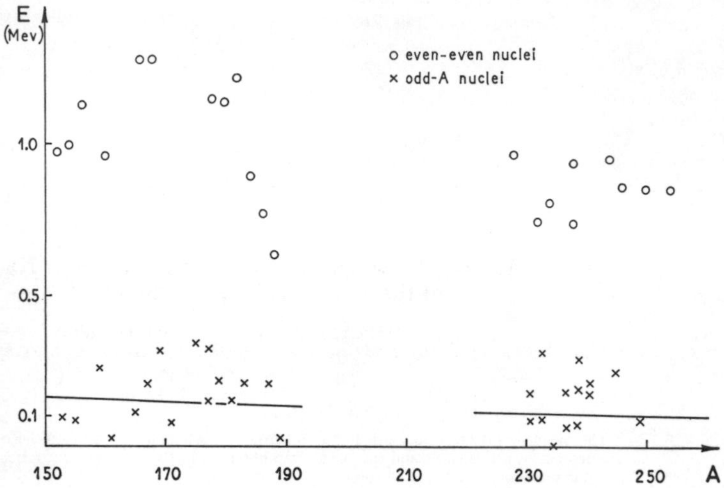

FIG. 1. Energies of first excited intrinsic states in deformed nuclei, as a function of the mass number. The experimental data may be found in *Nuclear Data Cards* [National Research Council, Washington, D. C.] and detailed references will be contained in reference 1 above. The solid line gives the energy $\delta/2$ given by Eq. (1), and represents the average distance between intrinsic levels in the odd-A nuclei (see reference 1).

The figure contains all the available data for nuclei with $150 < A < 190$ and $228 < A$. In these regions the nuclei are known to possess nonspherical equilibrium shapes, as evidenced especially by the occurrence of rotational spectra (see, e.g., reference 2). One other such region has also been identified around $A = 25$; in this latter region the available data on odd-A nuclei is still represented by Eq. (1), while the intrinsic excitations in the even-even nuclei in this region do not occur below 4 Mev.

We have not included in the figure the low lying $K=0$ states found in even-even nuclei around Ra and Th. These states appear to represent a collective odd-parity oscillation.

are not observed, and their absence implies significant correlations in the intrinsic nucleonic motion.

The appearance of a gap is reminiscent of the well-known repulsion effect between coupled levels, but in order to obtain a gap of the observed magnitude, which is several times larger than δ, it appears necessary to consider the coupling between a large number of states of independent particle motion. It seems likely that the resulting excitation spectrum may show regularities of collective type, and indeed there is some evidence for the occurrence of vibrational levels among the first intrinsic excitations in the spheroidal nuclei of even-even type.[2]

The correlations giving rise to the energy gap may also affect many other nuclear properties; thus, they appear to be responsible for the observed fact that the rotational moments of inertia are appreciably smaller than the values corresponding to rigid rotation.[3] Moreover, the well-known mass difference between even-even and odd-A nuclei[4] appears intimately connected with the occurrence of the gap. While we have here considered the nuclei of spheroidal type, similar differences between the intrinsic spectra of odd and even nuclei appear also for nuclei of spherical equilibrium shape. To exhibit the gap in these spectra one must, however, subtract the relatively low-lying collective excitations of vibrational type.

In the superconducting metal we may possibly be dealing with somewhat similar correlation effects in the electronic motion. Measurements of the thermal and electromagnetic properties of superconductors[5] indicate that the low-energy electronic excitation spectrum differs essentially from that of a Fermi gas in that there exists a finite energy gap between the ground state of the metal and the states representing electronic excitation.

Recently, new insight concerning the behavior of interacting fermions has been obtained from a detailed study of the correlations arising from the part of the interaction which acts between particles with equal and opposite momenta.[6] Treating only this part of the interaction, it was found that even very weak attractive interactions lead to a major change in the low-energy spectrum of the system. Quite apart from the extent to which additional interactions may further modify the spectrum, it would seem that the results obtained are already of considerable interest in connection with the features of the nuclear spectra discussed above and indicate that a modified structure of the Fermi surface is a general feature of Fermi systems with attractive interactions. This qualitative result is perhaps not

[3] A. Bohr and B. R. Mottelson, Kgl. Danske Videnskab. Selskab, Mat.-fys. Medd. **30**, 1 (1955).

[4] For a review of this effect, see C. D. Coryell, *Annual Review of Nuclear Science* (Annual Reviews, Inc., Stanford, 1953), Vol. 2, p. 304.

[5] For discussions of evidence for an energy gap, see Blevins, Gordy, and Fairbank, Phys. Rev. **100**, 1215 (1955); Corak, Goodman, Satterthwaite, and Wexler, Phys. Rev. **102**, 656 (1956); R. E. Glover and M. Tinkham, Phys. Rev. **104**, 844 (1956); **108**, 243 (1957).

[6] Bardeen, Cooper, and Schrieffer, Phys. Rev. **106**, 162 (1957), and Phys. Rev. **108**, 1175 (1957). This model has also been treated by N. N. Bogoliubov, J. Exptl. Theoret. Phys. (to be published) and J. Valatin (to be published).

surprising, since it may easily be shown that a perturbation treatment of the interactions leads to divergencies in the region of the Fermi surface.

Due to the simplicity of the argument, it may perhaps be useful to sketch such a perturbation calculation.[7] Consider two particles with opposite momenta and each having a kinetic energy $E_0=E_F-\epsilon$, where E_F is the Fermi energy. We evaluate the amplitude for their excitation to a level $E=E_F+\epsilon$, the other particles in the system remaining unperturbed. To first order we obtain, in obvious notation,

$$af^{(1)}=\frac{\langle 0|V|f\rangle}{2(E_0-Ef)}, \tag{2}$$

and to second order

$$af^{(2)}=\sum_i \frac{\langle 0|V|i\rangle\langle i|V|f\rangle}{4(E_0-E_i)(E_0-Ef)}$$

$$\approx af^{(1)}\int_{E_F}^{E_0+\Delta}\frac{VN(0)dE}{E-E_0}, \tag{3}$$

or

$$af^{(2)}\approx af^{(1)}N(0)V\ln[\Delta/(E_F-E_0)]. \tag{4}$$

We have approximated the interaction matrix element by a constant negative value $-V$ over an effective energy interval Δ. The density of the states at the Fermi surface is denoted by $N(0)$.

It is seen that the perturbation expansion represents a power series in the parameter

$$x=N(0)V\ln[\Delta/(E_F-E_0)]. \tag{5}$$

Thus, the series diverges for $x>1$, i.e., for E_0 in an energy region around the Fermi surface of extension

$$\epsilon\approx\Delta\exp[-1/N(0)V]. \tag{6}$$

This estimate corresponds to the result obtained in the above-mentioned model of superconductivity[6] for the energy region in which the particle motion is essentially correlated. It was also found[6] that this model leads to a gap in the energy spectrum of order given by (6).

It is of interest to attempt to apply these considerations to the nuclear case. Estimates of the quantity $N(0)V$ for the nucleus are somewhat uncertain, but indicate values of the order of $\frac{1}{5}$. Owing to the sensitivity of (6) to this quantity, it is difficult to make quantitative estimates of ϵ, but it appears likely that $\epsilon\ll\Delta$, with Δ representing an energy of the order of E_F. Under such circumstances the correlation effect would be relatively unimportant for bulk nuclear properties like the total binding energy, but would, of course, have essential effects on the low-energy excitation spectra. A quantitative estimate of ϵ would also be important for the derivation of a criterion for the occurrence of shell structure; thus, since the energy spacing between shells tends to zero as the size of the system increases, one would expect the shell structure to be washed out for a sufficiently large system.

It thus appears that there may exist interesting similarities between the low-energy spectra of nuclei and of the electrons in the superconducting metal. However, it must be stressed that the former are significantly influenced by the finite size of the nuclear system. Thus, the energy gap is observed to decrease with A, and the present data are insufficient to indicate the limiting value for the gap in a hypothetical infinitely large nucleus. Moreover, the degrees of freedom associated with the variation in shape play an especially important role in the low-energy nuclear spectra.

ACKNOWLEDGMENT

One of us (D. P.) would like to take this opportunity to thank Professor Niels Bohr and the members of the Institute for Theoretical Physics for the warm hospitality extended to him during the summer of 1957.

[7] A corresponding divergence in the two body scattering equation for particles in a Fermi gas has been pointed out by J. Goldstone (private communication).

Reprinted from THE PHYSICAL REVIEW, Vol. 121, No. 5, 1441–1456, March 1, 1961
Printed in U. S. A.

Nuclear Structure Studies in the Tin Isotopes with (d,p) and (d,t) Reactions*

BERNARD L. COHEN AND ROBERT E. PRICE
Radiation Laboratory, University of Pittsburgh, Pittsburgh, Pennsylvania

(Received July 22, 1960)

The neutron single-particle states in the odd isotopes of tin are identified by (d,p) angular distribution studies. The cross sections for exciting these states by (d,p) and (d,t) reactions are measured, and the results are analyzed to give values of V_j^2 (in Kisslinger-Sorenson notation), the fraction by which each of the single-particle states is full, for each subshell in each isotope. These are used to calculate ϵ_j, the unperturbed single-particle energies; the results are reasonably consistent. If the observed energies of single-particle states are used to predict the V_j, the agreement is generally good, but some discrepancies are noted and an explanation is offered.

Other weakly excited states are found in the region of the single-particle states. At higher excitation energies, several rather sharp levels are strongly excited in (d,p) reactions. Their energy, cross section, and regularities among the isotopes suggests that these are single-particle levels from the next major shell $(82<N\leq 126)$; however, their angular distributions cannot be used for identification as they are the same for all levels in this region and show little structure. This last fact is not easily explained.

Some of the two quasi-particle excitation states in the even isotopes of Sn are identified and the apparent pairing energy is thereby measured; it is surprisingly found to vary rapidly with mass number. Spectra from (d,p) and (d,t) reactions in isotonic pairs Cd^{114}-Sn^{116} and Cd^{116}-Sn^{118} are compared to show that the single-particle neutron states are much more radically affected by the addition of two protons than by the addition of two neutrons, contrary to the usual assumption in shell model theory.

Q values for (d,p) and (d,t) reactions on the major isotopes of tin are measured.

I. INTRODUCTION AND THEORY

FROM the simple shell-model viewpoint, the structure of nuclei with more than three particles (or holes) outside of closed shells is extremely complicated, and good theoretical calculations are essentially impossible. However, in the pairing theory approximation,[1,2] the structure becomes simple again provided, at least, that either the neutrons or protons have a closed shell. Such a situation arises among the isotopes

* Work done in the Sarah Mellon Scaife Radiation Laboratory and assisted by the National Science Foundation and the joint program of the Office of Naval Research and the U. S. Atomic Energy Commission.

[1] L. S. Kisslinger and R. A. Sorenson, Kgl. Danske Videnskab. Selskab, Mat.-fys. Medd. (to be published).
[2] M. Baranger (to be published).

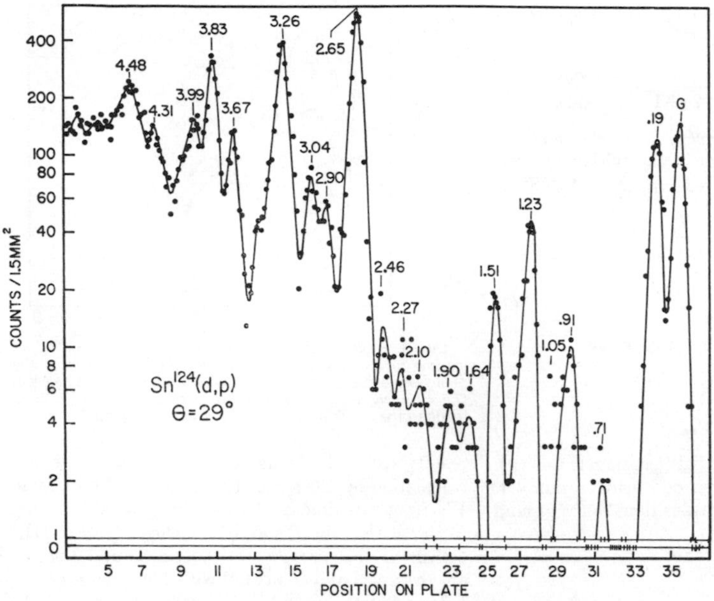

FIG. 1. Typical data for proton spectra from (d,p) reactions. Different symbols for ordinates equal to zero and one have no significance other than legibility. Figures are excitation energy in Mev.

of tin, where there is a closed shell of protons, and the neutron number outside of the closed shell varies from 16 to 24 (the hole number varies from 8 to 16).

The neutron subshells filling in this region are the $d_{5/2}$, $g_{7/2}$, $s_{1/2}$, $d_{3/2}$, and $h_{11/2}$. In the pairing theory approximation, the ground state of an even-even nucleus is characterized by a set of quantities[3] $V_{d5/2}$, $V_{g7/2}$, $V_{s1/2}$, etc., where $(V_{d5/2})^2$ is the fraction by which the $d_{5/2}$ shell is filled, etc. For simplicity, we introduce the notation

$$V_{2j}=(V_{lj})^2 \text{ of reference } 1=(v_{lj})^2 \text{ of reference } 2,$$

so that now the ground state of an even-even nucleus is specified by V_5, V_7, V_1, V_3, and V_{11}. In accordance with pairing theory, these quantities increase slowly and monotonically with mass number, in a manner which can be calculated from the unperturbed single particle level positions. Thus, the addition of two neutrons to an even-even nucleus changes the ground state-configuration only slightly. The low-lying states of odd-neutron isotopes consist essentially of an even-even core plus a particle (or hole) in one of the single-particle states. The spectrum of each of the odd isotopes of tin should thus be quite similar.

An especially useful technique for investigating these single-particle states is a study with the (d,p) and (d,t) stripping and pickup reactions. Firstly, they preferentially excite these single-particle and single-hole states; secondly, measurements of the angular distributions provide an assignment of each level to one of the single-particle states; and thirdly, measurements of the cross sections give determinations of the V's.

The dependence of the cross sections on the V's has been demonstrated rigorously by Yoshida,[4] but the following simple calculation (carried out independently) gives insight into the problem, and yields the correct results. The cross section for a (d,p) and a (d,t) reaction may be expressed as

$$\frac{d\sigma}{d\Omega}(d,p)=\frac{2I_f+1}{2I_i+1}P(l_n,Q,\theta)S(i,f),$$
$$\frac{d\sigma}{d\Omega}(d,t)=T(l_n,Q,\theta)S(i,f), \tag{1}$$

where I_f and I_i are the spins of initial and final nuclei, P and T are functions derivable, in principle, from reaction theory, and $S(i,f)=S(f,i)$ is a quantity derivable from nuclear structure theory which expresses the overlap between the initial and final nuclear states. In all stripping and pickup theories which have been conceived to date, P and T are functions of l_n, the orbital angular momentum of the "stripped" or "picked-up" neutron; Q, the energy release in the reaction; and θ, the angle between the incident deuteron and the emitted proton or triton.

If the initial and final state configurations differ only

[3] Reference 1 uses capital V's while reference 2 uses lower case v's. The former should not be confused with the capital V's used here which are their square.

[4] S. Yoshida (private communication).

in that one has j^n and the other has j^{n-1}, French[5] has shown that

$$S(n,n-1)=n \quad (n \text{ even})$$
$$=1-(n-1)/(2j+1) \quad (n \text{ odd}). \tag{2}$$

If the target nucleus is even-even, for a (d,t) reaction $S=n_i$, the number of particles in the initial nucleus; for a (d,p) reaction, $S=1-n_i/(2j+1)$. Since $n=(2j+1)V$, $I_i=0$, and $I_f=j$,

$$\frac{d\sigma}{d\Omega}(d,p)=(2j+1)PU_{2j}^{(i)},$$
$$\frac{d\sigma}{d\Omega}(d,t)=(2j+1)TV_{2j}^{(i)}, \quad \text{(target even)} \tag{3}$$

where

$$U_{2j}=1-V_{2j}, \tag{4}$$

and $V_{2j}^{(i)}$ means V_{2j} for the initial (i.e., target) nucleus. When the target nucleus has an odd neutron number, a similar calculation yields, for transitions to the ground state

$$\frac{d\sigma}{d\Omega}(d,p)=PV_{2j}^{(f)},$$
$$\frac{d\sigma}{d\Omega}(d,t)=TU_{2j}^{(f)}, \quad \text{(target odd)} \tag{5}$$

where $V_{2j}^{(f)}$ means V_{2j} for the final nucleus. The results (3) and (5) agree with those of a complete calculation by Yoshida.[4] The methods of obtaining the V's from experiments depends, in general, on forming ratios so that the P's and T's cancel. In Sec. III, the details of this process are described, and the results are discussed and compared with other data.

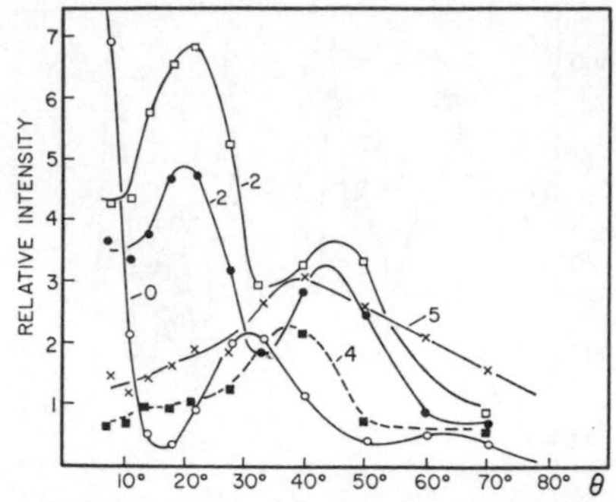

FIG. 3. Angular distributions of protons from $Sn^{116}(d,p)Sn^{117}$ leading to states of Sn^{117} with known spins and parities. Figures attached to the curves are l_n, the orbital angular momentum of the stripped neutron. Of the two curves with $l_n=2$, the upper leads to the $d_{3/2}$ state and the lower to the $d_{5/2}$ state.

In addition to yielding details of the shell being filled, (d,p) reactions leading to higher excited states should give information on the single-particle states in the next (empty) major shell. A considerable effort has been expended in this direction, although the results so far have led to little elucidation. This work is discussed in Sec. IV-A. Other parts of Sec. IV discuss the low-lying non-single-particle states, reactions on the odd isotopes of tin which give a direct measure of the pairing energy and show a strange behavior for the latter, a comparison of the neutron single-particle states in isotopes of Cd and Sn which have the same number of neutrons, and the experimental results for reaction Q values.

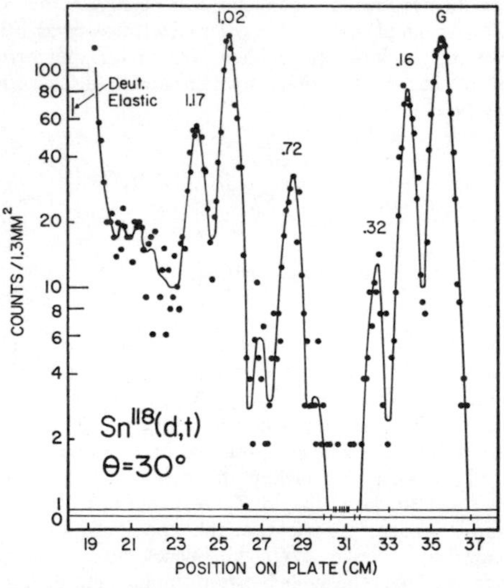

FIG. 2. Typical data for triton spectra from (d,t) reactions. See caption for Fig. 1.

II. EXPERIMENTAL

The experimental method has been described previously[6]; it consists of bombarding targets with 15-Mev deuterons from the University of Pittsburgh cyclotron, magnetically analyzing the reaction products with a 60° wedge magnet spectrograph, and allowing them to impinge on a nuclear track photographic emulsion located on its focal plane. After development, the emulsions are scanned under a microscope, and the number of tracks per unit area are counted as a function of position, thus determining intensity as a function of energy. The targets are isotopically enriched foils of each of the major isotopes of tin[7]; typical target

[5] J. B. French, *Nuclear Spectroscopy*, edited by F. Ajzenberg-Selove (Academic Press, Inc., New York, 1960).

[6] B. L. Cohen, J. B. Mead, R. E. Price, K. Quisenberry, and C. Martz, Phys. Rev. **118**, 499 (1960).

[7] The tin isotopes as metal foils were obtained from Stable Isotopes Division, Oak Ridge National Laboratory, Oak Ridge, Tennessee.

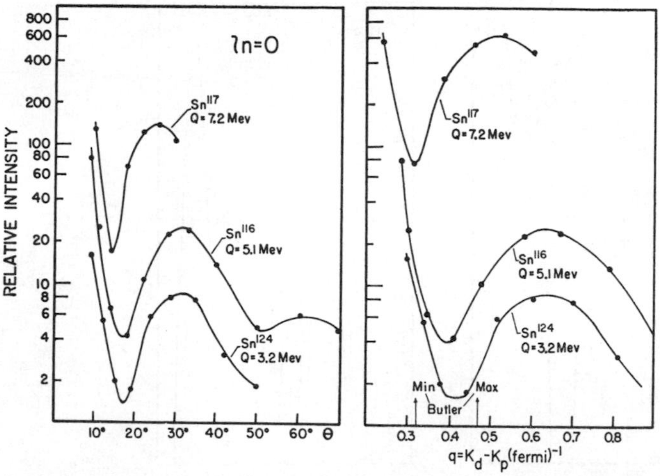

FIG. 4. Angular distributions from (d,p) reactions with $l_n=0$ but differing Q values. The plot on the right is the same data plotted against q, the momentum transferred to the nucleus. If Butler theory were valid, the plots vs q would all have maxima and minima at the same abscissas, namely those labelled "Butler Max" and "Min." A large amount of other data is consistent with that shown here.

thicknesses are 7 mg/cm^2, but by judicious target orientation,[8] the energy resolution is generally about 80 kev. In runs where protons are detected, the photographic emulsion is covered by sufficient absorber to stop all particles except protons; where tritons are detected, no particle selection is necessary as no other particle has as large a magnetic rigidity as $>$10-Mev tritons. Below 10 Mev, elastically and inelastically scattered deuterons produce a background which makes triton detection impossible. At small angles, the background from elastically scattered deuterons causes serious difficulty for triton energies up to $\sim$13 Mev.

Typical data are shown in Figs. 1 and 2. For reasons which are not very clear, data taken on the same day are most consistent. In some cases where data are taken several months apart, discrepancies in cross sections as large as 40% have been found. In measuring angular distributions it is thus important to expose plates at all angles on the same day. In deriving results from the data, these problems are taken into account in assigning weights to various experimental determinations. The best results are obtained when a measurement consists of determining the ratio of intensities of two peaks from the same plate exposure. Fortunately, some of the most important results in the experiment are obtained in this way. Portions of the plate used for quantitative data are scanned independently at least twice.

For other reasons which are also not clear, determinations of excitation energies for a given level vary by as much as 4% when plates are exposed at different times. More typical uncertainties in energies are about 1–2%. No extensive effort has yet been made to understand or to correct this difficulty.

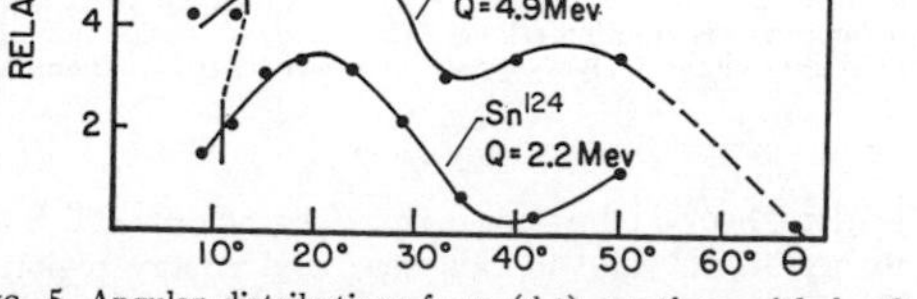

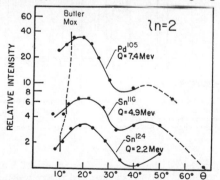

FIG. 5. Angular distributions from (d,p) reactions with $l_n=2$ but differing Q values. The solid vertical lines through each curve connected by dashed lines show the position of the first maximum predicted by Butler theory. A large amount of other data is consistent with that shown here; some is shown in Fig. 11.

[8] B. L. Cohen, Rev. Sci. Instr. 30, 415 (1959).

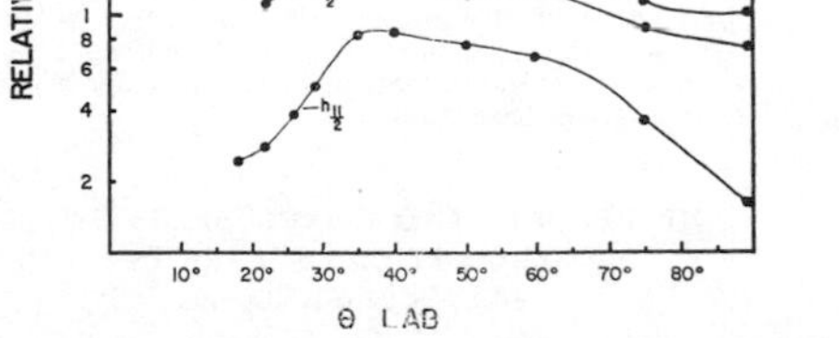

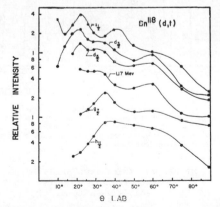

FIG. 6. Angular distributions of tritons from $Sn^{118}(d,t)Sn^{117}$ leading to states of Sn^{117} with known spins and parities designated by single-particle state attached to curves. The low-angle region is difficult to study because of deuteron background. The 1.17-Mev state was found to be $d_{5/2}$ from (d,p) reaction studies.

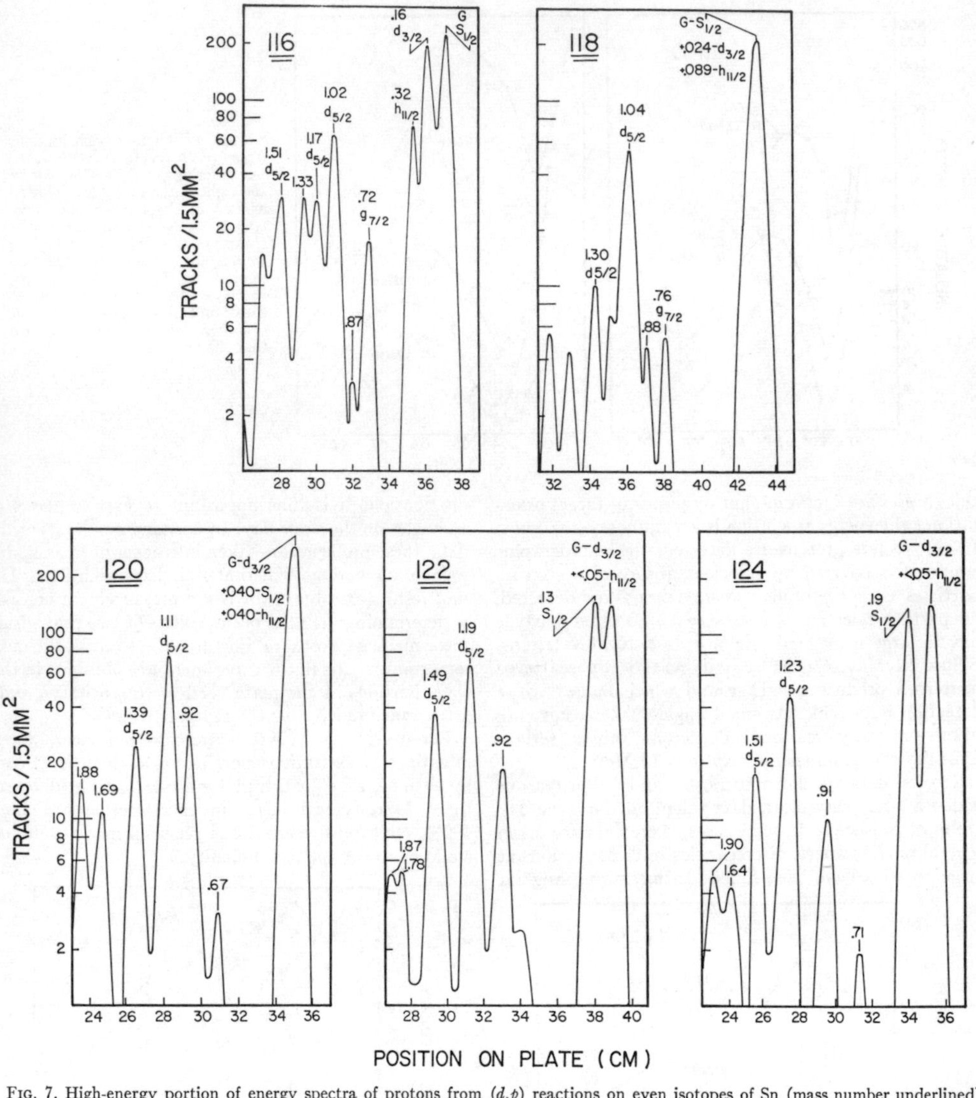

FIG. 7. High-energy portion of energy spectra of protons from (d,p) reactions on even isotopes of Sn (mass number underlined). Detection angle is 29°. Figures are excitation energy in Mev, and spectroscopic notation refers to assignment as single-particle level. Groups not so designated are not single-particle levels as evidenced by angular distribution studies. The energy determination of the $s_{1/2}$ level from $Sn^{120}(d,p)$ was obtained from the difference in apparent energy of the 1.11-Mev state at angles where $l_n=2$ and $l_n=0$ angular distributions have maxima.

III. RESULTS AND CONCLUSIONS ON SINGLE-PARTICLE STATES IN $50<N\leq 82$ SHELL

A. Angular Distributions

In light elements, values of l_n are determined straightforwardly by comparing angular distributions with Butler theory[9]; however, one does not expect Butler theory to be valid in this mass and energy region, so that the first task is to establish a systematics by measuring angular distributions for cases where l_n is known, for various values of Q.

[9] S. T. Butler, *Nuclear Stripping Reactions* (John Wiley & Sons, Inc., New York, 1957).

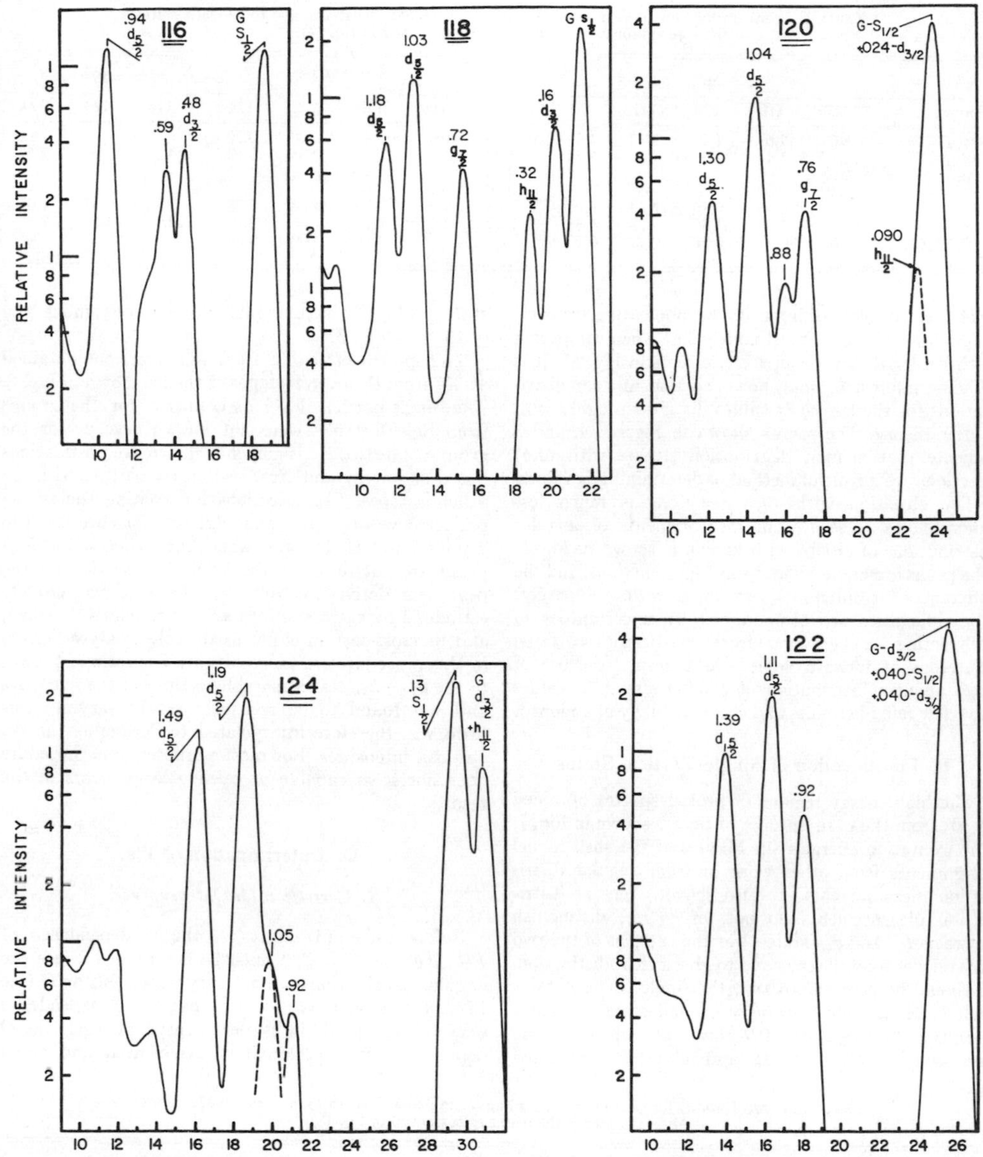

FIG. 8. Energy spectra of tritons form (d,t) reactions on even isotopes of Sn (mass number underlined). See caption for Fig. 7.

Figure 3 shows angular distributions for groups with $l_n=0$, 2, 4, and 5 from the reaction $Sn^{116}(d,p)Sn^{117}$. The shapes of the angular distributions and their variation with l_n fit well with expectations from experience with lighter elements; only the $l_n=0$ has a peak at forward angles, and the angle of the first peak in the other cases increases monotonically with l_n.

The dependence of these angular distributions on Q is shown in Figs. 4 and 5, where comparisons of positions of maxima and minima with Butler theory are also made. The changes in peak angle with Q are very slow, considerably slower than predictions from Butler theory and in the opposite direction. It is thus better to compare angular distributions directly rather than to con-

TABLE I. $d\sigma/d\Omega$ (mb/sr) for (d,p) reactions leading to single-particle states, and to 0.9-Mev states. Also tabulated is the quantity a, defined in Eq. (7).

	30°					45°					19°		
Target mass	116	118	120	122	124	116	118	120	122	124	116	120	124
$s_{1/2}$	2.6	1.6	1.7	1.7	1.4	0.40	~0.4	~0.4	0.40	0.20			
$d_{3/2}$	1.87	1.4	1.3	1.3	1.24	1.08	1.3	1.2	0.85	0.60	4.4	2.5	2.6
$h_{11/2}$	0.63					0.62							
$g_{7/2}$	0.19	0.09				0.10	0.10						
$d_{5/2}$	1.07	0.93	0.86	1.04	0.67	0.48	0.65	0.56	0.54	0.28	1.86	1.42	1.07
a	1.75	1.50	1.5	1.25	1.85	2.25	2.0	2.1	1.6	2.1	2.3	1.8	2.4
0.9 Mev	$\lesssim$0.03	0.04	0.27	0.23	0.10			0.17	0.09	0.06			

vert them to plots of intensity vs momentum transfer, q ($q=K_d-K_p$), as is most convenient when comparing with Butler theory (compare two plots in Fig. 4). It is of some interest to note, however, that angular distributions for the largest Q values do agree roughly with Butler theory. The results shown in Figs. 3, 4, and 5 indicate that angular distribution studies with (d,p) reactions are a fruitful method of determining l_n values.

The situation with (d,t) reactions is much less favorable as is seen from measurements of angular distributions of groups with known l_n shown in Fig. 6. The peaks are not as sharp as in (d,p) reactions, and the differences for different l_n are not as readily apparent. The difficulties are compounded by uncertainties in subtracting backgrounds from elastically scattered deuterons at forward angles. As a result, the use of (d,t) angular distributions for determining l_n values gave few reliable results and was eventually abandoned.

B. Identification of Single-Particle States

The high-energy regions of proton spectra obtained at 30° from the even isotopes of tin are shown in Fig. 7. The excitation energies (in Mev) and the shell model assignments from other work or from angular distribution measurements are also shown. Angular distribution measurements do not, of course, distinguish between $d_{5/2}$ and $d_{3/2}$ states, but the energies of the two are sufficiently well separated to give a clear distinction. It should be pointed out that the single-particle states include all the most strongly excited states; a slight exception to this is the 0.9-Mev state which will be discussed in Sec. IV-B. It, and all other unassigned states in Fig. 7, have angular distributions unlike any of those in Fig. 3.

The spectra of tritons from (d,t) reactions obtained at 30° from the even isotopes of tin are shown in Fig. 8. The single-particle level assignments for the groups from $Sn^{116}(d,t)Sn^{115}$ were not known (except for the ground state); the assignments shown are postulations based on energy and cross-section regularities with the other isotopes. Cross sections for exciting the single-particle levels by (d,p) and (d,t) reactions are listed in Tables I and II. In cases where the $s_{1/2}$, $d_{3/2}$, and $h_{11/2}$ peaks are not resolved, the total cross section for the peak was derived as follows: The $h_{11/2}$ was crudely estimated by extrapolation; since it is relatively small, and its cross section is not used in the analyses, errors in this procedure are unimportant. The ratio of the $s_{1/2}$ to the $d_{3/2}+h_{11/2}$ is measurable in three of the five cases and was found to be relatively slowly varying; this ratio was therefore interpolated to determine the $s_{1/2}$ and $d_{3/2}$ intensities. For most purposes, this procedure does not seem capable of causing large errors in the results.

C. Determination of V's

1. Correction for Q dependence.

Before using (3) and (5), the Q dependence of $P(l_n,Q,\theta)$ and $T(l_n,Q,\theta)$ must be determined. Since the angular distributions are not very dependent on Q (see Figs. 4 and 5), it is assumed that the Q dependence may be separated; in Butler theory,[9] at least, the Q dependence is approximately exponential and equal

TABLE II. $d\sigma/d\Omega$ (mb/sr) for (d,t) reactions leading to single-particle states, and to 0.9-Mev states. Also tabulated is the quantity b, defined in Eq. (8).

	30° Data					45° Data				
Target mass	116	118	120	122	124	116	118	120	122	124
$s_{1/2}$	1.31	1.31	1.6	2.0	2.1	1.27	2.20	3.2	3.4	3.6
$d_{3/2}$	0.50	0.66	1.05	1.4	1.8	0.32	0.71	1.2	1.8	1.8
$h_{11/2}$		0.09					0.22			
$g_{7/2}$		0.27					0.43			
$d_{5/2}$	2.15	1.88	1.94	2.24	2.86	1.27	2.06	2.20	3.00	2.85
b	0.23	0.35	0.54	0.62	0.63	0.25	0.34	0.55	0.60	0.65
0.9 Mev			0.16	0.38	0.06			0.20	0.52	0.07

TABLE III. V_3 and V_5 calculated for various values of A.

	Target mass / A	116	118	120	122	124
V_3	1.0	0.28	0.40	0.73	0.77	0.94
	1.12	0.26	0.36	0.60	0.66	0.76
	1.25	0.24	0.29	0.49	0.52	0.61
V_5	1.0	0.77	0.78	0.90	0.90	0.98
	1.12	0.78	0.80	0.87	0.87	0.94
	1.25	0.80	0.81	0.86	0.84	0.92

and opposite for P and T. We thus assume

$$P(l_n,Q,\theta)=P_{l_n}'(\theta)A^{-Q},$$
$$T(l_n,Q,\theta)=T_{l_n}'(\theta)A^{Q}, \quad (Q \text{ in Mev}). \quad (6)$$

This approximation is principally justified by the fact that the Q dependence is generally a small correction (with one exception to be noted). It is certainly unreliable if A is much different from unity, or if we compare states with much different Q values. In Butler[9] theory, $A \simeq 1.12$; from the ratios of the $d_{3/2}$ and $d_{5/2}$ states in the $Zr^{90}(d,p)Zr^{91}$ reaction, $A=1.14$; in the Pb isotopes, a recent study[10] gave $A=1.35$. It thus seems reasonable to expect A to be between 1.12 and 1.25; calculations were therefore made for these two values and for $A=1.00$.

2. *Determination of V_3 and V_5*

Inserting (6) in (3), taking the ratio of cross sections for exciting the $d_{3/2}$ and $d_{5/2}$ states, and dropping superscripts,

$$A^{(Q_3-Q_5)}\left[\frac{d\sigma}{d\Omega}(d,p) \to d_{3/2}\right] \Big/ \left[\frac{d\sigma}{d\Omega}(d,p) \to d_{5/2}\right] = a = \frac{4}{6}\frac{U_3}{U_5}, \quad (7)$$

where Q_3 and Q_5 designate the Q values for reactions leading to the $d_{3/2}$ and $d_{5/2}$ states, respectively, and a is the experimentally determined quantity on the left side of (7). Similarly,

$$A^{(Q_5-Q_3)}\left[\frac{d\sigma}{d\Omega}(d,t) \to d_{3/2}\right] \Big/ \left[\frac{d\sigma}{d\Omega}(d,t) \to d_{5/2}\right] = b = \frac{4}{6}\frac{V_3}{V_5}. \quad (8)$$

Experimental values for a and b are listed in Table I. There are some discrepancies in values of a determined at various angles due to differences in angular distributions. Equations (7) and (8) plus the two applicable equations (4) represent four equations in four unknowns (U_3, V_3, U_5, V_5) whose solution is

$$V_5=(a-\tfrac{2}{3})/(a-b),$$
$$V_3=(\tfrac{3}{2}a-1)b/(a-b)=\tfrac{3}{2}bV_5. \quad (9)$$

Values of V_3 and V_5 are listed for the various values of A in Table III.

Some information on the value of A may be obtained if one recognizes that P_2' and T_2' should be approximately constant for all cases at a given θ. Once the U's and V's are determined, P_2' and T_2' may be calculated from (3) and (6); results for $P_2'(30°)$ and $T_2'(30°)$ are listed in Table IV. These calculations are somewhat unreliable as they compare data obtained from different cyclotron runs made over an extended period of time, (in contrast to this, the determinations of V's depend on the relative areas under various peaks on the same photographic plate); they are furthermore quite sensitive to small changes in the experimental results. Nevertheless, they give ample reason to exclude $A=1.00$ and to favor $A=1.25$ over $A=1.12$. Weighting this with the value from the $Zr(d,p)$ reaction, we adopt $A=1.18$ to give our best values of V_3 and V_5 which are listed in Table V in columns labeled "Exp." It should be noted from Table III that V_3 and V_5 are generally not highly sensitive to the value of A. The final values of V_3 and V_5 are probably accurate within ± 0.06. The difference between V_3 and V_5 for successive isotopes are probably accurate within ± 0.03.

3. *Determination of V_1*

Since the ground states of the odd isotopes Sn^{117} and Sn^{119} are $s_{1/2}$ states, (d,p) and (d,t) reactions on these leading to the ground states of the final even-even nuclei give information on V_1 of the latter by use of (5). For example, V_1 for Sn^{118} can be obtained from (3), (5), and (6) as

$$A^{(Q_{78}-Q_{89})}\frac{d\sigma}{d\Omega}[Sn^{117}(d,p)Sn^{118}] \Big/ \frac{d\sigma}{d\Omega}[Sn^{118}(d,p)Sn^{119}] = c = [U_1/2V_1]_{Sn^{118}},$$

$$A^{(Q_{98}-Q_{87})}\frac{d\sigma}{d\Omega}[Sn^{118}(d,t)Sn^{117}] \Big/ \frac{d\sigma}{d\Omega}[Sn^{119}(d,t)Sn^{118}] = d = [2V_1/U_1]_{Sn^{118}}, \quad (10)$$

TABLE IV. Values of P_2' and T_2' from 30° data for various values of A (relative units for each A).

	Target mass / SP state / A	116 $d_{3/2}$	116 $d_{5/2}$	118 $d_{3/2}$	118 $d_{5/2}$	120 $d_{3/2}$	120 $d_{5/2}$	122 $d_{3/2}$	122 $d_{5/2}$	124 $d_{3/2}$	124 $d_{5/2}$
P_2'	1.0	65	78	54	67	120	144	142	173	560	560
	1.12	70	80	53	67	82	98	94	110	120	142
	1.25	75	86	51	65	66	80	66	74	69	77
T_2'	1.0	44	47	41	40	36	36	46	41	48	49
	1.12	50	49	46	45	43	42	50	48	54	54
	1.25	56	50	59	51	52	48	61	55	62	61

[10] B. L. Cohen, S. Mayo, and R. E. Price, Nuclear Phys. 20, 360 (1960); and B. L. Cohen, R. E. Price, and S. Mayo, Nuclear Phys. 20, 370 (1960).

TABLE V. Values of V for various single-particle states in even isotopes of tin. "Exp" denotes experimental values obtained in this work, K-S denotes values from Kisslinger-Sorenson calculation, and E denotes values obtained from observed energies by use of (17) or Fig. 9(b).

Mass No.	116			118			120			122			124		
SP state	Exp	K-S	E	Exp	K-S	E	Exp	K-S	E	Exp	K-S	E	Exp	K-S	E
$s_{1/2}$	0.42	0.37	~0.5	0.50	0.53	~0.5	0.61	0.65	0.57	0.69	0.75	0.69	0.74	0.88	0.74
$d_{3/2}$	0.25	0.25	0.20	0.33	0.39	0.33	0.55	0.53	~0.5	0.59	0.65	~0.5	0.68	0.75	~0.5
$d_{5/2}$	0.79	0.93	0.93	0.80	0.94	0.93	0.87	0.95	0.94	0.86	0.96	0.95	0.93	0.97	0.95
$g_{7/2}$	0.78	0.91	0.89	0.86	0.93	0.90	0.89	0.94	0.90	(0.92)	0.95		(0.95)	0.96	
$h_{11/2}$	0.27	0.11	0.13	0.33	0.19	0.25	0.35	0.27	0.34	0.47	0.38	~0.5	0.55	0.59	~0.5

where Q_{78}, Q_{87}, etc., are Q values for the reactions $Sn^{117}(d,p)Sn^{118}$, $Sn^{118}(d,t)Sn^{117}$, etc.; and c and d are the experimentally determined values of the ratios on the left. These plus the appropriate equation (4) give two independent determinations of V_1; they are listed in Table VI for the three values of A being considered. The results are consistent for $A=1.04$ with $V_1=0.45$.

This is an uncomfortably low value of A, and the whole analysis is somewhat questionable because of the large difference in Q values between reactions being compared (2.8 Mev). There may well be shifts in the angular distributions which render the separation (6) invalid. An alternative procedure was therefore followed: Angular distributions for the two reactions were measured and intensities were compared both at an angle near the peak of the angular distributions of each (27°) and at the peaks themselves; the results are the same from the two comparisons and are listed in Table VI. The results from the (d,p) and (d,t) comparisons are consistent for $A=1.12$ where each gives $V_1=0.50$; this value is adopted. The slight difference between the values of A used here and in the analyses of the $d_{3/2}$ and $d_{5/2}$ states need not be disturbing as the range of Q values covered is quite different, and A might be a function of l_n.

Once the value of A and of V_1 for Sn^{118} is determined, V_1 for the other isotopes may be obtained by assuming P' and T' are the same for all isotopes. In addition, V_1 for Sn^{116} and for Sn^{120} may be determined analogously with (10) from ratios of (d,t) cross sections for Sn^{117} and Sn^{116}, and from ratios of (d,p) cross sections from Sn^{119} and Sn^{120}. All values and weighted averages are listed in Table VII, and the weighted averages are listed in Table V. The values listed are probably accurate within ± 0.08, and the differences between V_1 for successive isotopes is probably accurate within ± 0.05. The data for Sn^{116} are somewhat less consistent than for the others, so that the error on its V_1 is perhaps 50% larger.

TABLE VI. Determinations of V_1 for Sn^{118}.

Method	Reaction	$A=1.00$	$A=1.12$	$A=1.25$
Average of 30° and 45° ratios	(d,p)	0.47	0.40	0.33
	(d,t)	0.43	0.51	0.59
Peaks in angular distribution	(d,p)	0.57	0.49	0.41
	(d,t)	0.42	0.50	0.57

4. Determination of V_7 and V_{11}

The methods used for the s and d states are not applicable to the $g_{7/2}$ and $h_{11/2}$, so that another method must be devised. Furthermore, a reasonably good determination of the $h_{11/2}$ cross section is only available for the two reactions leading to Sn^{117}. Since the $g_{7/2}$ cross sections are also well determined in these cases, we may obtain the experimental ratios

$$\left[\frac{d\sigma}{d\Omega}(d,p)\rightarrow g_{7/2}\right]\Big/\left[\frac{d\sigma}{d\Omega}(d,p)\rightarrow h_{11/2}\right]=e,$$

$$\left[\frac{d\sigma}{d\Omega}(d,t)\rightarrow g_{7/2}\right]\Big/\left[\frac{d\sigma}{d\Omega}(d,t)\rightarrow h_{11/2}\right]=f.$$

From (3)

$$\begin{aligned} e&=[(8P_4/12P_5)(U_7/U_{11})]_{Sn^{116}},\\ f&=[(8T_4/12T_5)(V_7/V_{11})]_{Sn^{118}}. \end{aligned} \qquad (11)$$

These can be solved for V_7 and V_{11} with the appropriate equations (4) provided we assume V_7 and V_{11} are the same for Sn^{116} and Sn^{118} (the inaccuracy in this is reduced by a perturbation treatment of the final results), and provided we know the ratios P_4/P_5 and T_4/T_5. As in a previous paper,[10] we assume

$$P_4/P_5=T_4/T_5=2^k. \qquad (12)$$

In $Pb(d,t)$ reactions,[10] we found $k\simeq 1.0$; in $Pb(d,p)$ reactions,[10] we found $k\simeq 0.7$. From Butler theory,[9] $k\simeq 1-1.5$, and this is in general agreement with experimental evidence in light elements. We thus might expect $k\sim 1$.

The values of V_7 and V_{11} obtained for Sn^{117} (an average between Sn^{116} and Sn^{118}) for various values of k are shown in Table VIII, and the total number of particles in the two states, $8\,V_7+12\,V_{11}$, are also listed.

TABLE VII. Values of V_1 for other isotopes by various methods assuming $V_1(Sn^{118})=0.50$, $A=1.12$.

Target mass	116	120	122	124
(d,p) σ ratios	0.32	0.54	0.54	0.67
(d,t) σ ratios	0.44	0.65	0.76	0.77
From (10)	0.48	0.62		
Weight av	0.42	0.61	0.69	0.74

TABLE VIII. V_7 and V_{11} as determined from 30° and 45° data as a function of k for Sn^{117}. The last row, the number of particles in these satates, should be 10.2.

	From 30° data				From 45° data		
k	0	0.75	1	2	0	1	2
V_7	0.62	0.82	0.86	0.99	0.84	0.96	1.02
V_{11}	0.13	0.30	0.38	0.86	0.28	0.64	1.36
$8\ V_7+12\ V_{11}$	6.6	10.2	11.4	18.2	10.1	15.4	···

However the latter quantity is directly obtainable by subtracting the number of s and d particles, $2\ V_1+V_3+6\ V_5$, from the total number of particles in the shell, 17. The result from Table V is 10.2; this is in agreement with the results in Table VIII for $k=0.75$ at 30°, and for $k=0$ at 45°; in both cases $V_7\simeq 0.83$ and $V_{11}\simeq 0.29$, so that these values are adopted. Incidentally, the low value for k at 45° is not unexpected, as the $l_n=5$ angular distribution is peaked at that angle while the $l_n=4$ is somewhat beyond its peak (see Fig. 3).

The change of V_7 and V_{11} with mass is difficult to obtain from the data because of the sparsity of cases where these levels are resolved. From the (d,p) data, one surmises that U_7 increases by a factor of 1.3 to 2.0 between Sn^{116} and Sn^{118} [the 45° data is somewhat unreliable as the $g_{7/2}$ angular distribution changes rapidly in that angular region (see Fig. 3)]. These two extremes would give $V_7=0.80-0.76$ and $0.85-0.88$ for Sn^{116} and Sn^{118}, respectively. In Table V, we adopt values midway between these two extremes. The ratio of (d,t) cross sections between Sn^{120} and Sn^{118}, with (3) and (6), indicate that V_7 increases by 5% between Sn^{118} and Sn^{120}, but this result is very sensitive to small experimental errors. For want of some better method, it is assumed in Table V that V_7 increases by 0.03 for each succeeding even isotope. This brings V_7 to 0.95 for Sn^{124}, which can hardly be off by more than ± 0.04 if V_7 for Sn^{118} is correct and the theory is applicable. The over-all uncertainties on V_7 are about ± 0.08.

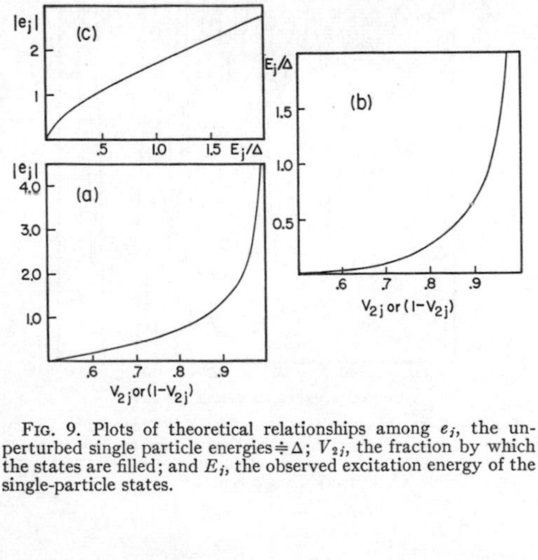

FIG. 9. Plots of theoretical relationships among e_j, the unperturbed single particle energies $\div\Delta$; V_{2j}, the fraction by which the states are filled; and E_j, the observed excitation energy of the single-particle states.

Since V_1, V_3, V_5, and V_7 are now chosen, values of V_{11} can be determined from the condition on the total number of particles. The values so obtained are listed in Table V; the uncertainties are about ± 0.20.

D. Discussion and Conclusions

Pairing theory relates two interesting quantities to the V's: the energies of the single-particle levels, ϵ_j, and the energies of the observed levels, E_j. These relationships are[1]:

$$V_{2j}=\frac{1}{2}\left[1-\frac{e_j}{(1+e_j^2)^{\frac{1}{2}}}\right], \tag{13}$$

where

$$e_j=(\epsilon_j-\lambda)/\Delta, \tag{14}$$

λ is the chemical potential, and Δ is half the energy gap, or about 1.1 Mev; and

$$E_j=\Delta[(1+e_j^2)^{\frac{1}{2}}-(1+e_{j-G}^2)^{\frac{1}{2}}], \tag{15}$$

where e_{j-G} is e_j for the ground state.

Solving (13) for V_{2j} and using (4), we obtain

$$e_j=\frac{U_{2j}-V_{2j}}{2(U_{2j}V_{2j})^{\frac{1}{2}}}. \tag{16}$$

The relationship (16) is plotted in Fig. 9(a). Values of ϵ_j obtained from the V_{2j} of Table V with (4), (14), and (16) are listed in Table IX where they are compared with the values for a Nilsson well.[11] The determinations of the single-particle energies for the various isotopes are reasonably consistent among themselves, although there are rather large fluctuations as might be expected. The agreement with the levels calculated for the Nilsson well is as good as one would expect in view of the uncertainty in the latter.

Another approach is to compare the experimental V's with those derived from the Nilsson-well single-particle energies by Kisslinger and Sorenson.[1] This is shown in Table V. The principal discrepancies which are far outside of experimental error are that the calculated

TABLE IX. Values of $\epsilon_j-\epsilon_{d5/2}$ calculated from V's of Table V and compared with the values for the Nilsson well used by Kisslinger and Sorenson. Energies are in Mev and are calculated using $\Delta=1.1$ Mev. The average of the experimental values is listed in the final column. For explanation of rows labeled "E," see text following Eq. (19).

Mass number		116	118	120	122	124	Nilsson K-S	Exp av
$s_{1/2}$	Exp	0.97	0.83	0.97	0.70	1.24	1.90	0.95
	E	1.65	1.72	1.57	1.40	1.37		
$d_{3/2}$	Exp	1.44	1.22	1.10	0.96	1.41	2.20	1.23
	E	2.45	2.12	1.87	1.85	1.94		
$d_{5/2}$	Exp	0	0	0	0	0	0	0
	E	0	0	0	0	0		
$g_{7/2}$	Exp	0.08	−0.33	−0.22			0.22	−0.16
	E	0.42	0.37	0.22				
$h_{11/2}$	Exp	1.34	1.22	1.54	1.22	1.75	2.80	1.41
	E	2.75	2.32	2.12	2.05	1.94		

[11] S. G. Nilsson, Kgl. Danske Videnskab. Selskab. Mat.-fys. Medd. 29, 16 (1955).

TABLE X. Energies of observed levels (E) and values of V obtained from them with (17) or Fig. 10. Energies are in Mev; Δ was taken as 1.1 Mev. Also listed are $\Sigma(2j+1)V_{2j}$ and N, the number of neutrons in the major shell.

Mass No.	115		117		119		121		123		125	
SP state	E	V	E	V	E	V	E	V	E	V	E	V
$s_{1/2}$	0	~0.5	0	~0.5	0	~0.5	0.04	0.64	0.13	0.73	0.19	0.76
$d_{3/2}$	0.49	0.14	0.16	0.26	0.024	0.40	0	~0.5	0	~0.5	0	~0.5
$d_{5/2}$	0.97	0.923	1.10	0.935	1.15	0.935	1.20	0.94	1.30	0.95	1.35	0.95
$g_{7/2}$	0.61	0.89	0.72	0.90	0.76	0.90	(1.1)	(0.94)	(1.2)	(0.94)	(1.2)	(0.94)
$h_{11/2}$			0.32	0.18	0.089	0.31	0.04	0.36	~0	~0.5	~0	~0.5
$\Sigma(2j+1)V_{2j}$		$14.2+12V_{11}$		17.0		19.1		20.7		~22.7		~22.7
N		15.0		17.0		19.0		21.0		23.0		25.0

values of V for $d_{5/2}$ and $g_{7/2}$ are too large, especially for the lighter isotopes. This would require that the single-particle energy differences between $d_{5/2}$, $g_{7/2}$, and $s_{1/2}$, $d_{3/2}$, $h_{11/2}$, be reduced from the Nilsson-well values, in agreement with Table IX.

The relationship between the observed energies and the V's may be obtained by solving (15) and (16), which gives

$$E_j=\Delta\left[\frac{1}{2(U_{2j}V_{2j})^{\frac{1}{2}}}-\frac{1}{2(U_GV_G)^{\frac{1}{2}}}\right],$$

where U_G and V_G are U and V for the single-particle level which is the ground state. Since V_G is always close to 0.5, that value may be substituted to give

$$E_j=\Delta\left[\frac{1}{2(U_{2j}V_{2j})^{\frac{1}{2}}}-1\right]. \tag{17}$$

The approximation in (17) is quite good for V_j anywhere between 0.3 and 0.7, which would apply to all cases of interest here. A plot of (17) is shown in Fig. 9(b).

The observed energies of the single-particle states are listed in Table X along with the V's calculated from them. The energies for the $d_{5/2}$ states are taken as the "center of gravity" of the observed levels weighted with the intensity with which they are excited. In the isotopes where the $g_{7/2}$ level is not observed, it is assumed to be under the large $d_{5/2}$ peak. As a check on the V's obtained from the observed energies, the sum $\sum(2j+1)V_{2j}$ is calculated and listed in Table X. This sum should be equal to the number of neutrons in the major shell, N, which is also listed in Table X. The agreement is excellent in all cases except Sn^{125} where it is within the uncertainty.

The V's from Table X for odd isotopes are interpolated for the even isotopes and listed in Table V. In Table V the agreement with Kisslinger-Sorenson values seems to be somewhat better than the agreement with the experimental values obtained from (d,p) and (d,t) cross sections.

On the other hand, the V's calculated from observed energies lead to difficulties when used to calculate single particle energies. This may be done either by using (16) and (17) in combination, or by noting from (16) that the second term in (15) is close to unity so that to a rather good approximation

$$E_j=\Delta[(1+e_j^2)^{\frac{1}{2}}-1]. \tag{18}$$

This may be solved for e_j to give

$$e_j=\pm\left[\left(\frac{E_j}{\Delta}+1\right)^2-1\right]^{\frac{1}{2}}. \tag{19}$$

This functional relationship is shown in Fig. 9(c). The

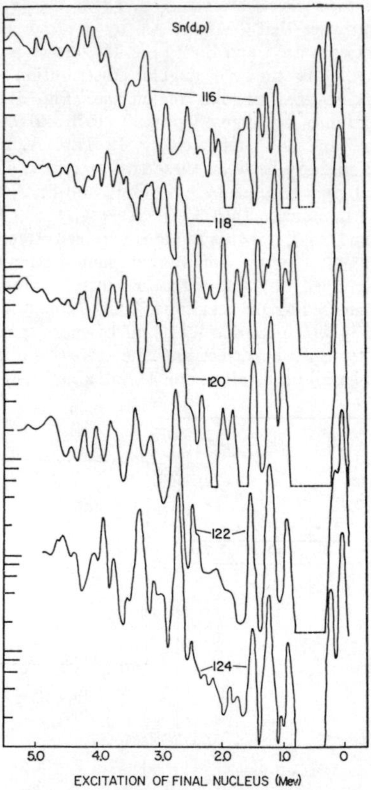

FIG. 10. Energy spectra of protons from (d,p) reactions on even isotopes of tin. Figures denote target mass number. Energy scale is only approximate: best values of energies of various peaks are listed in Table XI. Detection angle is 45°.

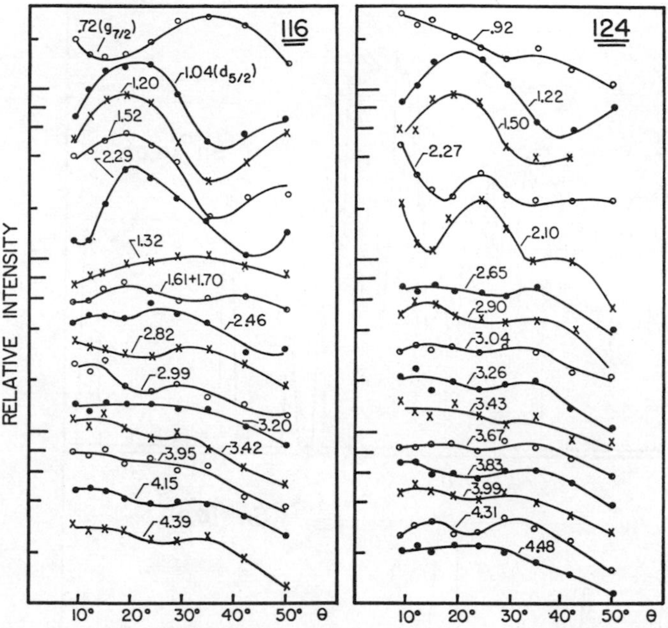

FIG. 11. Angular distributions of protons from (d,p) reactions on Sn^{116} and Sn^{124} leading to various excited states (excitation energy in Mev attached to curves) of final nuclei. Where there are discrepancies between energies shown here and those listed in Table XI, the latter are more accurate.

single particle energies derived from the observed energies of Table X (interpolated between adjacent masses) are listed in Table IX (rows designated "E"). It is seen there that the single particle energies calculated in this way shift rapidly and monotonically as a function of mass number. This behavior is most unexpected; it arises basically from the fact that the observed energy of a level as highly excited as the $d_{5/2}$ is expected from the theory to shift rapidly with mass number, contrary to observation. A similar situation was observed for the $s_{1/2}$ level in the mass 90–100 region. The most probable source of difficulty is that (15) is not completely accurate; there may well be other effects which shift the observed energies appreciably.[11a]

It thus seems most likely that the experimental values of the V's listed in Table V and the single-particle energies derived from these and listed in the last column of Table IX are reasonably accurate. The discrepancies with the Kisslinger-Sorenson values are certainly no larger than expected from their work. On the whole, the agreement between theory and experiment is quite good except for the discrepancy in the observed energies of the $d_{5/2}$ state.

IV. OTHER RESULTS AND CONCLUSIONS

A. Higher Excited States

The energy distributions from (d,p) reactions on the even isotopes of tin are shown in Fig. 10, and the peak energies and intensities at 30° are listed in Table XI. It is clear that the over-all intensity is relatively low at energies above the single-particle levels (~1.5 Mev), until it rises rather suddenly at about 2.6 Mev. The region above 2.6 Mev is characterized by several relatively sharp and very strongly excited levels.

This situation is entirely in line with expectations if

[11a] *Note added in proof.* R. Sorenson (private communication) has fit the observed energies without altering the V's by including the P_2-force in the calculation.

TABLE XI. Energies of levels observed in odd Sn isotopes with (d,p) reactions on even isotopes and their relative cross sections for excitation at 29°.

Sn^{117}		Sn^{119}		Sn^{121}		Sn^{123}		Sn^{125}	
E	$I(29°)$	E	$I(29°)$	E	$I(29°)$	E	$I(29°)$	E	$I(29°)$
0	200	0				0	180	0	140
0.16	190	0.77		0	300	0.12	100	0.19	115
0.31	72	0.92				0.91	13	0.91	11
0.72	16	1.08	58	0.92	29	1.20	75	1.23	43
1.02	60	1.35	13	1.11	72	1.50	25	1.51	24
1.18	28	1.57	5	1.39	25	1.79	7	1.64	
1.32	27	1.72	7	1.69	10	1.94	17	1.90	
1.52	30	1.95	7	1.88	13	2.30	15	2.10	7
1.61	10	2.09	10	2.21	16	2.42	20	2.27	8
1.70	10	2.35	16	2.41	22	2.69	400	2.46	14
2.06	40	2.63	60	2.53	···	3.10	150	2.65	520
2.25	18	2.88	60	2.62	250	3.32	300	2.90	54
2.41	43	3.07	50	2.87	73	3.70	200	3.04	78
2.47	35	3.16	50	3.01	140	3.93	180	3.26	380
2.60	~11	3.27	40	3.29	115	4.15	160	3.43	44
2.77	55	3.50	65	3.44	190	4.32	100	3.67	125
2.93	29	3.59	90	3.61	180	4.62	180	3.83	310
3.14	160	3.78	120	3.84	140	4.77	150	3.99	160
3.25	60	3.95	70	4.07	140			4.31	140
3.35	54	4.00	65	4.15	130				
3.52	46	4.36	90	4.35	120				
3.67	88	4.48	80	4.52	110				
3.75	95								
3.87	148								
4.06	185								
4.30	117								
4.48	135								
4.61	165								
4.72	150								

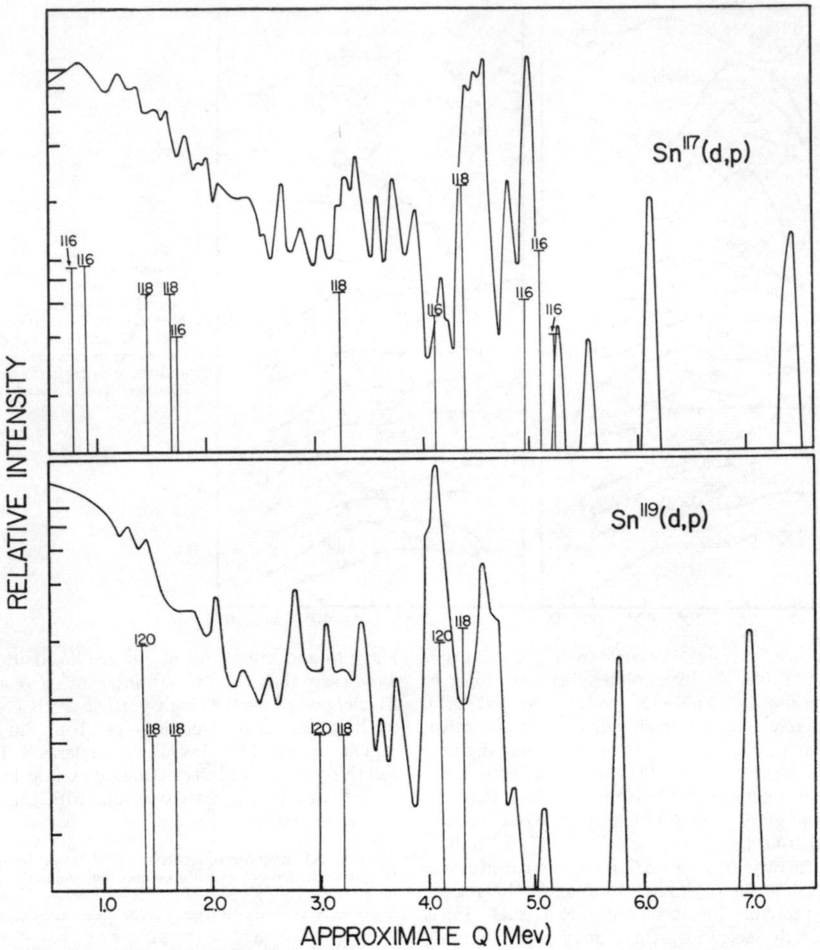

FIG. 12. Energy distributions of protons from (d,p) reactions on Sn^{117} and Sn^{119} at 45°. Vertical lines show positions of principal peaks from neighboring even isotopes (mass numbers stated); their height indicates the relative intensity.

these latter are the single-particle states of the next major shell which fills between neutron numbers 83 and 126. The energies are approximately those expected from the fact that the p-wave neutron giant resonance goes through zero neutron energy [i.e., $Q(d,p)=-2.2$ Mev] at $A=90$; the estimates of Cohen and Price[12] place the p states at an excitation energy of about 3 Mev in this mass region. The cross sections for the large peaks are approximately those expected for these single-particle states if we adopt (6) and (12) with the values of A and k used in the previous section. The regularities in energies and cross sections among the various isotopes is further evidence on this point; several of the peaks can be traced from isotope to isotope with very little imagination, although they become somewhat split up in Sn^{116} and Sn^{118}.

A considerable effort was expended in trying to further identify these levels with angular distribution studies. Some of the results are shown in Fig. 11 along with angular distributions for some of the low-lying levels for comparison. It is very apparent that all groups with excitation energy above 2.5 Mev have essentially the same angular distributions, and that these are almost completely lacking in sharp identifying features such as those possessed by the low-lying single-particle levels (see Figs. 3, 4, and 5).

It is very difficult to believe that this loss of feature in the angular distributions is only due to the fact that

[12] B. L. Cohen and R. E. Price, Nuclear Phys. 17, 129 (1960).

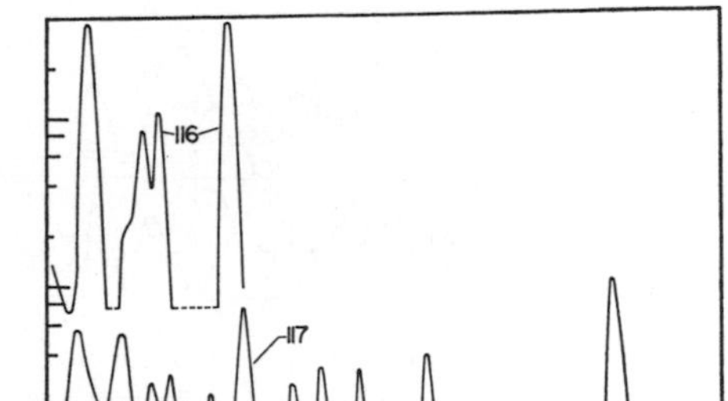

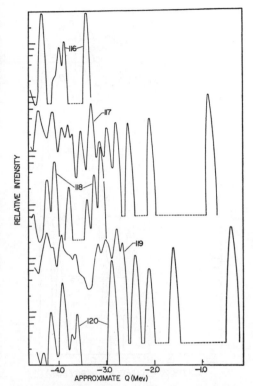

FIG. 13. Energy distributions of tritons from (*d,t*) reactions on Sn^{117}, Sn^{119}, and neighboring even isotopes (mass number shown). Detection angle is 45°.

their energy is low. The distributions shown in Figs. 4 and 5 show very little sensitivity to energy over a wide range, and indeed the lowest energy case from Fig. 5 has a proton energy corresponding to a 2.9-Mev excited state in Sn^{116}. The authors firmly believe that there is some deeper meaning to this anomaly. A similar situation was found in the Pb isotopes[9,10] although the low energy may have been a factor there.

B. Low-Lying Non-Single-Particle States

In the region below 2.6-Mev excitation energy, there are several states shown in Fig. 10 and listed in Table XI which were not classed as single-particle states. The angular distributions from some of these are shown in Fig. 11.

Basically, the explanation for these states, and for the fact that the $d_{5/2}$ states have more than one component, is that the model we are using is only a *model*, and is not a perfect representation of nuclei. States may occur due to other types of excitation, some of which perhaps have never been considered by nuclear theorists. If these states occur close to single-particle states and have the same spin and parity, they will mix with them; this is very probably the case with the $d_{5/2}$ levels. In other cases, the distance from the single-particle levels would seem to preclude mixing. For example, the angular distributions from the 2.10- and 2.27-Mev states from $Sn^{124}(d,p)$ bear strong similarities to $l_n=0$ distributions except that the minima and maxima occur at smaller angles (~15° vs 18° for the minima, and 24° vs 32° for the maxima). This could be explained by the low Q values, although the trend in Fig. 4 is in the opposite direction.

Perhaps the most interesting of the low-lying non-single-particle states is that occurring at about 0.9 Mev in essentially all the odd isotopes of Sn. The regularity of its occurrence, its low excitation energy, and its relatively large cross section are very suggestive. However, the evidence against its being a single-particle state is quite convincing: the angular distributions are completely untypical (see Fig. 11), and the variation of the cross section with mass is quite different. The evidence for the latter is shown in Tables I and II: The cross sections are much larger in Sn^{120} and Sn^{122} than in the other isotopes, whereas cross sections for single particle states vary monotonically and generally slowly with mass number. A state at 0.90 Mev in Sn^{119} has been reported from Coulomb excitation work,[13] so that this level might perhaps be strictly a collective one. However, it is still difficult to understand why it would not have a typical angular distribution pattern. The excitation of known collective levels in even-even nuclei by (*d,p*) and (*d,t*) reactions has been studied previously,[14] and the results are not inconsistent with theory.[1,3]

While there might be considerable interest in the low-lying, non-single-particle states, it should always be kept in mind that their excitation cross sections are low, so that no matter how they are interpreted, they would not appreciably affect the experimental determinations of the V's in Table V. It would seem most reasonable to attempt to study them by some other type of nuclear reaction in which they are strongly excited.

C. Reactions on Odd Isotopes of Tin; the Pairing Energy

The (*d,p*) and (*d,t*) reactions on the odd isotopes of tin lead to even-even final nuclei, so that they have large Q values. The low-lying states excited in these reactions have been studied in a previous paper,[14] and the excitation of ground states has been discussed in Sec. III-C-3 above.

One would expect the binding energies of a $d_{5/2}$, $d_{3/2}$, $g_{7/2}$, and $h_{11/2}$ neutron to an odd nucleus to be roughly the same as to an even nucleus, since they cannot form

[13] D. G. Alkhazov, D. S. Andrev, K. I. Erokhina, and I. K. Lemberg, J. Exptl. Theoret. Phys. (U.S.S.R.) **33**, 1346 (1957).
[14] B. L. Cohen and R. E. Price, Phys. Rev. **118**, 1582 (1960).

a pair with the odd nucleon ($s_{1/2}$ in both Sn^{117} and Sn^{119}). One therefore expects strongly excited levels at the same Q value in odd and even isotopes. There is good evidence for this in Figs. 12 and 13 where spectra from (d,p) and (d,t) reactions, respectively, in the odd targets are compared with those in neighboring even targets. The correspondence between groups of levels is readily apparent. The levels excited are principally the $d_{3/2}$ and $d_{5/2}$ forming two quasi-particle states of spin 1^+ and 2^+, and 2^+ and 3^+, respectively; the two groups are readily distinguishable by their energy difference. 0^+ levels in this region should not be excited by (d,p) and (d,t) reactions and this is in agreement with experiment.[14]

Since the $d_{3/2}$ and $s_{1/2}$ levels are very close in the odd nuclei, the separation between the ground state and the $(d_{3/2}s_{1/2})$ states in even nuclei gives an accurate measure of the pairing energy. This is 2.2 Mev in Sn^{116}, 2.6 Mev in Sn^{118}, and 2.9 Mev in Sn^{120} [note that determination for Sn^{118} from $Sn^{117}(d,p)$ and $Sn^{119}(d,t)$ both give 2.6 Mev]. This variation of pairing energy with mass number seems difficult to understand. The above results do not take into account the fact that in Sn^{116}, the $s_{1/2}$ is $\sim$0.2–0.3 Mev below the $d_{3/2}$ without pairing (this is an average between Sn^{115} and Sn^{117}); this would further enlarge the difference in pairing energies between Sn^{116} and the others.

D. Dependence of Neutron Single-Particle States on Coupling with Protons

It is a long-standing assumption of nuclear shell model theory[15] that the neutron single-particle states are essentially unaffected by the protons so long as the proton number is even. Since (d,p) and (d,t) reactions strongly excite neutron single-particle states, one would therefore expect strong similarities between spectra from these reactions when the target nuclei have the same number of neutrons but a different (even) number of protons. Two good cases for testing this are Cd^{114} and Sn^{116}, both of which have 66 neutrons; and Cd^{116} and Sn^{118}, both of which have 68 neutrons.

The energy spectra from (d,p) and (d,t) reactions on these isotopes are compared in Figs. 14 and 15. It is abundantly clear that the presence or absence of the two protons has a very strong effect on the neutron single-particle states. The energies of the single-particle levels in the Cd isotopes are all within $\sim$0.6 Mev of the ground state, whereas in the Sn isotopes, they extend to about 1.2 Mev; the $s_{1/2}$ state (the ground state in all cases) is relatively weakly excited by (d,p) reactions in Cd whereas it is quite strong in Sn; the multiplicity of levels is far larger in Cd; the intensity rise in (d,p) reactions due to states in the next major shell (discussed in Sec IV-A above) is at a lower energy for Cd ($\sim$2.0 Mev vs 2.6 Mev for Sn). In general, there is a much stronger similarity between the two Cd isotopes and between the two Sn isotopes than between Cd^{114}

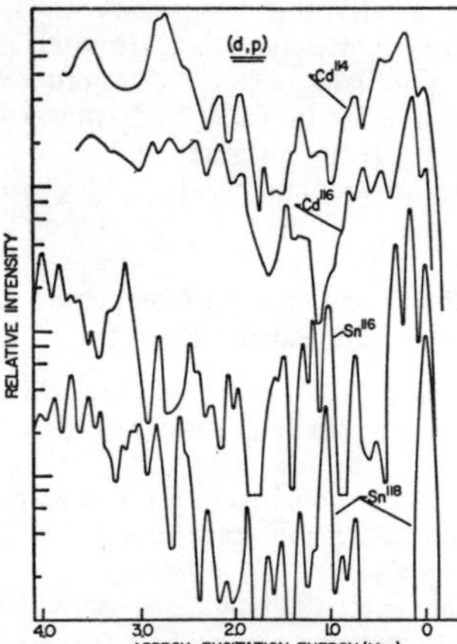

FIG. 14. Energy distribution of protons from (d,p) reactions on isotonic pairs Cd^{114}-Sn^{116} and Cd^{116}-Sn^{118}. Detection angle is 45°.

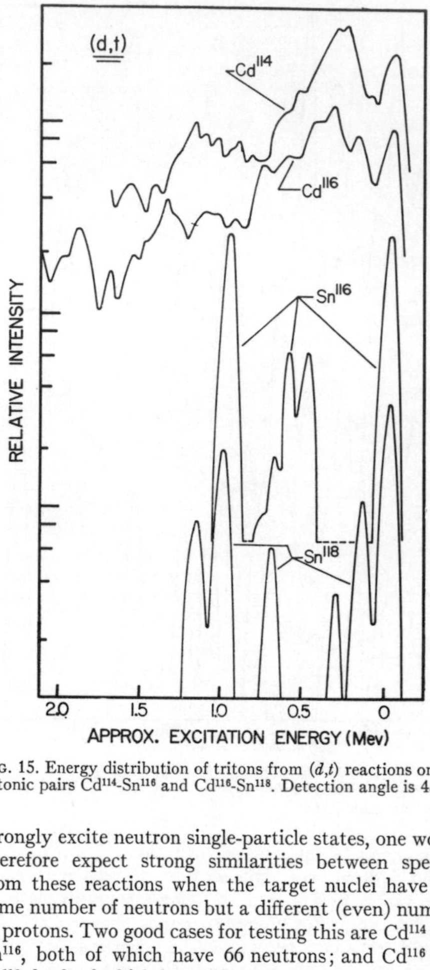

FIG. 15. Energy distribution of tritons from (d,t) reactions on isotonic pairs Cd^{114}-Sn^{116} and Cd^{116}-Sn^{118}. Detection angle is 45°.

[15] M. Mayer and J. H. D. Jensen, *Elementary Theory of Nuclear Shell Structure* (John Wiley & Sons, Inc., New York, 1955).

and Sn^{116}, and between Cd^{116} and Sn^{118}. Thus, the addition of two protons has a much more far reaching effect on the neutron single-particle states than the addition of two neutrons. This is the exact opposite from expectations from shell-model theory; on the other hand, it is not unexpected from pairing theory. It should be pointed out, of course, that the above conclusion is probably not a general one; the two protons added between Cd and Sn are those which close the major shell, which is something of a special case.

E. Ground-State Reaction Q Values

No systematic effort was made in these experiments to obtain accurate Q values, and in fact, there are some little understood experimental difficulties in doing this without apparatus. However, better determinations than any available in the literature are readily available from this work.

In (d,t) reactions, the deuteron elastic scattering peak always appears on the photographic plate at an apparent triton energy of $\frac{2}{3}$ the deuteron energy; thus, the Q value can be determined with little error due to the uncertainty in the energy of the incident deuteron beam. Once (d,t) Q values are determined, the (d,p) Q values for the four cases where initial and final nuclei are reversed in the two reactions may be calculated. Q values for other (d,p) reactions can be determined from positions of isotopic impurity peaks on plates where (d,p) Q values are known. In one case, a check was available from carbon and oxygen impurity peaks.

The Q values obtained are listed in Table XII where they are compared with best previously known data.[16] The error in these determinations is very probably less than 0.1 Mev, whereas the uncertainties in previous values[16] were about 0.3 Mev.

TABLE XII. Q values for (d,p) and (d,t) reactions on tin isotopes.

Isotope mass	$Q(d,p)$ (Mev) This work	$Q(d,p)$ (Mev) Previous	$-Q(d,t)$ (Mev) This work	$-Q(d,t)$ (Mev) Previous
116	4.85	4.97	3.40	3.11
117	7.20	6.98	0.80	0.94
118	4.40	4.56	3.15	2.94
119	7.05	6.73	0.35	0.53
120	4.15	3.93	3.00	2.70
122	3.85	3.70	2.70	2.46
124	3.45	3.51	2.30	2.16

[16] V. J. Ashby and H. C. Catron, University of California Radiation Laboratory Report UCRL-5419 (unpublished).

Reprinted from THE PHYSICAL REVIEW, Vol. 120, No. 3, 957–968, November 1, 1960
Printed in U. S. A.

Extension of the Shell Model for Heavy Spherical Nuclei

MICHEL BARANGER
Carnegie Institute of Technology, Pittsburgh, Pennsylvania
(Received June 16, 1960)

The Bardeen-Bogoliubov-Belyaev treatment of the pairing correlations is applied to spherical nuclei with a general nuclear force. The interaction between quasi-particles is treated by the method of linearized equations of motion. An advantage of this treatment is that the same equations describe single-particle excitations and collective excitations, so that the former are orthogonal to the latter and the total number of states is correct. Another advantage is that the spurious states due to the fluctuations in the number of particles are automatically eliminated. The equations to be solved resemble those for a two-body shell model calculation. Simple estimates, based on delta-function or quadrupole forces, are made for the vibrational frequencies in various modes and transition matrix elements. It is concluded that the method is as powerful as other known methods for dealing with collective states by the shell model, and that the same order of magnitude for the effective nuclear force seems capable of fitting all the data.

1. INTRODUCTION

THE past two years have seen some important developments in the theory of nuclear structure. The recent success in the theory of superconductivity[1] stimulated the application of the same ideas to nuclear physics.[2–5] According to the new point of view, the pairing correlations and the energy gap must play a fundamental role in our understanding of many nuclear properties. Belyaev[6] has discussed the influence of pairing correlations on the collective behavior of nuclei; and Kisslinger and Sorensen[7] have obtained good agreement with many detailed properties of single-closed-shell spherical nuclei, by using a simple interaction composed of a pairing force and a quadrupole force and treating it by the new methods. In a different line of research, there has been increasing success in accounting for collective effects starting from the ideas of the shell model. Here, we mention the work of Brown and Bolsterli[8] who showed that the location of the giant photoresonance could be explained by taking into account particle-hole interactions.

The present work represents another extension of these ideas. The aim is to develop an approximation suitable for calculating the properties of all low-lying levels of heavy spherical even-even nuclei, starting from a general shell-model Hamiltonian. To do this, we first perform the Bogoliubov-Valatin transformation[9] on the Hamiltonian (Sec. 2). The result can be interpreted in terms of a Hamiltonian of "quasi-particles" and an interaction between these quasi-particles. It is the existence of a gap in the spectrum of quasi-particles which restricts the low excited levels to two quasi-particles and makes possible a simple shell-model type of calculation. This is not quite true, however, because a few levels containing many quasi-particles may be brought down by collective effects. Fortunately, there is a well-known method which was devised to deal with this difficulty in other many-body problems, the method of linearized equations of motion. We use it (Sec. 3), and the resulting equations apply equally well to collective states and to noncollective states of two quasi-particles. This is a great advantage, as in the past one has had to treat the two kinds of states by different methods, with the result that one ended up with too many states and that often they were not mutually orthogonal. Also, one can now treat states which are only weakly collective, and for which the standard methods of dealing with collective states are not valid. Finally, we shall see that the spurious states due to the

[1] J. Bardeen, L. N. Cooper, and J. R. Schrieffer, Phys. Rev. **108**, 1175 (1957), referred to in the following as BCS.
[2] A. Bohr, B. R. Mottelson, and D. Pines, Phys. Rev. **110**, 936 (1958).
[3] A. Bohr, *Comptes Rendus du Congrès International de Physique Nucléaire, Paris, 1958* (Dunod, Paris, 1959).
[4] B. R. Mottelson, in *The Many-Body Problem* (John Wiley & Sons, Inc., New York, 1959).
[5] V. G. Soloviev, Nuclear Phys. **9**, 655 (1958).
[6] S. T. Belyaev, Kgl. Danske Videnskab. Selskab, Mat.-fys. Medd. **31**, No. 11 (1959). Some related work is due to A. Kerman (to be published).
[7] L. S. Kisslinger and R. A. Sorensen, Kgl. Danske Videnskab. Selskab, Mat.-fys. Medd. (to be published), referred to in the following as KS.
[8] G. E. Brown and M. Bolsterli, Phys. Rev. Letters **3**, 472 (1959).
[9] N. N. Bogoliubov, Nuovo cimento **7**, 794 (1958); J. G. Valatin, Nuovo cimento **7**, 843 (1958).

nonconstancy of the number of particles, a difficulty introduced by the Bogoliubov-Valatin transformation, can be easily eliminated. The equations resemble those for a two-body shell model calculation and should be easy to solve with a realistic nuclear force, except for the rather formidable problem of the choice of parameters. Here, we shall content ourselves with rough estimates based on quadrupole forces and δ-function forces. These are sufficient to show that the new method is as effective as older ones in dealing with quadrupole vibrations (Sec. 4A). We also apply it to collective vibrations of closed shells, in which case it is not necessary to perform the Bogoliubov-Valatin transformation, as the spacing between major shells already plays the role of an energy gap (Sec. 4B). One finds that the strength of the nuclear force, which is needed to bring the various pairing and collective effects into agreement with experiment, is of the same order of magnitude in all cases. Finally we show how one can estimate the enhancement of inelastic cross sections (Sec. 4C).

Many of the manipulations that we need to perform require the use of the algebra of angular momentum.[10] We shall not reproduce the details, as they are straightforward. We use the Condon and Shortley choice of phases[11] in all cases.

2. THE HAMILTONIAN

A. The Shell-Model Hamiltonian

Since we are concerned with heavy nuclei, we shall use j-j coupling, but we shall not use the isotopic spin formalism. The single-particle shell model states will be specified by various quantum numbers: the charge q, n, l, j, m. These states will be designated by Greek subscripts, and the corresponding creation and absorption operators will be called, for example, c_α^* and c_α. They satisfy the usual Fermion anticommutation rules,

$$c_\alpha c_\beta + c_\beta c_\alpha = c_\alpha^* c_\beta^* + c_\beta^* c_\alpha^* = 0, \tag{1a}$$

$$c_\alpha^* c_\beta + c_\beta c_\alpha^* = \delta_{\alpha\beta}. \tag{1b}$$

In association with the subscript α, we shall use the Roman subscript a, which stands for all quantum numbers above except the magnetic quantum number m. The starting Hamiltonian H has two parts. One is the sum of the single-particle energies,

$$H_{sp} = \sum\nolimits_\alpha \epsilon_a c_\alpha^* c_\alpha, \tag{2}$$

which runs over all values of the quantum numbers. The second part is the interaction Hamiltonian

$$H_i = \sum_{\alpha\beta\gamma\delta} \mathcal{V}_{\alpha\beta\gamma\delta} c_\alpha^* c_\beta^* c_\delta c_\gamma, \tag{3}$$

where the following antisymmetry relations must hold

$$\mathcal{V}_{\alpha\beta\gamma\delta} = -\mathcal{V}_{\beta\alpha\gamma\delta} = -\mathcal{V}_{\alpha\beta\delta\gamma} = \mathcal{V}_{\beta\alpha\delta\gamma}. \tag{4}$$

Next, we must write H_i in a way which exhibits its invariance under rotations and reflexions. This is accomplished by coupling two of the particles, say α and β, to angular momentum JM, coupling the other two also to JM, and writing an invariant tensor product. Thus, we are led to write $\mathcal{V}_{\alpha\beta\gamma\delta}$ in the form

$$\mathcal{V}_{\alpha\beta\gamma\delta} = -\tfrac{1}{2} \sum_{JM} G(abcdJ) C(j_\alpha j_\beta J; m_\alpha m_\beta M) \times C(j_\gamma j_\delta J; m_\gamma m_\delta M), \tag{5}$$

where the C's are the usual vector coupling coefficients. The minus sign is introduced for convenience, since the interactions are mostly attractive. The parity of $l_a + l_b$ must be the same as that of $l_c + l_d$, otherwise G vanishes. G must also conserve charge, i.e., $q_a + q_b = q_c + q_d$. There follows from Hermiticity of H_i and time-reversal invariance that G is real and

$$G(abcdJ) = G(cdabJ). \tag{6}$$

The relations (4) give, together with the symmetry properties of the C coefficients,

$$G(abcdJ) = -\theta(abJ) G(bacdJ) = -\theta(cdJ) G(abdcJ) = \theta(abcd) G(badcJ), \tag{7}$$

with the notation

$$\theta(abJ) = \theta(j_a j_b J) = (-)^{j_a + j_b + J}. \tag{8}$$

The relation between our G and the usual two-body matrix element of shell model calculations is

$$\langle abJM | H_i | cdJM \rangle = -\sigma_{ab} \sigma_{cd} G(abcdJ), \tag{9}$$

with

$$\sigma_{ab} = \begin{cases} 1 \text{ if } a \equiv b, \\ \sqrt{2} \text{ otherwise.} \end{cases} \tag{10}$$

But there was no compelling reason for coupling α and β together, and γ and δ together. We could also have coupled α and γ to $J'M'$, β and δ similarly; or alternatively α and δ to $J''M''$, as well as β and γ. This leads us to define another function F by

$$\begin{aligned} \mathcal{V}_{\alpha\beta\gamma\delta} &= -\tfrac{1}{2} \sum_{J'M'} F(acdbJ') s_\gamma C(j_\alpha j_\gamma J'; m_\alpha \bar{m}_\gamma M') \times s_\beta C(j_\delta j_\beta J'; m_\delta \bar{m}_\beta M') \\ &= +\tfrac{1}{2} \sum_{J''M''} F(adcbJ'') s_\delta C(j_\alpha j_\delta J''; m_\alpha \bar{m}_\delta M'') \times s_\beta C(j_\gamma j_\beta J''; m_\gamma \bar{m}_\beta M''). \end{aligned} \tag{11}$$

Here and in the following, $\bar{m}$ stands for $-m$. We had to introduce the symbol

$$s_\gamma = (-)^{j_\gamma - m_\gamma}, \tag{12}$$

because, in actuality, it is angular momentum j_α which is the sum of j_γ and J'. The same function F appears

[10] U. Fano and G. Racah, *Irreducible Tensorial Sets* (Academic Press, New York, 1959).

[11] E. U. Condon and G. H. Shortley, *The Theory of Atomic Spectra* (Cambridge University Press, New York, 1935).

with both coupling schemes by virtue of Eq. (4). It is related to the two-body matrix element for a particle and a hole. Its relationship to G involves a Racah coefficient:

$$F(acdbJ') = -\sum_J (2J+1) W(j_a j_b j_c j_d; JJ') G(bacdJ). \quad (13)$$

It is real and has the following symmetry properties:

$$F(acdbJ') = F(dbacJ') = \theta(abcd) F(cabdJ'), \quad (14)$$

but nothing simple happens if only a and c are interchanged.

The pairing force used by KS is (for charge-conserving matrix elements)

$$G(abcdJ) = \delta_{ab}\delta_{cd}\delta_{J0}(j_a+\tfrac{1}{2})^{\frac{1}{2}}(j_c+\tfrac{1}{2})^{\frac{1}{2}} g, \quad (15)$$

where g is a constant (which KS called G).

B. Treatment of the Pairing Correlations

In spherical nuclei with partially filled shells, the most important effect of the two-body force is to produce pairing correlations. Those must be treated quite accurately, even if other effects of the nuclear force are not. A suitable treatment was discovered by Bardeen, Cooper, and Schrieffer[1] for superconductors, and applied to nuclear physics by the Copenhagen school [2–4] and others.[5] In the BCS ground state of an even-even nucleus, the particles are distributed in pairs, all coupled to angular momentum 0; the method is a generalization of Racah's[12] seniority ideas. The simplest way to introduce these correlations in the wave function is to perform the Bogoliubov-Valatin[9] transformation. We define a new set of creation and absorption operators by

$$a_\alpha = u_a c_\alpha - s_\alpha v_a c_{-\alpha}^*, \quad a_\alpha^* = u_a c_\alpha^* - s_\alpha v_a c_{-\alpha}, \quad (16)$$

where $-\alpha$ is obtained from α by changing the sign of the magnetic quantum number, and u_a and v_a are real and related by

$$u_a^2 + v_a^2 = 1. \quad (17)$$

The a's satisfy the same anticommutation relations as the c's. They create and absorb "quasi-particles." For a level far above the Fermi level, $u_a \approx 1$, $v_a \approx 0$, and the quasi-particle is the same as a particle. For a level far below the Fermi level, $u_a \approx 0$, $v_a \approx 1$, and the quasi-particle is a hole. But for levels in the neighborhood of the Fermi level, a quasi-particle is partly particle and partly hole. The vacuum of the new operators is the BCS ground state. The converse of relations (16) are

$$c_\alpha = u_a a_\alpha + s_\alpha v_a a_{-\alpha}^*, \quad c_\alpha^* = u_a a_\alpha^* + s_\alpha v_a a_{-\alpha}. \quad (18)$$

We shall express H in terms of the operators a_α. A difficulty arises because the number of quasi-particles does not commute with the number of neutrons $\mathfrak{N}_n$ and that of protons $\mathfrak{N}_p$,

$$\mathfrak{N}_n = \sum_n c_\alpha^* c_\alpha, \quad \mathfrak{N}_p = \sum_p c_\alpha^* c_\alpha, \quad (19)$$

where $\sum_n$ runs over all neutron states and $\sum_p$ all proton states. This forces us to introduce two chemical potentials λ_n and λ_p, and instead of diagonalizing H, we try to diagonalize

$$\mathfrak{H} = H - \lambda_n \mathfrak{N}_n - \lambda_p \mathfrak{N}_p, \quad (20)$$

subject to the condition that the expectation values of $\mathfrak{N}_n$ and $\mathfrak{N}_p$ are the given numbers of neutrons and protons in the nucleus. This procedure has the unfortunate consequences that our equations really represent a mixture of neighboring even-even nuclei, and that some of their solutions are "spurious," i.e., do not correspond to any state of a single nucleus; the damage will be partially repaired in Sec. 3.

The task of expressing $\mathfrak{H}$ in terms of the a's is straightforward and will only be sketched. We introduce the notation N for the normal product[13] of an operator, obtained by rewriting all quasi-particle creation operators to the left of the absorption operators, changing the sign whenever two Fermion operators are inverted, but ignoring commutators. For instance,

$$N(c_\alpha^* c_\gamma) = u_a u_c a_\alpha^* a_\gamma - s_\alpha s_\gamma v_a v_c a_{-\gamma}^* a_{-\alpha} + s_\alpha v_a u_c a_{-\alpha} a_\gamma + u_a s_\gamma v_c a_\alpha^* a_{-\gamma}^*. \quad (21)$$

A well-known theorem[14] enables one to write any operator as a sum of normal products, for instance

$$\begin{aligned} c_\alpha^* c_\beta^* c_\delta c_\gamma = {} & N(c_\alpha^* c_\beta^* c_\delta c_\gamma) \\ & + \delta_{\alpha,-\beta} s_\alpha u_a v_a N(c_\delta c_\gamma) + \delta_{\gamma,-\delta} s_\gamma u_c v_c N(c_\alpha^* c_\beta^*) \\ & + \delta_{\alpha\gamma} v_a^2 N(c_\beta^* c_\delta) + \delta_{\beta\delta} v_b^2 N(c_\alpha^* c_\gamma) \\ & - \delta_{\alpha\delta} v_a^2 N(c_\beta^* c_\gamma) - \delta_{\beta\gamma} v_b^2 N(c_\alpha^* c_\delta) \\ & + \delta_{\alpha,-\beta}\delta_{\gamma,-\delta} s_\alpha s_\gamma u_a v_a u_c v_c + (\delta_{\alpha\gamma}\delta_{\beta\delta} - \delta_{\alpha\delta}\delta_{\beta\gamma}) v_a^2 v_b^2. \quad (22) \end{aligned}$$

This is substituted in H_i and use is made of well-known properties of the C coefficients. For instance, in view of the relation

$$\sum_{m_\alpha M} C(j_\alpha j_\beta J; m_\alpha m_\beta M) C(j_\alpha j_\delta J; m_\alpha m_\delta M) = (2J+1)(2j_\beta+1)^{-1} \delta_{j_\beta j_\delta} \delta_{m_\beta m_\delta}, \quad (23)$$

the first term of the third line of (22), when substituted in H_i, gives

$$-\tfrac{1}{2} \sum_{\alpha\beta\delta J} G(abadJ)(2J+1) \times (2j_\beta+1)^{-1} \delta_{j_\beta j_\delta} \delta_{m_\beta m_\delta} v_a^2 N(c_\beta^* c_\delta). \quad (24)$$

At this point we introduce an essential simplification. We assume that, among all our levels a, b, $\cdots$, a given

[12] G. Racah, Phys. Rev. **63**, 367 (1943).

[13] S. S. Schweber, H. A. Bethe, and F. de Hoffmann, *Mesons and Fields* (Row, Peterson and Company, Evanston, 1955), Vol. I. p. 203.

[14] Reference 13, p. 210. The theorem is closely related to Wick's theorem.

combination of charge, parity, and j value occurs only once. This enables us to replace $\delta_{j\beta j\delta}$ in (24) by δ_{bd} and to sum immediately over δ. In practice, this restriction is not serious, as it is satisfied in most shell model calculations. The same assumption has to be invoked for all the terms in the middle three lines of (22).

Introduce the notations

$$\Delta_a=(2j_a+1)^{-\frac{1}{2}}\sum_c(2j_c+1)^{\frac{1}{2}}u_cv_cG(aacc0), \quad (25)$$

$$\mu_a=2(2j_a+1)^{-1}\sum_{bJ}(2J+1)v_b{}^2G(ababJ)$$
$$=2(2j_a+1)^{-\frac{1}{2}}\sum_b(2j_b+1)^{\frac{1}{2}}v_b{}^2F(aabb0), \quad (26)$$

$$\eta_a=\epsilon_a-\mu_a-\lambda_a. \quad (27)$$

After the Bogoliubov-Valatin transformation, $\mathcal{H}$ can be written as the sum of four parts,

$$\mathcal{H}=\mathcal{H}_1+\mathcal{H}_2+\mathcal{H}_3+\mathcal{H}_4. \quad (28)$$

The first part is a pure number, the energy of the ground state,

$$\mathcal{H}_1=\sum_a[v_a{}^2(\eta_a+\tfrac{1}{2}\mu_a)-\tfrac{1}{2}u_av_a\Delta_a]. \quad (29a)$$

The others are

$$\mathcal{H}_2=\sum_\alpha[(u_a{}^2-v_a{}^2)\eta_a+2u_av_a\Delta_a]a_\alpha{}^*a_\alpha, \quad (29b)$$

$$\mathcal{H}_3=\sum_\alpha s_\alpha[u_av_a\eta_a+\tfrac{1}{2}(v_a{}^2-u_a{}^2)\Delta_a]$$
$$\times(a_\alpha{}^*a_{-\alpha}{}^*+a_{-\alpha}a_\alpha), \quad (29c)$$

$$\mathcal{H}_4=\sum_{\alpha\beta\gamma\delta}\mathcal{V}_{\alpha\beta\gamma\delta}N(c_\alpha{}^*c_\beta{}^*c_\delta c_\gamma). \quad (29d)$$

One chooses the u's and v's in such a way that $\mathcal{H}_3$ vanishes. This is what Bogoliubov[9] calls "the elimination of the dangerous terms"; it is equivalent to the BCS procedure of minimizing $\mathcal{H}_1$. The result is

$$2u_av_a=\Delta_a/E_a, \quad u_a{}^2-v_a{}^2=\eta_a/E_a, \quad (30)$$

with

$$E_a=(\eta_a{}^2+\Delta_a{}^2)^{\frac{1}{2}}. \quad (31)$$

Then, $\mathcal{H}_2$ takes the form

$$\mathcal{H}_2=\sum_\alpha E_aa_\alpha{}^*a_\alpha, \quad (32)$$

which shows that E_a is the energy of a quasi-particle. Δ_a is half the energy gap. The quantity η_a is the single-particle energy, corrected for the self-energy μ_a, and counted from the Fermi level λ_a. The two λ's are determined by writing that the expectation value of $\mathfrak{N}$ for the ground state is a given number n, for both neutrons and protons, for instance

$$n_n=\sum_n v_a{}^2=\tfrac{1}{2}\sum_n(1-\eta_a/E_a). \quad (33)$$

As for $\mathcal{H}_4$, it is the residual interaction between quasi-particles. Its explicit expression in terms of the a operators involves sixteen terms.

In the case of a general nuclear force G, the values of Δ_a, μ_a, λ_a can only be obtained by solving the complicated set of coupled equations given above. The problem simplifies itself[7] in the case of the pairing force (15), because μ_a can be neglected and one sees that Δ_a depends only on the charge. For a more realistic force, the various Δ_a's for a given charge are still roughly equal; hence the notion of an energy gap, without reference to a single-particle state, is still a meaningful one.

3. THE APPROXIMATION PROCEDURE

A. Basic Equations

If the interaction were really a pairing force, $\mathcal{H}_2$ would be the most important part of the Hamiltonian and $\mathcal{H}_4$ could be treated by perturbation theory, at least for states with $J\neq 0$, because F would be small and would have only diagonal elements. In this case, one obtains the picture of nearly independent quasi-particles, the creation of a pair of quasi-particles requiring an energy at least equal to the energy gap. KS have shown that this picture agrees well with many detailed properties of heavy nuclei, hence the pairing force is certainly an important element in the real force. But, to properly take into account other parts of the force, a better treatment of $\mathcal{H}_4$ must be given. The first idea that comes to mind is to diagonalize $\mathcal{H}_4$ exactly between all two-quasi-particle states. The neglect of states containing four or more quasi-particles is justified by saying that, since there is an energy gap, their excitation requires more energy. In the language of Feynman diagrams, the method consists in summing exactly all diagrams similar to Fig. 1(a). It is also known as the Tamm-Dancoff approximation. The calculation is very similar to a standard shell-model calculation for two particles, which is not hard. This procedure cannot yield collective states, which necessarily contain a large number of quasi-particles.

The method which we propose to use is more powerful and almost as easy. It is well known in the theory of

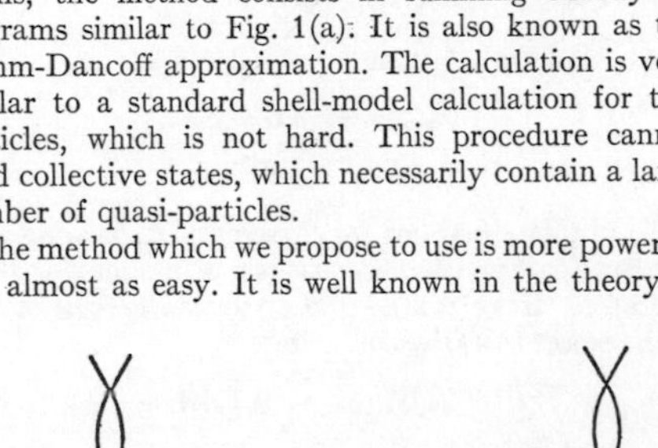

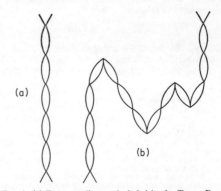

FIG. 1. (a) Feynman diagram included in the Tamm-Dancoff approximation. The lines are quasi-particles. No arrows are shown since a quasi-particle is part particle, part hole. There are two quasi-particles present at all times. The complete interaction between quasi-particles, $\mathcal{H}_4$, acts at each vertex. (b) Additional diagram included in the approximation of linearized equations of motion. The chain may double upon itself any number of times. There may be 2, 6, 10, $\cdots$ quasi-particles at once.

superconductors, under such varied names as random phase approximation,[15] method of linearized equations of motion,[15] method of approximate second quantization.[16] It is also allied to Dyson's new Tamm-Dancoff method.[17] It is equivalent to summing all diagrams[18] similar to Fig. 1(b). Our treatment will be closest to that of Anderson.[15] Let us define some creation and absorption operators for pairs of quasi-particles coupled to JM,

$$A^*(abJM)=\sum_{m_\alpha m_\beta} C(j_\alpha j_\beta J;m_\alpha m_\beta M)a_\alpha{}^*a_\beta{}^*, \quad (34a)$$

$$A(abJM)=\sum_{m_\alpha m_\beta} C(j_\alpha j_\beta J;m_\alpha m_\beta M)a_\beta a_\alpha. \quad (34b)$$

Upon interchange of a and b, we have for instance

$$A(baJM)=-\theta(abJ)A(abJM). \quad (35)$$

Let Ψ_0 be the real ground state (not the BCS approximate state) and Ψ_{BM} an excited state with angular momentum JM, the subscript B being used to distinguish it from other excited states. We define two amplitudes ψ and φ (independent of M) by

$$\psi_{abB}=\langle\Psi_0|A(abJM)|\Psi_{BM}\rangle, \quad (36a)$$

$$\varphi_{abB}=s_{JM}\langle\Psi_0|A^*(abJ\bar{M})|\Psi_{BM}\rangle, \quad (36b)$$

with

$$s_{JM}=(-)^{J-M}.$$

The symmetry relations for ψ and φ are

$$\psi_{baB}=-\theta(abJ)\psi_{abB}, \quad (37a)$$

$$\varphi_{baB}=-\theta(abJ)\varphi_{abB}. \quad (37b)$$

To obtain equations for these amplitudes, one takes matrix elements of the equations of motion for the A operators. If we call ω_B the excitation energy of Ψ_{BM} with respect to Ψ_0, we can write

$$\langle\Psi_0|[A,\mathcal{H}]|\Psi_{BM}\rangle=\omega_B\langle\Psi_0|A|\Psi_{BM}\rangle, \quad (38)$$

since both Ψ_0 and Ψ_{BM} are eigenstates of $\mathcal{H}$. If the commutator of $\mathcal{H}$ with one of the A operators of (34) is calculated, it is found to contain terms with two a operators and terms with four a operators. The approximation consists in dropping the latter terms, i.e., linearizing the equations of motion, on the grounds that they involve more energetic excitations. A serious discussion of the validity of this approximation is very difficult and we shall not attempt it. We are left with a set of linear, homogeneous equations for matrix elements of pairs of quasi-particle operators. Of course, we must include combinations of products of the type $a_\alpha{}^*a_\beta$ as well as the combinations of Eq. (34). But these other combinations are found to be completely uncoupled from each other and from the A's. Amplitudes of the type

$$\langle\Psi_0|a_\alpha{}^*a_\beta|\Psi_{BM}\rangle, \quad (39)$$

must therefore be set equal to 0, since they vanish in the limit of independent quasi-particles,[19] $\mathcal{H}_4=0$. Define two functions P and R through the equations

$$[A(abJM),\mathcal{H}] =\textstyle\sum_{cd} P(abcdJ)A(cdJM) +\sum_{cd} R(abcdJ)s_{JM}A^*(cdJ\bar{M}) + \text{terms in } a^*a + \text{terms with four } a\text{'s}. \quad (40a)$$

$$[s_{JM}A^*(abJ\bar{M}),\mathcal{H}] =-\textstyle\sum_{cd} P(abcdJ)s_{JM}A^*(cdJ\bar{M}) -\sum_{cd} R(abcdJ)A(cdJM) + \text{terms in } a^*a + \text{terms with four } a\text{'s}. \quad (40b)$$

They satisfy the symmetry relations

$$P(cdabJ)=P(abcdJ),\quad R(cdabJ)=R(abcdJ). \quad (41)$$

With our approximations, the quantities ψ, φ, and ω are solutions of the eigenvalue equation

$$\begin{aligned}\omega_B\psi_{abB}&=\textstyle\sum_{cd} P(abcdJ)\psi_{cdB} +\sum_{cd} R(abcdJ)\varphi_{cdB},\\ -\omega_B\varphi_{abB}&=\textstyle\sum_{cd} P(abcdJ)\varphi_{cdB} +\sum_{cd} R(abcdJ)\psi_{cdB}.\end{aligned} \quad (42)$$

This simple system of equations resembles very much the equations for a two-particle shell-model calculation, but we shall see in the next subsection that it also includes some collective solutions. It is clear that the problem is equivalent to diagonalizing a nonsymmetric matrix whose number of lines and columns is twice the number of two-particle states. For every solution B with $\omega_B>0$, there exists another solution B' with $\omega_{B'}=-\omega_B$ and ψ and φ interchanged. The latter solution must be rejected; only solutions with $\omega_B>0$ have physical significance.

The task of expressing P and R in terms of the nuclear force G or F of Sec. 2 involves a fair amount of manipulating and only the results will be given. It is convenient

[15] P. W. Anderson, Phys. Rev. **112**, 1900 (1958). The method was applied to the electron gas by D. Bohm and D. Pines, Phys. Rev. **92**, 609 (1953); K. Sawada, Phys. Rev. **106**, 372 (1957); K. Sawada, K. A. Brueckner, N. Fukuda, and R. Brout, Phys. Rev. **108**, 507 (1957).

[16] N. N. Bogoliubov, V. V. Tolmachev, and D. V. Shirkov, *A New Method in the Theory of Superconductivity* (Consultants Bureau, New York, 1959). See also V. M. Galitskii, J. Exptl. Theoret. Phys. (U.S.S.R.) **34**, 1011 (1958) [translation: Soviet Phys.-JETP **34**, **(7)**, 698 (1958)].

[17] F. J. Dyson, Phys. Rev. **91**, 1543 (1953). The present approximation keeps an infinite subset of new Tamm-Dancoff amplitudes.

[18] The importance of these backward-going diagrams in the treatment of nuclear collective oscillations has been emphasized repeatedly by S. Fallieros and R. Ferrell, who have also discussed the corresponding modification (69) of the normalization. See in particular S. Fallieros, Ph.D. thesis, University of Maryland, 1959 (Physics Department Technical Report No. 128), and R. A. Ferrell, Bull. Am. Phys. Soc. **4**, 59 (1959).

[19] The amplitude φ also vanishes in that limit, but it is coupled to ψ.

for the following to define two new amplitudes by

$$f_{abB}=\psi_{abB}+\varphi_{abB}, \tag{43a}$$

$$g_{abB}=\psi_{abB}-\varphi_{abB}. \tag{43b}$$

The equations for f and g are found to be

$$\begin{aligned}\omega_B f_{abB}&=(E_a+E_b)g_{abB}-\sum_{cd} U(abcdJ)g_{cdB},\\ \omega_B g_{abB}&=(E_a+E_b)f_{abB}-\sum_{cd} V(abcdJ)f_{cdB},\end{aligned} \tag{44}$$

with

$$U(abcdJ)=(u_au_b+v_av_b)(u_cu_d+v_cv_d)G(abcdJ) +(u_av_b-v_au_b)(u_cv_d-v_cu_d)H(abcdJ), \tag{45a}$$

$$V(abcdJ)=(u_au_b-v_av_b)(u_cu_d-v_cv_d)G(abcdJ) +(u_av_b+v_au_b)(u_cv_d+v_cu_d)K(abcdJ), \tag{45b}$$

$$H(abcdJ)=F(abcdJ)+\theta(cdJ)F(abdcJ), \tag{46a}$$

$$K(abcdJ)=F(abcdJ)-\theta(cdJ)F(abdcJ). \tag{46b}$$

It is important to note that, in all this work, the summations run over all values of the indices, which means that a given pair of distinct single-particle levels appears twice. Since, upon interchange of the indices, the amplitudes f and g transform in the same way as ψ and φ, i.e., by Eq. (37), the matrices U and V should have the following symmetry properties:

$$\begin{aligned}U(abcdJ)&=U(cdabJ)\\ &=-\theta(abJ)U(bacdJ)=-\theta(cdJ)U(abdcJ)\\ &=\theta(abcd)U(badcJ),\end{aligned} \tag{47}$$

and similarly for V. It can be checked that they do. One of the two functions, say g, can be eliminated from Eq. (44). Then f is seen to be the eigenvector of a non-symmetric matrix for eigenvalue ω_B^2.

More will be said in the next subsection about the significance of Eqs. (42) or (44). But first, we shall show how the Tamm-Dancoff approximation referred to earlier is recovered in the limit of weak coupling, i.e., small $\mathcal{H}_4$. In that case, it is clear from Eq. (44) that f and g are about equal (since $\omega_B>0$), i.e., $\varphi\ll\psi$. If we neglect φ in Eq. (42) and realize that R is also small compared to P (because $\mathcal{H}_2$ does not contribute to R), we get an equation for ψ alone,

$$\omega_B\psi_{abB}=\sum_{cd} P(abcdJ)\psi_{cdB}. \tag{48}$$

This same equation would come out of the Tamm-Dancoff method. Then, one would define ψ by

$$\psi_{abB}=\langle 0|A(abJM)|\Psi_{BM}\rangle, \tag{49}$$

where $\langle 0|$ is the BCS ground state, and neglect all other amplitudes. The Schrödinger equation would be

$$W_B\psi_{abB}=\tfrac{1}{2}\sum_{cd}\langle 0|A(abJM)\mathcal{H}A^*(cdJM)|0\rangle\psi_{cdB}, \tag{50}$$

where W_B is the energy, and one would normalize ψ (which is real) by

$$\sum_{ab}(\psi_{abB})^2=2. \tag{51}$$

The appearance of the factors $\frac{1}{2}$ and 2 is due to the fact, already mentioned, that our summations involve most pairs of levels twice. The matrix element in (50) can be written

$$\begin{aligned}&\langle 0|[A(abJM),\mathcal{H}]A^*(cdJM)|0\rangle +\langle 0|\mathcal{H}A(abJM)A^*(cdJM)|0\rangle\\ &=P(abcdJ)-\theta(cdJ)P(abdcJ) +W_0[\delta_{ac}\delta_{bd}-\theta(cdJ)\delta_{ad}\delta_{bc}],\end{aligned} \tag{52}$$

where W_0 is the energy of the ground state. In view of the various symmetry relations, Eq. (48) would be obtained.

B. Collective Vibrations

To show how collective vibrations arise out of the formalism, we shall repeat the derivation of Eq. (42) somewhat differently. Let us look for some operators Q_{BM}, Q_{CM}, $\cdots$ with the following property

$$[Q_{BM},\mathcal{H}]=\omega_BQ_{BM}, \tag{53a}$$

$$[Q_{BM}^*,\mathcal{H}]=-\omega_BQ_{BM}^*, \tag{53b}$$

where ω_B is some number. Let us assume that the Q's can be expressed as linear combinations of the A's of a given J, with real coefficients,

$$Q_{BM}=\sum_{ab} X_{abB}A(abJM) -\sum_{ab} Y_{abB}s_{JM}A^*(abJ\bar{M}), \tag{54a}$$

$$s_{JM}Q_{B\bar{M}}^*=\sum_{ab} X_{abB}s_{JM}A^*(abJ\bar{M}) -\sum_{ab} Y_{abB}A(abJM). \tag{54b}$$

If we substitute this expansion in Eqs. (53), and if we decide, as we did in subsection A, to ignore in the commutator terms of the form a^*a or terms containing four a's, we obtain the following set of equations for the X's and Y's:

$$\begin{aligned}\omega_BX_{abB}&=\sum_{cd} P(cdabJ)X_{cdB} +\sum_{cd} R(cdabJ)Y_{cdB},\\ -\omega_BY_{abB}&=\sum_{cd} P(cdabJ)Y_{cdB} +\sum_{cd} R(cdabJ)X_{cdB},\end{aligned} \tag{55}$$

which is identical with the set (42). Thus, X and Y are proportional to ψ and φ. In the following, we consider only solutions of these equations for which ω_B is positive. One can easily deduce[20] from the equations a kind of orthogonality relation,

$$\sum_{ab}(X_{abB}X_{abC}-Y_{abB}Y_{abC})=0, \tag{56a}$$

which holds for two different solutions B and C of the same J. Since one obtains another solution of Eq. (55) by exchanging X_B and Y_B, the following also holds for any two solutions with positive ω and the same J:

$$\sum_{ab}(Y_{abB}X_{abC}-X_{abB}Y_{abC})=0. \tag{56b}$$

[20] Multiply Eqs. (55) by X_{abC} and Y_{abC}, respectively, and add. Repeat the procedure with B and C interchanged. Subtract the two and use Eq. (41).

Equations (53) show that Q_{BM}^* and Q_{BM} are the raising and lowering operators of a harmonic oscillator. Q_{BM}^* creates a vibrational quantum of energy ω_B and Q_{BM} destroys it. The ground state may be defined by the set of all equations

$$Q_{BM}|\Psi_0\rangle=0, \tag{57}$$

and a particular excited state would be, for instance

$$|\Psi_{BM}\rangle=Q_{BM}^*|\Psi_0\rangle, \tag{58}$$

whose energy with respect to $|\Psi_0\rangle$ is ω_B. The ground state so defined is more accurate than the BCS ground state, as it includes the zero-point motion of the oscillators. For most of the applications, it is not necessary to have an explicit form for $|\Psi_0\rangle$. But, if one were desired, one could assume the most general expansion

$$|\Psi_0\rangle=\chi_0|0\rangle+\sum_{\alpha\beta}\chi_2(\alpha\beta)a_\alpha^*a_\beta^*|0\rangle + \sum_{\alpha\beta\gamma\delta}\chi_4(\alpha\beta\gamma\delta)a_\alpha^*a_\beta^*a_\gamma^*a_\delta^*|0\rangle+\cdots, \tag{59}$$

and, after having solved Eqs. (55), determine the χ's from Eqs. (57). It will easily be seen that only terms with 0, 4, 8, $\cdots$ quasi-particles occur. On the other hand, the excited state (58) has only 2, 6, 10, $\cdots$ quasi-particles. This is consistent with our statement that the amplitude (39) vanishes. The χ's are determined by a set of recurrence relations which connect χ_n to χ_{n-4}. But since the sum in (59) actually has a finite number of terms, trouble will occur unless the χ's become small before the end of the sum is reached. A related cause of trouble is the Pauli principle, which requires that any χ with two equal arguments vanish and makes the number of equations larger than the number of χ's. We see therefore that it is essential for the validity of the approximation that the average number of quasi-particles in the ground state, ν_0, be small compared to the total number of states, which we call Ω. In other words, we wish to treat the Q operators as boson operators, i.e., creation and absorption operators for oscillator quanta; but since the Q's are actually made up of products of operators that obey the Pauli principle, this is possible only if the number of states available is much larger than the number of fermions present. Otherwise, the fermions start to get into each other's way and the whole picture breaks down. This would happen, presumably, if the interaction was made so strong that many vibrational frequencies were very low. It might be noted in this connection[4] that the BCS ground state itself is good only for large Ω.

If this interpretation is to be consistent, it must be verified that two different singly excited states, $|\Psi_{BM}\rangle$ and $|\Psi_{CM'}\rangle$, are orthogonal. We write

$$\begin{aligned}\langle\Psi_0|Q_{BM}Q_{CM'}^*|\Psi_0\rangle &=\langle\Psi_0|[Q_{BM},Q_{CM'}^*]|\Psi_0\rangle\\ &=\sum_{abcd} X_{abB}X_{cdC}\langle\Psi_0|[A(abJM),A^*(cdJ'M')]|\Psi_0\rangle\\ &\quad -s_{JM}s_{J'M'}\sum_{abcd} Y_{abB}Y_{cdC}\\ &\qquad\times\langle\Psi_0|[A(cdJ'\bar{M}'),A^*(abJ\bar{M})]|\Psi_0\rangle,\end{aligned} \tag{60}$$

using Eq. (57) and the fact that two A^*'s or two A's commute. The commutator of an A with an A^* is found to be

$$\begin{aligned}[A(abJM),A^*(cdJ'M')] &= \sum_{m_\alpha m_\beta m_\gamma m_\delta} C(j_\alpha j_\beta J;m_\alpha m_\beta M)C(j_\gamma j_\delta J';m_\gamma m_\delta M')\\ &\quad\times[\delta_{\alpha\gamma}\delta_{\beta\delta}-\delta_{\alpha\delta}\delta_{\beta\gamma}-\delta_{\alpha\gamma}a_\delta^*a_\beta\\ &\qquad -\delta_{\beta\delta}a_\gamma^*a_\alpha+\delta_{\beta\gamma}a_\delta^*a_\alpha+\delta_{\alpha\delta}a_\gamma^*a_\beta],\end{aligned} \tag{61}$$

hence we need to know vacuum expectation values of products such as $a_\gamma^*a_\alpha$. This certainly vanishes unless the charge, the parity, and the angular momentum of α are the same as those of γ. If we invoke again the simplifying assumption made in Sec. 2B, this means that α must be the same as γ. Calling ν_a the average number of quasi-particles of type α in the ground state, we write

$$\langle\Psi_0|a_\gamma^*a_\alpha|\Psi_0\rangle=\delta_{\alpha\gamma}\nu_a. \tag{62}$$

After performing the summation over magnetic quantum numbers, one finds

$$\begin{aligned}\langle\Psi_0|[Q_{BM},Q_{CM'}^*]|\Psi_0\rangle &=2\delta_{JJ'}\delta_{MM'}\textstyle\sum_{ab}(X_{abB}X_{abC}-Y_{abB}Y_{abC})\\ &\qquad\times(1-2\nu_a).\end{aligned} \tag{63}$$

The quantity ν_a is of order ν_0/Ω, which we assumed to be small and can be neglected. Then, the orthogonality relation (56a) shows that the expression vanishes for $B\neq C$. The case $B=C$ gives us the normalization, which we want to be

$$\langle\Psi_0|Q_{BM}Q_{BM}^*|\Psi_0\rangle=1, \tag{64}$$

and therefore, if $J_B=J_C$,

$$\textstyle\sum_{ab}(X_{abB}X_{abC}-Y_{abB}Y_{abC})=\frac{1}{2}\delta_{BC}. \tag{65}$$

The argument can be extended to show that the Q's satisfy approximately the commutation relations

$$[Q_{BM},Q_{CM'}]=[Q_{BM}^*,Q_{CM'}^*]=0, \tag{66a}$$

$$[Q_{BM},Q_{CM'}^*]=\delta_{BC}\delta_{MM'}, \tag{66b}$$

as far as all matrix elements between low excited states are concerned, relations (66a) being a consequence of Eq. (56b). Thus, as long as ν_0/Ω is small, we have truly a system of independent bosons and we can consider higher excited states such as $Q_{BM}^{*2}|\Psi_0\rangle$ or $Q_{BM}^* Q_{CM'}^*|\Psi_0\rangle$, with energies $2\omega_B$ and $\omega_B+\omega_C$. Of course, the higher the excitation, the worse the approximations become. And, in any case, it is not allowed to carry these ideas to excitations larger than twice the gap, where we would get mixing with configurations that we have not properly taken into account. Since most ω's, by far, are larger than the gap, the corresponding Q^*'s can be applied only once and do not give rise to a vibrational spectrum, properly speaking, since there is only one excited state. Those are the excitations that can be described as of the single-particle type. We know that these excitations are also given correctly by our method, since it is an improvement upon the Tamm-Dancoff method that would normally be used for them. It is the virtue of the present approximation that the same equations describe single-particle and collective states, as well as all shades in between. Consequently, the various states are automatically orthogonal to each other (approximately) and the total number of states is correct. The main result of this section is therefore that, due to the special treatment of the pairing correlations and the importance of the energy gap, it has become possible to perform a certain type of shell-model calculation that will give the low excited states of spherical, nonclosed-shell nuclei, including the vibrational states, and whose difficulty is not much greater than that of a two-body shell-model calculation, except for the choice of parameters.

There remains to establish the connection between X and Y on the one hand and ψ and φ on the other. We defined ψ in Eq. (36a) by

$$\psi_{abB}=\langle\Psi_0|A(abJM)Q_{BM}^*|\Psi_0\rangle$$
$$=\langle\Psi_0|[A(abJM),Q_{BM}^*]|\Psi_0\rangle. \quad (67)$$

All we have to do is express Q_{BM}^* in terms of the A's by Eq. (54b) and insert the previously given value of the commutator of A and A^*, neglecting terms of order ν_0/Ω as earlier. The result is

$$\psi_{abB}=2X_{abB}, \quad \varphi_{abB}=2Y_{abB}, \quad (68)$$

and the orthonormalization conditions become[18]

$$\textstyle\sum_{ab}(\psi_{abB}\psi_{abC}-\varphi_{abB}\varphi_{abC})=2\delta_{BC}, \quad (69a)$$

$$\textstyle\sum_{ab}(\varphi_{abB}\psi_{abC}-\psi_{abB}\varphi_{abC})=0, \quad (69b)$$

provided $J_B=J_C$. We note that this agrees with Eq. (51) in the limit where φ is small. In terms of f and g, these equations become simpler, namely

$$\textstyle\sum_{ab} f_{abB}g_{abC}=2\delta_{BC}, \quad (J_B=J_C). \quad (70)$$

One can also derive a simple sum rule. For this, it is more convenient to sum over a given pair of levels only once. We designate the pair (ab) or (ba), coupled to J, by the single Greek index Γ, and furthermore we define

$$f_{\Gamma B}'=\begin{cases} f_{abB} & \text{if} \quad a\neq b \\ f_{abB}/\sqrt{2} & \text{if} \quad a\equiv b \end{cases} \quad (71)$$

and $g_{\Gamma B}'$ similarly. Then Eq. (70) becomes

$$\textstyle\sum_\Gamma f_{\Gamma B}'g_{\Gamma C}'=\delta_{BC}, \quad (J_B=J_C). \quad (72)$$

The number of possible values taken by Γ is also the number of possible values for B or C. If one assumes that the vectors $f_{\Gamma B}'$, for instance, form a complete set, then the following sum rule holds:

$$\textstyle\sum_B f_{\Gamma B}'g_{\Delta B}'=\delta_{\Gamma\Delta}, \quad (J_\Gamma=J_\Delta), \quad (73)$$

since it is true when applied to every vector of the set. This sum rule is not accurate in the case $J=0$, because then the physical solutions of our equations do not form a complete set, due to the existence of spurious solutions to be discussed next.

C. The Spurious States

It is well known[4,7] that the independent quasi-particle picture yields too many states. There is one extra state of $J=0$ among all states containing a pair of neutron quasi-particles, and another one for proton pairs. Their existence is due to the fact that, since the BCS ground state is not eigenstate of $\mathfrak{N}_n$ or $\mathfrak{N}_p$, the states $\mathfrak{N}_n|0\rangle$ and $\mathfrak{N}_p|0\rangle$ are different from $|0\rangle$ and their components on two-quasi-particle states are spurious; only states orthogonal to them have equivalents in a physical nucleus. But the two-quasi-particle states resulting from an approximate diagonalization of the Hamiltonian are usually not orthogonal to the spurious states, with the result that the spurious states are mixed with various percentages among all the states that one calculates. It is a major advantage of the present method that this difficulty does not arise, as was pointed out by Anderson.[15] Here, two of the solutions of our equations are entirely spurious and the others not at all. The spurious solutions have positive parity, $J=0$, $\omega=0$, $f=0$, and

$$g_{aa0}=(2j_a+1)^{\frac{1}{2}}u_a v_a, \quad (74)$$

a being a neutron state in one case, a proton in the other. It can easily be verified that these are solutions of Eqs. (44), provided one appeals once again to the assumption that the charge, the parity, and the angular momentum determine the state; as a consequence, for states of two neutrons and positive parity for instance, g_{ab0} exists only if $a\equiv b$.

The existence of these simple solutions is due to the fact that $\mathfrak{N}_n$ and $\mathfrak{N}_p$ satisfy Eq. (53) for Q_{BM} with $\omega_B=0$, since they commute exactly with $\mathcal{H}$. They can be written

$$\mathfrak{N}_n=\textstyle\sum_n\{v_a^2+(u_a^2-v_a^2)a_\alpha^*a_\alpha$$
$$+(2j_a+1)^{-\frac{1}{2}}u_a v_a[A(aa00)+A^*(aa00)]\}, \quad (75)$$

and $\mathfrak{N}_p$ similarly. Therefore, two of our Q's are immediately known,

$$Q_n=\textstyle\sum_n(2j_a+1)^{-\frac{1}{2}}u_a v_a[A(aa00)+A^*(aa00)], \quad (76)$$

and Q_p similarly. We cannot apply to them all the

arguments of Sec. 2B because they are Hermitian. But the orthogonality relations (56) are still satisfied, and therefore we can repeat the argument leading to Eq. (63) to show that

$$\langle\Psi_0|\mathfrak{N}_n Q_{B0}^*|\Psi_0\rangle\approx 0, \tag{77}$$

for instance, where B is any other $J=0$ excited state. This shows that the other solutions of our equations are orthogonal to $\mathfrak{N}_n|\Psi_0\rangle$ and are nonspurious in the sense used above. They are not, however, eigenstates of $\mathfrak{N}_n$ or $\mathfrak{N}_p$. The states still describe a mixture of neighboring even-even nuclei, and in fact the expectation value of $\mathfrak{N}_n$ or $\mathfrak{N}_p$ varies from state to state, depending on the relative amounts of hole or particle character in the excitations. But, at least, the number of states is correct.

4. APPLICATIONS

We have seen that Eqs. (44), when used with a realistic effective two-body force, should be capable of accounting approximately for the properties of all low-lying levels of even-even spherical nuclei. A calculation of this type is necessarily lengthy and none have yet been performed. Here, we propose only to demonstrate the power of the method in dealing with collective effects. We shall use very simple forces and the calculations will be quite rough. We have never given explicit expressions for the various wave functions, but this is not so serious because we shall see that, for many applications, the amplitudes f and g are just what one needs.

A. Quadrupole Vibrations

Here, the aim is to understand the relatively small vibrational frequency and the large electric quadrupole matrix element between the first 2^+ excited state and the ground state.[21] We follow KS and take an interaction composed of a pairing force, Eq. (15), and a quadrupole force of the type introduced by Elliott[22] (the discussion is limited to particles of a single charge),

$$H_Q=-\tfrac{1}{2}\chi\sum_{\alpha\beta\gamma\delta\mu}(-)^\mu q_\mu(\alpha\gamma)q_{\bar\mu}(\beta\delta)c_\alpha^*c_\beta^*c_\delta c_\gamma, \tag{78}$$

$$q_\mu(\alpha\gamma)=\langle\alpha|r^2Y_{2\mu}(\theta,\varphi)|\gamma\rangle. \tag{79}$$

Essentially, the pairing force contributes only to $\mathcal{H}_2$ and the quadrupole force only to $\mathcal{H}_4$. The method used by KS to get the collective state consists in picking a collective coordinate, in this case the quadrupole moment Q; calculating the energy for a fixed value of Q; nvoking the adiabatic approximation and using this energy as potential energy for the motion of Q; deriving a kinetic energy from Inglis' cranking formula; and finally solving the Schrödinger equation for Q, in this case a harmonic oscillator equation. We shall see on an example that Eqs. (44) give results that are nearly the same, without invoking the adiabatic approximation.

It is convenient to change the phases of the states of two particles (abJ). We multiply them all by

$$S_{abJ}=(-)^{j_b+\frac{1}{2}}\times\operatorname{sgn} C(j_aj_bJ;\tfrac{1}{2}-\tfrac{1}{2}0). \tag{80}$$

We prime the matrices expressed with these new phases. For instance,

$$V'(abcdJ)=S_{abJ}S_{cdJ}V(abcdJ). \tag{81}$$

Their symmetry properties are simpler, namely

$$\begin{aligned}V'(abcdJ)&=V'(cdabJ)=V'(badcJ)\\&=(-)^JV'(bacdJ)=(-)^JV'(abdcJ).\end{aligned} \tag{82}$$

We need the matrices G', H', and K' for $J=2$. It turns out that G' and H' are small because, through recoupling of the angular momenta, the strength of the quadrupole force is distributed between many J values. But K' contains a large term for 2^+ states,

$$K'(abcd2^+)\approx(\chi/20\pi)L_{ab}^{\frac{1}{2}}L_{cd}^{\frac{1}{2}}, \tag{83}$$

$$L_{ab}=\mathcal{R}_{ab}^2(2j_a+1)(2j_b+1)\times[C(j_aj_b2;\tfrac{1}{2}-\tfrac{1}{2}0)]^2, \tag{84}$$

$$\mathcal{R}_{ab}=\int_0^\infty R_a(r)R_b(r)r^4dr. \tag{85}$$

The fact that all matrix elements of K' are positive leads us to expect a collective solution. Equations (44) become (for $J=2^+$)

$$\begin{aligned}\omega f_{ab}&=(E_a+E_b)g_{ab},\\ \omega g_{ab}&=(E_a+E_b)f_{ab}-(\chi/20\pi)\sin(x_a+x_b)L_{ab}^{\frac{1}{2}}\\&\quad\times\sum_{(cd)2^+}\sin(x_c+x_d)L_{cd}^{\frac{1}{2}}f_{cd},\end{aligned} \tag{86}$$

with

$$u_a=\cos x_a,\quad v_a=\sin x_a. \tag{87}$$

Solution is easy and the secular equation is[23]

$$\frac{20\pi}{\chi}=\sum_{(ab)2^+}\frac{\sin^2(x_a+x_b)L_{ab}(E_a+E_b)}{(E_a+E_b)^2-\omega^2}. \tag{88}$$

The collective solution is that value of ω which is below all (E_a+E_b). If it does not exist because χ is too large, then the nucleus is not spherical and this method cannot be applied.

As an example, we pick the following parameters which are very close to those used by KS for Sn^{118}: $\eta(h_{11/2})=0.80$, $\eta(d_{3/2})=0.24$, $\eta(s_{1/2})=-0.04$, $\eta(g_{7/2})=-1.70$, $\eta(d_{5/2})=-1.90$, $\Delta=1.02$, all in Mev; $\chi=0.090$ Mev α^4; $\alpha=(m\omega_0/\hbar)^{\frac{1}{2}}$, where ω_0 is the frequency of the oscillator well used; $\alpha^{-4}=2.46\times10^{-51}$ cm^4. We find the vibrational frequency to be $\omega=1.17$ Mev. The same

[21] G. S. Goldhaber and J. Weneser, Phys. Rev. **98**, 212 (1955).
[22] J. P. Elliott, Proc. Roy. Soc. (London) **A245**, 128, 562 (1958).

[23] Dr. Sorensen points out that this equation reduces to Eq. (32) of KS in the limit of small ω.

value is obtained with the method of KS if one takes $\chi=0.091$ Mev α^4. The deviations between the two methods would be larger for larger ω, but for states that are truly collective they are equivalent.

The strength of the electric quadrupole transition between the first excited state and the ground state is measured by[24]

$$B(E2)=\sum_{M\mu}|\langle\Psi_0|\mathfrak{M}(E2,\mu)|\Psi_{2^+M}\rangle|^2, \quad (89)$$

with

$$\mathfrak{M}(E2,\mu)=\int r^2Y_{2\mu}(\theta,\varphi)\rho(\mathbf{x})d^3x, \quad (90)$$

$$\rho(\mathbf{x})=e\sum_{m_s}\phi^*(\mathbf{x}m_s)\phi(\mathbf{x}m_s), \quad (91)$$

where $\phi(\mathbf{x}m_s)$ destroys a particle at position $\mathbf{x}$ with spin m_s, and e is the effective charge. To calculate $B(E2)$, one expresses the ϕ operators in terms of the c's,

$$\phi(\mathbf{x}m_s)=\sum_\alpha\langle\mathbf{x}m_s|\alpha\rangle c_\alpha, \quad (92)$$

then the c's in terms of the a's by Eqs. (18), then one introduces the amplitudes ψ and φ by Eqs. (36), and one finds

$$B(E2)=(5e^2/80\pi)[\sum_{(ab)2^+}L_{ab}^{\frac{1}{2}}\sin(x_a+x_b)f_{ab}]^2. \quad (93)$$

It is essential here to have the correct normalization. This is given by Eq. (70) and the final result is

$$B(E2)=\frac{50\pi e^2}{\chi^2\omega}\left[\sum_{(ab)2^+}\frac{\sin^2(x_a+x_b)L_{ab}(E_a+E_b)}{[(E_a+E_b)^2-\omega^2]^2}\right]^{-1}. \quad (94)$$

For the example above, setting e equal to unity, one finds $B(E2)=2.8\times10^{-49}$ cm^4, while the method of KS gives 3.0 and the experimental value[25] is 2.3. One can also use Eq. (73) to derive a sum rule for $B(E2)$. One multiplies Eq. (93) by ω to be able to replace ωf_{ab} by $(E_a+E_b)g_{ab}$, and one finds easily

$$\sum_B\omega_B[B(E2)]_B$$
$$=(5e^2/40\pi)\sum_{(ab)2^+}\sin^2(x_a+x_b)L_{ab}(E_a+E_b), \quad (95)$$

where the sum on the left runs over all solutions of Eqs. (86). For our numerical example, the collective solution contributes 79% of the total sum.

Finally, we note that collective effects can be much stronger when protons are present as well as neutrons. The next section is an example.

B. Collective Oscillations of Closed Shells

Some collective phenomena vary smoothly through the periodic table without change at the magic numbers. They do not depend on the composition of the unfilled shells and must therefore involve transitions between whole shells. The giant photoresonance is evidence of 1^- oscillations with this property. There are also 3^- oscillations[26] which manifest themselves through large radiative matrix elements and anomalous inelastic scattering. Pairing correlations are not so important here, because the large spacing between shells already plays the role of an energy gap. Then, one can use the equations of Sec. 3, but set u equal to 1 for a particle and to 0 for a hole. Since we are interested in states composed of a particle and a hole, the G term does not appear in Eqs. (45).

We assume δ-function forces,

$$[V_S(1-\boldsymbol{\sigma}_1\cdot\boldsymbol{\sigma}_2)/4+V_T(3+\boldsymbol{\sigma}_1\cdot\boldsymbol{\sigma}_2)/4]\delta(\mathbf{x}_1-\mathbf{x}_2). \quad (96)$$

The triplet part acts only between a neutron and a proton. All standard force mixtures have[27]

$$V_S=0.6V_T. \quad (97)$$

The matrix elements involve radial integrals such as

$$F_S=(V_S/4\pi)\int_0^\infty R_a(r)R_b(r)R_c(r)R_d(r)r^2dr, \quad (98)$$

and F_T which is similarly defined. We follow Brown and Bolsterli[8] in keeping only those integrals which are obviously large and setting them all equal. We need matrix elements of H and K, both for (a,b,c,d) all of one charge and for (a,b) of one charge, (c,d) of the other. For odd J and parity, one finds that the largest elements by far (i.e., by a factor 3) are those of H between non-identical particles. We keep only those. Let a and c be particles, b and d be holes. We keep only terms where a and b belong to adjacent major shells, and for which $l_b=l_a+1$; this gives R_a and R_b the same number of nodes and makes the radial integral large.[8] We do the same for c and d. Adopting again the phases (80), we find

$$H'(abcdJ)=\tfrac{1}{2}Fh_{ab}^{\frac{1}{2}}h_{cd}^{\frac{1}{2}}, \quad (99)$$

$$h_{ab}=\tfrac{1}{2}(2J+1)^{-1}(2j_a+1)(2j_b+1)\times[C(j_aj_bJ;\tfrac{1}{2}-\tfrac{1}{2}0)]^2, \quad (100)$$

$$F=F_S+3F_T. \quad (101)$$

We keep only terms with $j_b=j_a+1$, as they give bigger C coefficients in (100). The hole b associated with a given particle a is now completely determined and we shall use a single subscript, Roman for proton particle-hole pairs, Greek for neutrons.

With these rather drastic approximations, Eq. (44)

[24] K. Alder *et al.*, Revs. Modern Phys. **28**, 432 (1956).
[25] P. H. Stelson and F. K. McGowan, Phys. Rev. **110**, 489 (1958).
[26] A. M. Lane and E. D. Pendlebury, Nuclear Phys. **15**, 39 (1960).
[27] J. P. Elliott and A. M. Lane, *Encyclopedia of Physics* (Springer-Verlag, Berlin, 1957), Vol. XXXIX, p. 337.

takes the form

$$\begin{aligned}\omega f_a &= E_0 g_a - F h_a^{\frac{1}{2}} \textstyle\sum_\alpha h_\alpha^{\frac{1}{2}} g_\alpha,\\ \omega g_a &= E_0 f_a,\\ \omega f_\alpha &= E_0 g_\alpha - F h_\alpha^{\frac{1}{2}} \textstyle\sum_a h_a^{\frac{1}{2}} g_a,\\ \omega g_\alpha &= E_0 f_\alpha,\end{aligned} \tag{102}$$

where E_0 is the distance between major shells. The secular equation is

$$(E_0^2-\omega^2)^2 = F^2 E_0^2 (\textstyle\sum_a h_a)(\sum_\alpha h_\alpha). \tag{103}$$

There are two solutions: one for which $E_0^2-\omega^2$ is positive and in which the protons and the neutrons oscillate in phase (i.e., f_a and f_α have the same sign); and the other for which $E_0^2-\omega^2$ is negative, f_a and f_α have opposite signs, the protons and the neutrons are in opposite phase. For light nuclei, those would be called $T=0$ and $T=1$, respectively. Oscillation in phase gives an attraction, out of phase a repulsion. For a numerical estimate, we took $\sum_a h_a$ and $\sum_\alpha h_\alpha$ equal, and calculated it using the 50–82 major shell for the particle and the 82–126 major shell for the hole. We found it equal to 9 for $J=1$ and 2.9 for $J=3$. We took E_0 equal to 7 Mev.

For the 3^- case and oscillation in phase, the experimental value of ω seems to be[26] 2.6 Mev. This is achieved by taking $F=2.1$ Mev. The 1^- in-phase solution corresponds to motion of the center of mass of the whole nucleus and is spurious.[28] The 1^- out-of-phase case is the giant dipole resonance which has been discussed by Brown and Bolsterli.[8] Our treatment differs from theirs in that we include the diagrams of Fig. 1(b), while they have only those of Fig. 1(a). Including diagrams 1(b) actually enhances the effect for the in-phase case, but decreases it for out-of-phase. Of course, one may wonder about the validity of either method when applied to such large excitation as that of the giant resonance. Be that as it may, one can get the experimental value, $\omega=15$ Mev (for heavy nuclei), by taking $F=2.8$ Mev.

The two values of F thus obtained are in rough agreement. Another estimate of F can be gotten from the work of KS, since the $J=0$ part of the G matrix for the pairing force is almost the same as for a δ-function force. Their value of F_S (their G) is (25 Mev)/A. By Eqs. (97) and (101), F should be six times larger. For heavy nuclei, this gives $F=0.8$ Mev. One possible reason why this estimate is smaller, is that the true force has a finite range, whose effect is to increase hole-particle matrix elements compared to particle elements. However, it should also be noted that, in his theory of the lead isotopes with δ-function forces, Pryce[29] uses values of F_S around 0.3 or 0.4 Mev, corresponding to $F\approx 2$ Mev. Finally, a meaningful comparison can also be made with the numbers of Sec. 4A because, for a δ-function force and identical particles, one has

$$\begin{aligned}&K'(abcd2^+)\\ &\quad=(F_S/10)[(2j_a+1)(2j_b+1)(2j_c+1)(2j_d+1)]^{\frac{1}{2}}\\ &\qquad\times|C(j_aj_b2;\tfrac{1}{2}-\tfrac{1}{2}0)C(j_cj_d2;\tfrac{1}{2}-\tfrac{1}{2}0)|.\end{aligned} \tag{104}$$

This is very close to Eq. (83). Since $\mathcal{R}_{aa}^2$ is $(11/2)^2\alpha^{-4}$ for most values of a, one can identify F_S with $(\chi/2\pi)(11/2)^2\alpha^{-4}$. The value of F that one obtains this way is 2.6 Mev.

In conclusion, one can say that the order-of-magnitude agreement between these various estimates of the nuclear force makes it appear likely that, in the future, it will be possible to obtain a good fit of all these phenomena with the same effective two-body interaction.

C. Anomalous Inelastic Scattering

Anomalously large inelastic scattering has been observed with protons,[30] deuterons,[31] and α particles.[32] This happens in particular for scattering into the first quadrupole vibrational state, but there are other large anomalies at other energies. The main one is around 2.5 Mev in all heavy spherical nuclei. Cohen[33] has suggested that collective effects are responsible in all cases, and strong evidence[34] has been offered that the 2.5-Mev anomaly is due to 3^- vibrations. It might be that, in nuclei with proton and neutron shells both partially filled, there is also a contribution from the one-phonon 4^+ vibrational state[35] which must lie near the top of the gap.

A proper theory of this effect must take into account absorption, refraction, and diffraction of the projectile.[36] Here, we do not wish to attempt to calculate the absolute cross section or the angular distribution, but only try to make a very rough estimate of the enhancement compared to the single-particle value. For this, it might be enough to use a model where the projectile is spinless and interacts with the nucleons in Born approximation through a zero-range, spin-independent, charge-independent potential. Then, the scattering amplitude with

---

[28] J. P. Elliott and T. H. R. Skyrme, Proc. Roy. Soc. (London) **A232**, 561 (1955).

[29] M. H. L. Pryce, Nuclear Phys. **2**, 226 (1956/57); D. E. Alburger and M. H. L. Pryce, Phys. Rev. **95**, 1482 (1954).

[30] B. L. Cohen, Phys. Rev. **105**, 1549 (1957); B. L. Cohen and A. G. Rubin, Phys. Rev. **111**, 1568 (1958).

[31] J. L. Yntema and B. Zeidman, Phys. Rev. **114**, 815 (1959); B. L. Cohen and R. E. Price (to be published).

[32] D. R. Sweetman and N. S. Wall, *Comptes Rendus du Congrès International de Physique Nucléaire, Paris, 1958* (Dunod, Paris, 1959); H. W. Fulbright, N. O. Lassen, and N. O. Roy Poulsen, Kgl. Danske Videnskab. Selskab, Mat.-fys. Medd. **31**, No. 10 (1959); J. L. Yntema, B. Zeidman, and B. J. Raz (to be published); D. K. McDaniels, J. S. Blair, S. W. Chen, and G. W. Farwell (to be published).

[33] B. L. Cohen, Phys. Rev. **116**, 426 (1959).

[34] See reference 26 and D. K. McDaniels *et al.*, reference 32.

[35] Not to be confused with the 4^+ component of the two-phonon 2^+ vibration.

[36] N. Austern and E. Rost (to be published); J. S. Blair, Phys. Rev. **115**, 928 (1959); S. I. Drozdov, J. Exptl. Theoret. Phys. (U.S.S.R.) **28**, 734, 736 (1955) [Translation: Soviet Phys.-JETP **1**, 588, 591 (1955)].

momentum transfer **k** is proportional to

$$\int d^3x\, e^{i\mathbf{k}\cdot\mathbf{x}}\langle\Psi_0|\sum_{m_sq}\phi^*(\mathbf{x}m_sq)\phi(\mathbf{x}m_sq)|\Psi_{BM}\rangle, \quad (105)$$

where $\phi(\mathbf{x}m_sq)$ destroys a particle with position **x**, spin m_s, charge q. We shall calculate the quantity

$$\int d^3x|\langle\Psi_0|\sum_{m_sq}\phi^*(\mathbf{x}m_sq)\phi(\mathbf{x}m_sq)|\Psi_{BM}\rangle|^2, \quad (106)$$

which is a measure of the total strength of the transition. This can be expressed in terms of f and g by methods used earlier. With the phases (80), it is found equal to

$$\tfrac{1}{2}\sum_{abcd} Z(abcd)h_{ab}^{\frac{1}{2}}h_{cd}^{\frac{1}{2}}(u_av_b+v_au_b)\times(u_cv_d+v_cu_d)f_{ab}f_{cd}, \quad (107)$$

for even J and even parity, and to

$$\tfrac{1}{2}\sum_{abcd} Z(abcd)h_{ab}^{\frac{1}{2}}h_{cd}^{\frac{1}{2}}(u_av_b-v_au_b)\times(u_cv_d-v_cu_d)g_{ab}g_{cd}, \quad (108)$$

for odd J and odd parity, with

$$Z(abcd)=(4\pi)^{-1}\int_0^\infty R_a(r)R_b(r)R_c(r)R_d(r)r^2dr, \quad (109)$$

and h_{ab} as defined by Eq. (100). Other combinations of J and parity give a vanishing result. The charges of a and b must be the same, and those of c and d likewise. Once again, we shall set all large radial integrals equal and neglect the others.

For a single-particle transition, only two states are important, say a particle state a and a hole b. The amplitudes f_{ab} and g_{ab} are equal to each other, and to unity in view of the normalization (70). We can average h_{ab} over J, which gives $\frac{1}{2}$. Then, formulas (107) and (108) become just Z. Therefore, the enhancement over the single-particle transition is given by (107) or (108), but with Z omitted, provided that we include in the sum only terms whose Z is large.

It is a simple matter to apply this to the case of 3^- oscillations, using the approximations and parameters of Sec. 4B. The enhancement is given by $(4E_0/\omega)\sum_a h_a$, which is equal to 30. This is of the same order of magnitude as the enhancement of $B(E3)$ for heavy nuclei, quoted in reference 26. A more direct comparison with experiment is difficult.

ACKNOWLEDGMENTS

Special thanks are due E. U. Baranger for instructing the author in nuclear spectroscopy and R. Sorensen for extensive discussions and correspondence concerning the work of the Copenhagen school and his own work with L. Kisslinger. We are grateful to A. Bohr, B. Cohen, L. Kisslinger, S. Meshkov, L. Wolfenstein, and S. Yoshida for helpful conversations, and to K. Kumar for checking some of the algebra.

After completion of this work, we learned from Drs. Bohr and Sorensen that investigations of a similar nature are going on elsewhere. Equation (88) has been derived by A. Bohr (unpublished). A simplified version of it which assumes degeneracy of the single-particle levels was derived two years ago by B. Mottelson and developed by D. R. Bès and B. Mottelson (unpublished). The same equation has recently been given by Kobayasi and Marumori.[37] The work of Arvieu and Véneroni[38] comes closest to the spirit of ours. These authors also propose the use of the Sawada method for determining collective oscillations in spherical nuclei. Their equations differ from ours by the absence of the G term in (45a) and (45b). This has little effect on the collective states, but these terms are essential if the equations are to be used also for other two-quasi-particle states, with a realistic nuclear force. They are also necessary for the elimination of the spurious states.[39]

[37] M. Kobayasi and T. Marumori, Progr. Theoret. Phys. (Kyoto) 23, 387 (1960).

[38] R. Arvieu and M. Véneroni, Compt. rend. 250, 992, 2155 (1960).

[39] *Note added in proof.* Related papers recently appeared include T. Marumori, Progr. Theoret. Phys. (Kyoto) 24, 331 (1960) and G. E. Brown, J. A. Evans, and D. J. Thouless, preprint.

Reprinted from THE PHYSICAL REVIEW, Vol. 123, No. 6, 2122–2130, September 15, 1961
Printed in U. S. A.

Studies of Stripping and Pickup Reactions on the Basis of the Pairing Plus Quadrupole-Quadrupole Interaction Model*

SHIRO YOSHIDA†
Radiation Laboratory, University of Pittsburgh, Pittsburgh, Pennsylvania
(Received November 16, 1960)

Cross sections for (d,p) and (d,t) reactions in units of the single-particle cross sections (the spectroscopic factors) are calculated for spherical nuclei. It is assumed that the protons fill a closed shell and that only neutrons in an unfilled shell interact with each other through the pairing and quadrupole-quadrupole interactions. First the pairing interactions problem is solved by introducing quasi-particles according to Belyaev. Next the quadrupole-quadrupole interaction is diagonalized, taking into accout two quasi-particle states for the first excited state of even-even nuclei. Using these wave functions the spectroscopic factors are obtained in simple form, and are evaluated numerically for the case of the Sn isotopes. Comparison is made with experiments for the transitions to the ground states of even-even and even-odd isotopes as well as to the vibrational states of even-even isotopes. Agreement in both cases is fairly good.

1. INTRODUCTION

THE importance of deuteron stripping and pickup reactions as a tool of nuclear spectroscopy has been emphasized by many authors. These reactions provide rather direct information on the wave functions of low-lying nuclear states. Macfarlane and French[1] gave the most elaborate and complete reviews of these reactions, mainly based on the shell model, while Satchler[2] summarized studies of the stripping reactions based on the collective model. For deformed nuclei with rotational spectra Satchler gave a straightforward prescription for analysis of experimental data and work has been published along this line.[3] However for the vibrational spectra further detailed calculations like the intermediate coupling theory may be necessary to analyze experimental data.

Recently another aspect of nuclear structure was revealed by the Copenhagen group[4] in analogy with superconductivity in solid state physics. The pairing force is responsible for this new aspect of structure and the existence of an energy gap in the intrinsic spectra of deformed even-even nuclei was the first experimental support for it. The powerful mathematical method of superconductivity[5] was applied in the nuclear case by Belyaev[6] and further detailed comparisons with experiments have been carried out successfully by Kisslinger and Sorensen.[7] The latter authors treated single closed-shell nuclei and calculated the energy spectra, electromagnetic moments, and transition rates. To study the

* This work was supported by the Office of Naval Research.
† On leave of absence from Institute for Nuclear Study, University of Tokyo, Tokyo, Japan.
[1] M. H. Macfarlane and J. B. French, Revs. Modern Phys. **32**, 567 (1960).
[2] G. R. Satchler, Ann. Phys. **3**, 275 (1958).
[3] A. E. Litherland, H. McManus, E. B. Paul, D. A. Bromley, and H. E. Gove, Can. J. Phys. **36**, 378 (1958).
[4] A. Bohr, B. R. Mottelson, and D. Pines, Phys. Rev. **110**, 936 (1958).
[5] J. Bardeen, L. N. Cooper, and J. R. Schrieffer, Phys. Rev. **108**, 1175 (1957). N. N. Bogoliubov, Nuovo cimento **7**, 794 (1958). J. G. Valatin, *ibid.* **7**, 843 (1958). N. N. Bogoliubov, V. V. Tolmachev, and D. V. Shirko, *A New Method in the Theory of Superconductivity* (Consultants Bureau, New York, 1959).
[6] S. T. Belyaev, Kgl. Danske Videnskab. Selskab, Mat.-fys. Medd. **31**, No. 11 (1959).
[7] L. S. Kisslinger and R. A. Sorensen, Kgl. Danske Videnskab. Selskab, Mat.-fys. Medd. **32**, No. 9 (1960).

vibrational states they assumed the cranking model.[8] These states also have been studied by Baranger and other people[9] using more refined methods.

The pairing forces cause a strong configuration mixing among the nucleon states in the unfilled shell, which is difficult to treat by usual shell model calculations. This configuration mixing gives rise to the energy gap, and to secondary effects, like the deviation of the moment of inertia from the rigid-body value.[10] However its effects may be seen directly by studying the stripping and pickup process. In fact Cohen and Price[11] have made experiments with (d,p) and (d,t) reactions in a wide range of atomic numbers, and found many facts which seem difficult to explain by the simple shell model. This paper was inspired by their work and will give theoretical considerations of the (d,p) and (d,t) reactions based on the superconductive nature of nuclei. For the vibrational state the Tamm-Dancoff method will be applied and rather simple and explicit formulas for the reduced width will be presented.

The (d,p) and (d,t) cross sections may be expressed as[1]

$$d\sigma_{d,x}/d\Omega = R_{d,x} \textstyle\sum_l S_l \phi_{d,x}(l,Q,\theta), \quad x=p,t \qquad (1.1)$$

where $R_{d,x}$ is the statistical factor and is given by

$$R_{d,p}=(2J_f+1)/(2J_i+1), \quad R_{d,t}=1. \qquad (1.2)$$

J_i and J_f are the spin of the target and residual nucleus respectively. The second factor in Eq. (1.1), S_l, is called the spectroscopic factor, which gives the probability of the appearance of the single particle state in the parent nuclear wave function. The last factor is the single-particle cross section and is considered as a function of orbital angular momentum l of the stripped or captured neutron, the Q value, and the angle of the outgoing particle θ.

The spectroscopic factor S_l may be expressed as a sum of overlap integrals between the parent nucleus and a free state composed of the daughter nucleus and a captured or stripped neutron with angular momentum j. That is,

$$S_l = \textstyle\sum_{j=l\pm\frac{1}{2}} S_j, \qquad (1.3)$$

where

$$S_j = A\langle \Psi_{JM} | \Phi_{JM}(j,J_0)\rangle^2. \qquad (1.4)$$

In the last equation, A is the mass number of the parent nucleus and Ψ_{JM} is its wave function, J and M being its spin and the Z component. $\Phi_{JM}(j,J_0)$ is given by

$$\Phi_{JM}(j,J_0) = \sum_{m,M} (jmJ_0M_0|JM)\phi_{jm}\Psi_{J_0M_0}, \qquad (1.5)$$

where $(jmJ_0M_0|JM)$ is the Clebsch-Gordan coefficient, ϕ_{jm} is the spin-angle part of the captured or stripped neutron, and $\Psi_{J_0M_0}$ is the wave function of the daughter nucleus with spin J_0 and Z component M_0. This spectroscopic factor corresponds also to the reduced width in units of the single-particle reduced width.

As for the single-particle cross section $\phi(l,Q,\theta)$, the dependences on l, Q, and θ are known empirically.[11] Therefore the knowledge of the spectroscopic factor is sufficient to discuss the cross section. The spectroscopic factor may be calculated easily once the wave functions are given. In Sec. 2 the necessary formulas for the nuclear wave function based on the pairing interaction model will be summarized. Then the spectroscopic factor will be calculated in Sec. 3 for the ground states or single-particle states. Section 4 will be devoted to the construction of the wave function of the vibrational states and in the following section (Sec. 5), these wave functions will be applied to the calculation of the spectroscopic factor for vibrational states. These results will be compared with experiments in Sec. 6 and discussions will be presented.

[8] D. R. Inglis, Phys. Rev. **96**, 1059 (1954); **97**, 701 (1955).

[9] M. Baranger, Phys. Rev. **120**, 957 (1960). For similar works see references in Baranger's paper.

[10] A. B. Migdal, J. Exptl. Theoret. Phys. (U.S.S.R.) **37**, 249 (1959); [translation Soviet Phys.—JETP **10**, 176 (1960)]. J. J. Griffin and M. Rich, Phys. Rev. **118**, 850 (1960).

[11] B. L. Cohen and R. E. Price, Phys. Rev. **118**, 1582 (1960).

2. PAIRING INTERACTION

In this section the nuclear model based on the pairing interaction will be summarized in order to give necessary wave functions for the calculation of the spectroscopic factor. We follow the work of Belyaev[6] but use the Condon and Shortley[12] phase for the wave function. It is also assumed that only one kind of nucleons (neutrons) are active while the other kind of nucleons (protons) form a closed shell and will not be taken into account in the calculation. The vacuum state $|0\rangle$ will be understood to stand for the state where all states in filled shells are occupied and none of the unfilled shell is occupied. The Hamiltonian for the pairing interaction then is given by

$$H_0 = \sum_{j,m} \epsilon_j a_{jm}^\dagger a_{jm} - \tfrac{1}{4}G \sum_{j'm'} (-)^{j'-m'} a_{j'm'}^\dagger a_{j'-m'}^\dagger \times \sum_{jm} (-)^{-j+m} a_{j-m} a_{jm}, \qquad (2.1)$$

where the first term of the right-hand side represents the sum of the single-particle energies (of the shell model states) while the second term represents the pairing interactions among nucleons in the unfilled shell. $a_{jm}^\dagger$ and a_{jm} are the creation and annihilation operators of the shell model state with spin j and Z component m. Also ϵ_j is the single-particle energy of the shell model state j, and G is the strength of the pairing interaction. To specify a shell model state, quantum numbers other than j and m will be necessary, but they will be suppressed unless they are needed.

Following the procedure of Bogoliubov and Valatin[5] the operators $a_{jm}^\dagger$ and a_{jm} now will be transformed into new operators by a canonical transformation. As this transformation mixes states with different mass

[12] E. U. Condon and G. H. Shortley, *The Theory of Atomic Spectra* (Cambridge University Press, New York, 1951).

number, it is necessary to introduce the auxiliary Hamiltonian

$$H_0'=H_0-\lambda\sum_{j,m} a_{jm}{}^\dagger a_{jm}, \tag{2.2}$$

where λ is the chemical potential, serving as a Lagrange multiplier to take into account the constraint that for the solution Ψ the average occupation number equals the number n of nucleons in the unfilled shell; $\langle\Psi|\sum a_{jm}{}^\dagger a_{jm}|\Psi\rangle=n$. The Bogoliubov and Valatin[5] transformation is given by

$$a_{jm}=U_j\alpha_{jm}+V_j(-)^{j-m}\alpha_{j-m}{}^\dagger, \tag{2.3}$$

where U_j and V_j satisfy

$$U_j^2+V_j^2=1. \tag{2.4}$$

The coefficients U_j and V_j are chosen so that the new Hamiltonian in terms of α_{jm} and $\alpha_{jm}{}^\dagger$ will not contain terms like $\alpha^\dagger\alpha^\dagger$ and $\alpha\alpha$. Therefore the following equations are obtained

$$\tfrac{1}{4}G\sum_j \frac{2j+1}{[(\epsilon_j-\lambda)^2+\Delta^2]^{\frac{1}{2}}}=1, \tag{2.5}$$

where

$$\Delta=\tfrac{1}{2}G\sum_j(2j+1)U_jV_j, \tag{2.6}$$

and

$$U_j^2=\tfrac{1}{2}\left[1+\frac{\epsilon_j-\lambda}{[(\epsilon_j-\lambda)^2+\Delta^2]^{\frac{1}{2}}}\right], \tag{2.7}$$

$$V_j^2=\tfrac{1}{2}\left[1-\frac{\epsilon_j-\lambda}{[(\epsilon_j-\lambda)^2+\Delta^2]^{\frac{1}{2}}}\right]. \tag{2.8}$$

The transformed Hamiltonian takes the form

$$H_0'=\text{const}+\sum E_j\alpha_{jm}{}^\dagger\alpha_{jm} +\text{terms containing four } \alpha\text{'s}, \tag{2.9}$$

where the second term represents the transformed single-particle energy, and

$$E_j=[(\epsilon_j-\lambda)^2+\Delta^2]^{\frac{1}{2}}. \tag{2.10}$$

In this new representation the nuclear state is specified by the various occupation numbers of the new particle states which are called the quasi-particle states. The last term of (2.9) will be neglected. The quasi-particle states are the elementary excitations with respect to a new vacuum, which is the ground state of an even-even nucleus. In terms of the old representation, the wave function of the new vacuum is expressed as

$$\Psi_0=\prod_{j,m>0}(U_j+V_j(-)^{j-m}a_{jm}{}^\dagger a_{j-m}{}^\dagger)|0\rangle. \tag{2.11}$$

It is easily shown that

$$\alpha_{jm}\Psi_0=0. \tag{2.12}$$

The odd nucleus then is the state with one quasi-particle and the wave function is given by

$$\alpha_{JM}{}^\dagger\Psi_0. \tag{2.13}$$

The number of nucleons is obtained as

$$n=\sum_j\frac{2j+1}{2}\left[1-\frac{\epsilon_j-\lambda}{[(\epsilon_j-\lambda)^2+\Delta^2]^{\frac{1}{2}}}\right] +\sum_{i=1}^{r}\frac{\epsilon_i-\lambda}{[(\epsilon_i-\lambda)^2+\Delta^2]^{\frac{1}{2}}}, \tag{2.14}$$

where the first term represents the contribution from the new vacuum and the second term is the contribution from the quasi-particles.

Equations (2.5) and (2.14) are the basic equations, and Δ and λ will be obtained if ϵ_j, G, and n are given, Δ is the lowest energy of the quasi-particle as seen from (2.10). After Δ and λ are derived U_j and V_j may be calculated from (2.7) and (2.8) and accordingly the energy and the wave function will be obtained. Numerical values of Δ and λ are tabulated by Kisslinger and Sorensen[7] for the single closed shell nuclei.

It is noted that the values of U_j and V_j differ from one nucleus to another and change smoothly with increasing mass number. In the next section it will become necessary to treat the even-even nucleus with nucleon number n and the even-odd nucleus with nucleon number $n\pm1$ in calculating the overlap integral. If the former wave function is denoted by Ψ_0, in which U_j and V_j are adjusted to give the average nucleon number n, then the latter wave function given by Eq. (2.13) $\alpha_{JM}{}^\dagger\Psi_0$ will no longer correspond to the state with a nucleon number $n\pm1$. Instead for this nucleus Eq. (2.14) once again gives the average nucleon number n, because the contribution from the one quasi-particle JM is very small if the odd nucleus is in the ground or low excited state, where $\epsilon_J\approx\lambda$. In order to get the odd-nuclear wave function with nucleon number $n\pm1$, it is necessary to use slightly different U_j' and V_j' from those used in the even-even nucleus. Let that vacuum state be denoted by Ψ_0' which gives the average nucleon number $n\pm1$, and those quasi-particle operators by $\alpha_{jm}'^\dagger$ and α_{jm}' which are obtained by replacing U_j and V_j by U_j' and V_j'. Then the vacuum state with prime may be expressed in terms of the original vacuum state and its operators as

$$\Psi_0'=\prod_{j,m>0}(V_jV_j'+U_jU_j')[1-(U_jV_j'-U_j'V_j) \times(V_jV_j'+U_jU_j')^{-1}(-)^{j-m}\alpha_{j-m}{}^\dagger\alpha_{jm}{}^\dagger]\Psi_0. \tag{2.16}$$

Neglecting the higher order terms, the last equation is expressed approximately

$$\Psi_0'\simeq\left[1+\tfrac{1}{2}\sum_{j,m}\frac{\Delta U_j}{V_j}(-)^{j-m}\alpha_{j-m}{}^\dagger\alpha_{jm}{}^\dagger\right]\Psi_0, \tag{2.17}$$

where

$$\Delta U_j = U_j' - U_j. \tag{2.18}$$

For the one quasi-particle state it is easy to prove that

$$\alpha_{jm}'^{\dagger}\Psi_0' \simeq \alpha_{jm}^{\dagger}\Psi_0', \tag{2.19}$$

where higher order terms are neglected.

3. GROUND-STATE SPECTROSCOPIC FACTOR

The spectroscopic factor is expressed in the second quantization form as

$$S_j = \langle \Psi_{JM} | \Phi_{JM}(j,J_0)\rangle^2, \tag{3.1}$$

where Ψ_{JM} is the wave function of the parent nucleus with spin J and Z component M, while

$$\Phi_{JM}(j,J_0) = \sum_{m,M_0} (jmJ_0M_0|JM) a_{jm}^{\dagger}\Psi_{J_0M_0}. \tag{3.2}$$

In the last equation $\Psi_{J_0M_0}$ is the wave function of the daughter nucleus with spin J_0 and Z component M_0, and j and m are the spin and Z component of the captured or stripped nucleon.

We first consider the case of the odd parent nucleus. If the ground state of the even-even nucleus is denoted by Ψ, and the parent even-odd nucleus by $\alpha_{JM}'^{\dagger}\Psi_0'$, then the spectroscopic factor is expressed as

$$S_j = \langle \alpha_{JM}'^{\dagger}\Psi_0' | a_{jm}^{\dagger}\Psi_0\rangle^2. \tag{3.3}$$

By using (2.17), (2.19), and (2.3), the last equation gives the result

$$S_j = \delta_{Jj} U_J^2, \tag{3.4}$$

where U_J^2 is the probability of the orbit with spin J in the even-even nucleus being empty. The correction factor given by (2.17) plays no role in this expression, in which U_j and V_j apply to the daughter nucleus, but would if the U_j and V_j of the parent nucleus were used. If we use the U_j and V_j for the parent nucleus, then we have

$$S_j = \langle \alpha_{JM}^{\dagger}\Psi_0 | a_{jm}^{\dagger}\Psi_0'\rangle^2 = \delta_{Jj}(U_J + \Delta U_J)^2,$$

which agrees with (3.4) because of the correction term ΔU_J. Equation (3.4) may be given the interpretation that one nucleon is captured by the even-even nucleus into the orbit j and that the probability is proportional to the probability of the orbit j being empty.

Next let us consider the case of an even-even parent nucleus. If the wave function of the parent nucleus is denoted by Ψ_0 and that of the odd nucleus by $\alpha_{J_0M_0}'^{\dagger}\Psi_0'$, then the spectroscopic factor is obtained

$$S_j = \delta_{J_0j}(2J_0+1)V_{J_0}^2, \tag{3.5}$$

where $V_{J_0}^2$ is again the probability of the orbit with spin J_0 in the even-even nucleus being occupied. The interpretation is similar to the previous case; one nucleon at the level j is stripped from the even-even nucleus and the probability is proportional to the number of nucleons occupying the orbit j, that is $(2J_0+1)V_{J_0}^2$ [see (2.14)]. It is noted that the spectroscopic factor is described by U and V of the even-even nucleus irrespective of which nucleus actually is the parent. In our treatment the state of the odd nucleus has been described as being the ground state, but in fact it may be any state of that nucleus. For any single quasi-particle state the formulas (3.4) and (3.5) should be valid. These two facts make it possible to obtain all the values of U_j and V_j for the even-even nucleus from the set of experimental cross section of (d,p) and (d,t) reaction for single quasi-particle states.[13]

Here we have to remember that the number of nucleons has not been taken into account exactly, due to the introduction of the Bogoliubov and Valatin[5] transformation. It is expected that the error in the nucleon number n may be proportional to $\sqrt{n}$, and our results also may contain some errors. To test this it is convenient to compare our results with the shell model results in a simple case. Let us assume that the configuration is pure j^n, then the equations (2.5)–(2.8) and (2.14) become very simple and the following solution may be obtained easily

$$\epsilon - \lambda = G(2j+1-2n)/4, \quad \Delta = G[n(2j+1-n)]^{\frac{1}{2}}/2, \tag{3.6}$$

where ϵ is the single particle energy of the orbit j. From (2.7) and (2.8) we obtain

$$U_j^2 = 1 - \frac{n}{2j+1}, \quad V_j^2 = \frac{n}{2j+1}. \tag{3.7}$$

If these are put into (3.4) and (3.5), then

$$\begin{aligned} S_j &= \delta_{jJ}\left[1 - \frac{n}{2j+1}\right] \quad \text{for odd parent nucleus,} \\ &= \delta_{jJ_0} n \quad \text{for even-even parent nucleus,} \end{aligned} \tag{3.8}$$

where n is the number of nucleons j in the even-even nuclei. These results agree exactly with those obtained from the usual shell model calculation.[1] From this we may expect that our results should be very accurate despite the inaccurate treatment of nucleon number.

4. VIBRATIONAL STATE

In considering the vibrational state of even-even nuclei, the quadrupole-quadrupole interaction,[14]

$$H_{Q-Q} = -\tfrac{1}{2}x \sum_{\mu j_1 j_1' j_2 j_2'} (-)^{\mu}\langle j_1'm_1' | Y_{2\mu}v | j_1m_1\rangle$$
$$\times \langle j_2'm_2' | Y_{2-\mu}v | j_2m_2\rangle a_{j_1'm_1'}^{\dagger} a_{j_2'm_2'}^{\dagger} a_{j_2m_2} a_{j_1m_1}, \tag{4.1}$$

is taken into account in addition to the pairing interaction. In the last equation, x is the coupling constant

---

[13] B. L. Cohen and R. E. Price, Phys. Rev. **121**, 1441 (1961).

[14] J. P. Elliott, Proc. Roy. Soc. (London), **A245**, 128, 562 (1958).

[this corresponds to $(\hbar/m\omega_0)^2\chi$ in the Kisslinger and Sorensen paper[7]] and $Y_{2\mu}$ are the second order spherical harmonics. Harmonic oscillator single-particle wave functions are assumed in order to make the calculation easy. The dimensionless oscillator potential v is given by

$$v=(m\omega_0/\hbar)r^2, \tag{4.2}$$

where r is the radial coordinate of the single particle, m is the mass of the nucleon, and ω_0 is the angular frequency of the harmonic oscillator.

After applying the Bogoliubov and Valatin transformation[5] (2.3), the Q–Q interaction is expressed in a normal form:

$$\begin{aligned}H_{Q-Q}=-(x/10)&\sum_{j_1j_1'j_2j_2'}(j_2'\|Y_2v\|j_2)(j_1'\|Y_2v\|j_1)\\
&\times\Big[\tfrac{1}{4}u_{j_2'j_2}u_{j_1'j_1}\sum_\mu(-)^\mu A^\dagger(j_2'j_22-\mu)A^\dagger(j_1'j_12\mu)\\
&+u_{j_2'j_2}v_{j_1'j_1}\sum_\mu(-)^\mu A^\dagger(j_2'j_22-\mu)A^0(j_1'j_12\mu)\\
&+\tfrac{1}{2}u_{j_2'j_2}u_{j_1'j_1}\sum_\mu A^\dagger(j_2'j_22\mu)A(j_1'j_12\mu)\\
&+v_{j_2'j_2}u_{j_1'j_1}\sum_\mu A^0(j_2'j_22\mu)A(j_1'j_12\mu)\\
&+\tfrac{1}{4}u_{j_2'j_2}u_{j_1'j_1}\sum_\mu(-)^\mu A(j_2'j_22\mu)A(j_1'j_12-\mu)\\
&-5(-)^{j_2-j_1'}v_{j_2'j_2}v_{j_1'j_1}\sum_{\nu\kappa}(-)^\nu W(j_2'j_2j_1'j_1;2\nu)\\
&\qquad\times A^\dagger(j_1'j_2'\nu\kappa)A(j_1j_2\nu\kappa)\Big],\end{aligned} \tag{4.3}$$

where

$$\begin{aligned}A^\dagger(j_1j_2\lambda\mu)&=\sum_{m_1m_2}(j_1m_1j_2m_2|\lambda\mu)\alpha_{j_1m_1}{}^\dagger\alpha_{j_2m_2}{}^\dagger,\\
A(j_1j_2\lambda\mu)&=\sum_{m_1m_2}(j_1m_1j_2m_2|\lambda\mu)\alpha_{j_2m_2}\alpha_{j_1m_1},\\
A^0(j_1j_2\lambda\mu)&=\sum_{m_1m_2}(-)^{j_2+m_2}(j_1m_1j_2m_2|\lambda\mu)\\
&\qquad\times(\alpha_{j_1m_1}{}^\dagger\alpha_{j_2-m_2}-\tfrac{1}{2}\delta_{j_1j_2}\delta_{m_1,-m_2}).\end{aligned} \tag{4.4}$$

The first two lines of (4.4) represent a pair of quasi-particle creation and annihilation operators, respectively, and the last line represents the quadrupole transition operator (for $\lambda=2$). Also $u_{j_1j_2}$ and $v_{j_1j_2}$ are the following combinations of U_j and V_j:

$$u_{j_1j_2}=U_{j_1}V_{j_2}+V_{j_1}U_{j_2},\quad v_{j_1j_2}=U_{j_1}U_{j_2}-V_{j_1}V_{j_2}. \tag{4.5}$$

In Eq. (4.3), $(j'\|Y_2v\|j)$ is the reduced matrix element of the nondimensional quadrupole transition operator and is given by

$$\begin{aligned}(N'l'j'\|Y_2v\|Nlj)=&\frac{1}{(4\pi)^{\frac{1}{2}}}(-)^{j'-j}[5(2j'+1)]^{\frac{1}{2}}\\
&\times(j'\tfrac{1}{2}20|j\tfrac{1}{2})\frac{1+(-)^{l+l'}}{2}(N'l'|v|Nl),\end{aligned} \tag{4.6}$$

TABLE I. The radial integrals $(N'l'|v|Nl)$.

N'	l'	$(N'l'\|v\|Nl)$
N	l	$N+\frac{3}{2}$
$N\pm2$	l	$-\frac{1}{2}[(N+l+2\pm1)(N-l+1\pm1)]^{\frac{1}{2}}$
$N\pm2$	$l\pm2$	$\frac{1}{2}[(N+l+1\pm2)(N+l+3\pm2)]^{\frac{1}{2}}$
N	$l\pm2$	$-[(N+l+2\pm1)(N-l+1\mp1)]^{\frac{1}{2}}$
$N\mp2$	$l\pm2$	$\frac{1}{2}[(N-l\mp2)(N-l+2\mp2)]^{\frac{1}{2}}$

where N is the principal quantum number of the harmonic oscillator wave function, such that the energy is $\hbar\omega_0(N+\frac{3}{2})$. The radial integrals $(N'l'|v|Nl)$ are given in Table I.

The transformed Q–Q interaction has terms like $\alpha^\dagger\alpha^\dagger$, $\alpha\alpha$, and $\alpha^\dagger\alpha$ which were not included in Eq. (4.3). However, these terms need not be carried because they should have been eliminated together with corresponding terms in the pairing interaction by choosing an appropriate transformation (2.3), or should have been included in the single quasi-particle energy given in (2.9). Constant terms were also neglected, because we have no interest in them.

The problem of the pairing plus the Q–Q interaction may be solved in various approximations and is known to give rise to the vibrational spectra in some circumstances. Kisslinger and Sorensen[7] used the cranking model[8] under the adiabatic assumption, but their wave function is not convenient for our purpose. Baranger[9] used the method of the linearized equation of motion, which is believed to be the most refined treatment so far obtained, but with this method it is difficult to give the explicit form of the wave function. The Tamm-Dancoff approximation, which is a further approximation to the latter method,[9] gives the explicit wave function. We will use this approximation. The wave function for the excited state with spin 2 of the even-even nucleus is assumed to be a superposition of two quasi-particle states with resultant angular momentum 2, whose coefficients are chosen so that the Hamiltonian is diagonalized. The first excited state wave function is written as

$$\Psi_{2M}=Q_{2M}{}^\dagger\Psi_0, \tag{4.7}$$

where

$$Q_{2M}{}^\dagger=\sum_{j_1j_2}f_{j_1j_2}A^\dagger(j_1j_22M). \tag{4.8}$$

Then the Schrödinger equation is expressed as

$$\begin{aligned}0=(H-\hbar\omega)\Psi_{2M}=\Big[&\sum_{j_1j_2}f_{j_1j_2}(E_{j_1}+E_{j_2}-\hbar\omega)A^\dagger(j_1j_22M)\\
&-(x/20)\sum_{j_3j_4j_3'j_4'}(j_3'\|Y_2v\|j_4')(j_3\|Y_2v\|j_4)\\
&\times u_{j_3'j_4'}u_{j_3j_4}\sum_\mu A^\dagger(j_3'j_4'2\mu)A(j_3j_42\mu)\\
&\times\sum_{j_1j_2}f_{j_1j_2}A^\dagger(j_1j_22M)\Big]\Psi_0,\end{aligned} \tag{4.9}$$

where $\hbar\omega$ is the excitation energy of the state. The term in (4.3) with the Racah coefficient was neglected as it is unimportant and makes the calculation complex.[9] Using the following relation:

$$A(j_1'j_2'\lambda'\mu')A^\dagger(j_1j_2\lambda\mu)\Psi_0=\delta_{\lambda'\lambda}\delta_{\mu'\mu}(\delta_{j_1'j_1}\delta_{j_2'j_2}+(-)^{j_1'-j_2'-\lambda'}\delta_{j_1'j_2}\delta_{j_2'j_1})\Psi_0, \quad (4.10)$$

which is easily verified, the equation becomes

$$f_{j_1j_2}(E_{j_1}+E_{j_2}-\hbar\omega)-(x/10)(j_1\|Y_{2v}\|j_2)u_{j_1j_2}\times\sum_{j_1'j_2'}f_{j_1'j_2'}(j_1'\|Y_{2v}\|j_2')u_{j_1'j_2'}=0. \quad (4.11)$$

The solution is easily obtained as

$$f_{j_1j_2}=C\frac{(j_1\|Y_{2v}\|j_2)u_{j_1j_2}}{E_{j_1}+E_{j_2}-\hbar\omega}, \quad (4.12)$$

where C is a constant to be determined later. The eigenvalue equation is

$$1=(x/10)\sum_{j_1j_2}\frac{(j_1\|Y_{2v}\|j_2)^2u_{j_1j_2}^2}{E_{j_1}+E_{j_2}-\hbar\omega}, \quad (4.13)$$

from which $\hbar\omega$ may be determined. The normalization of the wave function requires

$$\langle\Psi_0|Q_{2\mu}Q_{2\mu'}^\dagger|\Psi_0\rangle=\delta_{\mu\mu'}, \quad (4.14)$$

from which we obtain

$$\sum_{j_1j_2}f_{j_1j_2}^2=\tfrac{1}{2}. \quad (4.15)$$

The constant C in (4.12) is determined by (4.15), and we obtain

$$f_{j_1j_2}=\frac{1}{\sqrt{2}}\frac{(j_1\|Y_{2v}\|j_2)u_{j_1j_2}}{E_{j_1}+E_{j_2}-\hbar\omega}\times\left[\sum_{j_1'j_2'}\left\{\frac{(j_1'\|Y_{2v}\|j_2')u_{j_1'j_2'}}{E_{j_1}+E_{j_2}-\hbar\omega}\right\}^2\right]^{-\frac{1}{2}}. \quad (4.16)$$

The operators $Q_{\lambda\mu}^\dagger$ and $Q_{\lambda\mu}$ satisfy the following approximate boson commutation relations

$$[Q_{\lambda'\mu'},Q_{\lambda\mu}^\dagger]=\delta_{\lambda'\lambda}\delta_{\mu'\mu},\quad [Q_{\lambda'\mu'},Q_{\lambda\mu}]=[Q_{\lambda'\mu'}^\dagger,Q_{\lambda\mu}^\dagger]=0, \quad (4.17)$$

whose vacuum expectation values are exact, and which are expected to be approximately valid for the case of a small number of quasi-particles. From the Schrödinger equation (4.9) we obtain

$$HQ_{2\mu}^\dagger\Psi_0\simeq\hbar\omega Q_{2\mu}^\dagger\Psi_0,\quad Q_{2\mu}^\dagger H\Psi_0\simeq0,$$

from which the approximate commutation relation,

$$[H,Q_{2\mu}^\dagger]\simeq\hbar\omega Q_{2\mu}^\dagger, \quad (4.18)$$

follows. The second excited state may be described as

$$\Psi_{JM}^{(2)}=\frac{1}{\sqrt{2}}\sum_{\mu\mu'}(2\mu'2\mu|JM)Q_{2\mu'}^\dagger Q_{2\mu}^\dagger\Psi_0, \quad (4.19)$$

both because this wave function satisfies the following approximate Schrödinger equation

$$H\Psi_{JM}^{(2)}\simeq2\hbar\omega\Psi_{JM}^{(2)}, \quad (4.20)$$

which is easily verified by using (4.18), and because it satisfies the normalization equation

$$\langle\Psi_{JM}^{(2)}|\Psi_{JM}^{(2)}\rangle=1. \quad (4.21)$$

Therefore it is seen that the choice of the wave functions (4.7) and (4.8) give rise in fact to the vibrational spectra if the commutation relations (4.17) and (4.18) are satisfied in a good approximation.

When the second-excited vibrational state of an even-even nucleus is considered in a stripping calculation, an improved wave function for the odd nucleus becomes necessary. The three quasi-particle states should be included in addition to the one quasi-particle state. The simplest way to get the improved wave function is to take the Q–Q force as a perturbation and to make a first order calculation. The result is shown as

$$\Psi_{JM}=[\alpha_{JM}^\dagger+\sum_j C_j\sum_{\mu m}(2\mu jm|JM)Q_{2\mu}^\dagger\alpha_{jm}^\dagger]\Psi_0, \quad (4.22)$$

where

$$C_j=-\frac{x}{[5(2J+1)]^{\frac{1}{2}}}(j\|Y_{2v}\|J)v_{jJ}\times\sum_{j_1j_2}(j_1\|Y_{2v}\|j_2)u_{j_1j_2}f_{j_1j_2}/(E_J-E_j-\hbar\omega). \quad (4.23)$$

5. SPECTROSCOPIC FACTOR FOR VIBRATIONAL STATES

We are now ready to calculate the spectroscopic factor for the vibrational states using the wave functions that were obtained in the last section. Let us begin with the first vibrational state. First the parent nucleus is assumed to be even-odd, for which the notations without prime will be used. The notations with prime will be used for the even-even daughter nucleus. Then the spectroscopic factor (3.1) may be expressed by using (3.2), (4.7), and (4.23) as

$$S_j=\langle[\alpha_{JM}^\dagger+\sum_{j'}C_{j'}\sum_{\mu'm'}(2\mu'j'm'|JM)Q_{2\mu'}^\dagger\alpha_{j'm'}^\dagger]\Psi_0\times|\sum_{mM_0}(jmJ_0M_0|JM)(U_j\alpha_{jm}^\dagger+V_j(-)^{j-m}\alpha_{j-m})Q_{J_0M_0}'^\dagger\Psi_0'\rangle^2, \quad (5.1)$$

where JM and J_0M_0 are the spin and its Z component for the parent and daughter nucleus, respectively.

Using the following relation:

$$A'^{\dagger}(j_1j_22\mu)\Psi_0' \simeq A^{\dagger}(j_1j_22\mu)\Psi_0', \quad (5.2)$$

which may be proved easily, Eq. (5.1) is simplified as

$$S_j = \left| 2\left(\frac{2J_0+1}{2J+1}\right)^{\frac{1}{2}} V_j f_{jJ}' - C_j U_j \right|^2, \quad (5.3)$$

where U_j and V_j are referred to the even-odd nucleus while f_{jJ}' is referred to the even-even nucleus. In obtaining the first term in the absolute square of the last equation, Eq. (2.17) was utilized, but the second term is calculated neglecting the difference between Ψ_0 and Ψ_0'.

The treatment of the case of the even-even parent nucleus is similar to the previous case. Only the result is presented:

$$S_j = \left| 2U_j f_{jJ_0}' + \left(\frac{2J_0+1}{2J+1}\right)^{\frac{1}{2}} C_j V_j \right|^2, \quad (5.4)$$

where U_j and V_j are referred to the even-odd nucleus again and f_{jJ}' is referred to the even-even nucleus. J and J_0 are spin of the parent and daughter nuclei, respectively, just as in the previous case.

Next the second-excited state is considered. The wave function (4.19) is used instead of (4.7) which was used in the previous cases, and the commutation relation (4.17) is fully utilized to simplify the expression. The calculation is not so much different from the previous case, so the results only will be presented. If the parent nucleus is even-odd, the spectroscopic factor is given by

$$S_j = 40(2J_0+1)V_j^2 \left| \sum_{j'} C_{j'} W(2j'J_0j;J2) f_{j'j}' \right|^2, \quad (5.5)$$

while if the parent nucleus is even-even, then

$$S_j = 40(2J_0+1)U_j^2 \left| \sum_{j'} C_{j'} W(2j'Jj;J_02) f_{j'j}' \right|^2. \quad (5.6)$$

In the above two equations U_j and V_j are referred to the odd nucleus and $f_{j'j}'$ is referred to the even-even nucleus. J and J_0 are the spin of the parent and the daughter nucleus, respectively. The correction factor for the difference between Ψ_0 and Ψ_0' is omitted. It should be mentioned that the results (5.5) and (5.6) are only given in crude approximation as the approximate commutation relations (4.18) were used, and the correction term given by (2.17) is omitted. The wave function (4.19) itself is also approximate because the wave functions of the second-excited states with 2 and 0 may be expected to be mixed with the first-excited state and the ground state, respectively, even if the number of the quasi-particles is restricted to 4. It may be very interesting to study the second- or higher-excited states of even-even nuclei through the stripping and pickup process by using improved wave functions.

6. DISCUSSIONS AND COMPARISON WITH EXPERIMENTS

In this section the theoretical predictions for the reactions of Sn isotopes will be compared with the experimental results of Cohen and Price.[11] Later the validity of the approximations involved in the present theory will be discussed. The cross section is given by (1.1), in which the single-particle cross section $\phi(l,Q,\theta)$ is considered first. Cohen and Price[11] obtained the following empirical rule for $\phi(l,Q,\theta)$ from experimental data of known reactions:

$$\phi_{dp}(l,Q,\theta) = F_p(l,\theta)A^{-Q}, \quad \phi_{dt}(l,Q,\theta) = F_t(l,\theta)A^{Q}, \quad (6.1)$$

where $F_p(l,\theta)$ and $F_t(l,\theta)$ are functions of angle and angular momentum transfer, and at a certain angle near 30°, the dependence on l was found to be

$$F_x(l,\theta)/F_x(l+1,\theta) \simeq 2. \quad (6.2)$$

In Eq. (6.1), A is a constant and its value is around 1.18. Q is the Q value of the reaction, measured in Mev.

The spectroscopic factor may be calculated using the results of the preceding sections. The parameters ϵ_j, λ, and Δ are adopted from Kisslinger and Sorensen,[7] from which U_j and V_j are calculated. For the vibrational state, the strength of the Q–Q interaction x is fixed by (4.13) inserting the experimental value of the $\hbar\omega$ for the even-even nucleus. Then the coefficient C_j for the three quasi-particle state in the odd nucleus wave function is obtained from (4.23). Then formulas (5.3)–(5.6) give the spectroscopic factors for the vibrational state.

The theoretical and experimental[11] cross-section ratios for the ground state transitions are listed in Table II. The ratio is taken of the reaction with odd target nucleus to that with even target nucleus. The agreement is fairly good considering the experimental errors and the theoretical uncertainty concerning the single particle energy spectra ϵ_j.[13] Here it may be instructive to present in contrast the interpretation by the simple shell model.[11] The transitions $Sn^{117}(d,p)Sn^{118}$ and $Sn^{118}(d,p)Sn^{119}$ are considered as $(h_{11/2})^2 s_{1/2} \rightarrow (h_{11/2})^4$ and $(h_{11/2})^4 \rightarrow (h_{11/2})^4 s_{1/2}$, respectively. The former transition is forbidden, so the ratios of these two reactions should be zero. The case of $Sn^{119}(d,p)$ is the same. On the other hand for the (d,t) reaction, $Sn^{118}(d,t)Sn^{117}$ is forbidden and the ratio listed in the table should be infinite. But these do not agree with experiment. In our theory the pairing interaction is taken into account and because of the strong configuration mixing resulting from the pairing interaction, transitions like $Sn^{117}(d,p)Sn^{118}$ no longer are forbidden.

For the first-excited state the strength of the Q–Q interaction x is calculated as explained before and its values are 0.129, 0.125, and 0.127 Mev for Sn^{116}, Sn^{118}, and Sn^{120}, respectively. The calculated results are given in Table III together with the experimental data.[11] The agreement is not bad. It is noted that the correction

TABLE II. The ratio of the ground-state cross sections, (even-odd → even-even)/(even-even → even-odd).

Transition	Theoretical	Experimental[11]
$Sn^{117}(d,p)/Sn^{118}(d,p)$	0.41	0.27
$Sn^{119}(d,p)/Sn^{118}(d,p)$	0.51	0.27
$Sn^{117}(d,t)/Sn^{118}(d,t)$	0.83	0.76
$Sn^{119}(d,t)/Sn^{118}(d,t)$	0.63	0.67

TABLE III. The ratio of the first excited vibrational state cross section to the ground-state cross section.

Transition	Theoretical	Experimental[11]
$Sn^{117}(d,p)$	0.33	0.13
$Sn^{119}(d,p)$	0.14	0.13
$Sn^{117}(d,t)$	0.24	0.26
$Sn^{119}(d,t)$	0.36	0.26

term with C_j in (5.3) and (5.4) is not important and its effect to the spectroscopic factor is less than 10% in the case of Sn. The orbital angular momentum l of the captured or stripped neutron is fixed uniquely by the selection rule in the case of Sn isotopes because the spin of the odd isotopes is $\frac{1}{2}$. However in the general case, many values of l are allowed and the theory may predict each contribution.

As we used many approximations in our calculation, it may be important to discuss their validity. The effect of the inaccurate treatment of the nucleon number was already considered in Sec. 3. In the following discussion approximations concerning the vibrational state will be examined.

First of all we used the Tamm-Dancoff method in obtaining the wave function of the vibrational state. However it is known that the method of linearized equations of motion is superior to the present method.[9] One reason why we did not use the better approximation is that a similar approximation has not yet become available for the odd nucleus and therefore the improvement only of the wave function of the even-even nucleus has little meaning. But it is interesting to compare these two approximations with each other and with other approximations.

The method of linearized equations of motion gives the following eigenvalue equation[9]

$$1=\frac{x}{5}\sum\frac{(j_1\|Y_{2v}\|j_2)^2u_{j_1j_2}{}^2(E_{j_1}+E_{j_2})}{(E_{j_1}+E_{j_2})^2-(\hbar\omega)^2}. \tag{6.3}$$

On the other hand, Kisslinger and Sorensen[7] used the cranking model to evaluate the excitation energy of the vibrational state. The excitation energy is given by

$$\hbar\omega=\left[\sum\frac{(j_1\|Y_{2v}\|j_2)^2u_{j_1j_2}{}^2}{E_{j_1}+E_{j_2}}\Big/\sum\frac{(j_1\|Y_{2v}\|j_2)^2u_{j_1j_2}{}^2}{(E_{j_1}+E_{j_2})^3}\right]^{\frac{1}{2}}\times\left[1-\frac{x}{5}\sum\frac{(j_1\|Y_{2v}\|j_2)^2u_{j_1j_2}{}^2}{E_{j_1}+E_{j_2}}\right]^{\frac{1}{2}}. \tag{6.4}$$

The third method we consider is the simplified generator coordinate method used by Ferrell and Visscher.[16] The trial-wave function is constructed by first solving the deformed single-particle potential problem,

$$H_M=H_0-\beta\hbar\omega\textstyle\sum_i v_iY_{20}(\theta_i\varphi_i), \tag{6.5}$$

where H_0 represents the spherical, independent quasi-particle Hamiltonian and the last term represents the deformed part of the independent-particle potential. β is the deformation parameter and r_i, θ_i, and φ_i are the polar coordinates of the ith nucleon. v_i is given by (4.2) with r replaced by r_i. The solution of (6.5) is obtained as a function of β and denoted by $\Psi(\beta)$. Then the wave function for the vibrational state is given by

$$\Psi_{20}=N[(\partial/\partial\beta)\Psi(\beta)]_{\beta=0}, \tag{6.6}$$

with spin 2 and Z component 0. N is the normalization constant. The result is expressed as

$$\Psi_{20}=\sum_{j_1j_2}f_{j_1j_2}A^\dagger(j_1j_220)\Psi_0, \tag{6.7}$$

where $f_{j_1j_2}$ is slightly different from that for the Tamm-Dancoff method, namely

$$f_{j_1j_2}=\frac{(j_1\|Y_{2v}\|j_2)u_{j_1j_2}}{E_{j_1}+E_{j_2}}\times\left[\sum_{j_1j_2}\left\{\frac{(j_1\|Y_{2v}\|j_2)u_{j_1j_2}}{E_{j_1}+E_{j_2}}\right\}^2\right]^{-\frac{1}{2}}. \tag{6.8}$$

The excitation energy is obtained as the expectation value of the original Hamiltonian $H=H_0'+H_{Q-Q}$;

$$\hbar\omega=\left\{\sum_{j_1j_2}\frac{(j_1\|Y_{2v}\|j_2)^2u_{j_1j_2}{}^2}{E_{j_1}+E_{j_2}}\Big/\sum_{j_1j_2}\left[\frac{(j_1\|Y_{2v}\|j_2)u_{j_1j_2}}{E_{j_1}+E_{j_2}}\right]^2\right\}\times\left[1-\frac{x}{10}\sum_{j_1j_2}\frac{(j_1\|Y_{2v}\|j_2)^2u_{j_1j_2}{}^2}{E_{j_1}+E_{j_2}}\right]. \tag{6.9}$$

Figure 1 shows the excitation energy $\hbar\omega$ as a function of the strength of the Q–Q force, calculated using various of these methods. The calculation was carried through for Sn^{118}, and Kisslinger and Sorensen's U_j and V_j were used again. The experimental value of $\hbar\omega$ for Sn^{118} is indicated in Fig. 1. It is noted that the cranking model gives excellent agreement with the curve obtained for large x by the method of linearized equations of motion. However the Tamm-Dancoff and the simplified generating coordinate methods are poor approximations

[15] S. G. Nilsson, Kgl. Danske Videnskab. Selskab, Mat.-fys. Medd. **29**, No. 16 (1959).
[16] R. A. Ferrell and W. M. Visscher, Phys. Rev. **102**, 450 (1956); **104**, 475 (1956).
[17] V. Fano and G. Racah, *Irreducible Tensorial Sets* (Academic Press, Inc., New York, 1959).

for the strong-coupling case. Therefore an improvement of the wave function by using the method of linearized equations of motion is very desirable, especially for the case of strong coupling. However for the case of the Sn isotopes the results of the Tamm-Dancoff method do not seem so bad.

Next we consider the accuracy of the commutation relations (4.18) which were used in the calculation of the spectroscopic factor. These approximate commutation relations made the calculations simple. For the zero quasi-particle state they are correct, so they are also expected to be a good approximation for states with a small number of quasi-particles. To show this the normalization integrals for the three quasi-particle state and for the second excited state of the even-even nucleus were calculated. They are given by

$$\langle \sum (2\mu' j' m' | JM) Q_{2\mu'}{}^{\dagger} \alpha_{j'm'}{}^{\dagger} \Psi_0 \times | \sum (2\mu j m | JM) Q_{2\mu}{}^{\dagger} \alpha_{jm}{}^{\dagger} \Psi_0 \rangle = 1 + 20 \sum_{j'} f_{jj'}{}^2 (-)^{J-j'} W(j'jjJ;22), \quad (6.10)$$

$$\langle \sum (2\mu_1' 2\mu_2' | JM) Q_{2\mu_1'}{}^{\dagger} Q_{2\mu_2'}{}^{\dagger} \Psi_0 \times | \sum (2\mu_1 2\mu_2 | JM) Q_{2\mu_1}{}^{\dagger} Q_{2\mu_2}{}^{\dagger} \Psi_0 \rangle = 1 - 200 \sum f_{j_1 j_2} f_{j_3 j_4} f_{j_1 j_3} f_{j_2 j_4} X \begin{Bmatrix} j_1 & j_3 & 2 \\ j_2 & j_4 & 2 \\ 2 & 2 & J \end{Bmatrix}, \quad (6.11)$$

where $X(\quad)$ is the Wigner $9-j$ symbol. If the commutation relations (4.17) are used both these normalization constants should be unity. Numerical calculations were carried out for the case of Sn^{118} and the following results are obtained: The three quasi-particle normalization constants are 0.83, 0.99, and 0.99 for $J=1/2$, $j=3/2$; $J=1/2$, $j=5/2$; $J=j=11/2$, respectively. For the second vibrational states the calculation was done only for $J=0$, and the result is 0.70.

In treating the vibrational state the term with the Racah coefficient in the Q–Q interaction (4.3) has not been taken into account, and the interaction has been assumed to take place only among nucleons in the incomplete shell. To examine these two effects it is convenient to use the method of the simplified generating coordinate. An actual calculation was done for Sn^{118} and the contribution to the excitation energy from the term with the Racah coefficient was found to be 5% of the principal contribution. The contribution to the vibrational state wave function from the excitation of two quasi-particles other than the two quasi-particles in the unfilled shell was estimated to be 40% of the total contribution for Sn^{118}. If this effect is taken into account in the calculation of the spectroscopic factor, then the results may be changed. However in this case also the wave function of the odd state should be treated on a similar basis.

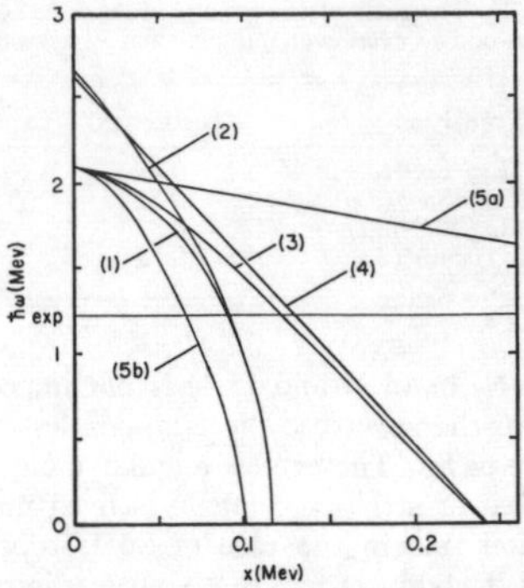

FIG. 1. Excitation energy of the first vibrational state for even-even nuclei as a function of the strength of the Q–Q interaction. The curves are calculated by using the following various approximations for Sn^{118}: (1) method of the linearized equation of motion; (2) cranking model; (3) Tamm-Dancoff method; (4) simplified generator coordinate method; (5a) the first-order perturbation calculation; (5b) the second-order perturbation calculation.

ACKNOWLEDGMENTS

The author wishes to thank N. Austern, Elizabeth Baranger, Michel Baranger, B. L. Cohen, and S. Meshkov for stimulating discussions.

1.C Nuclear Physics 31 (1962) 211—230; © North-Holland Publishing Co., Amsterdam

TIME-DEPENDENT HARTREE-FOCK EQUATIONS AND ROTATIONAL STATES OF NUCLEI

D. J. THOULESS † and J. G. VALATIN

Department of Mathematical Physics, University of Birmingham

Received 17 July 1961

Abstract: The connection between translational and rotational degeneracies in the solutions of the time independent Hartree-Fock equations and the existence of solutions of the time-dependent equations which represent uniform translational or rotational motions is investigated. With a non-spherical equilibrium shape, the equations give rotating solutions in which the self-consistent rotating potentials are determined by the motion of the particles. With no axial symmetry, and neglecting higher order effects in the angular velocities, there are time-dependent solutions corresponding to the general motion of a classical top. For an equilibrium shape with axial symmetry, the only rotational motions are uniform rotations about an axis perpendicular to the symmetry axis. The equations are studied in the density matrix formulation in which the results can be immediately extended to include the effect of pairing correlations. Solutions representing a uniform translational motion can be explicitly constructed. For the rotational motion, the changes in the density matrix are determined for small angular velocities by a linear equation. This contains a correction to the cranking model equation which expresses the effect of a transformation to a moving frame of reference on the velocity-dependent self-consistent potentials. The connection between vibrational and rotational solutions of the time-dependent Hartree-Fock equations is discussed. The rotational modes are related to zero-frequency solutions of the equations for small oscillations, and in the linear space of small variations the infinitesimal rotational and translational changes define an independent subspace. This leads to a separation of the rotational and translational energies in the Hamiltonian of the random phase approximation.

1. Introduction

Moments of inertia which can be defined from the rotational sequences of nuclear energy levels have been calculated by means of the cranking model [1,2]) in which the motion of the nucleons is investigated in a potential driven round with a constant angular velocity. If the effect of the pairing correlations is taken into account the values of moments of inertia obtained from the model are in satisfactory agreement with experiment [3]). The inertial parameters are determined in the model as a result of a rotation enforced from outside the system. The reasons for the rotation and its self-consistency are beyond the original scope of the cranking model, though there have been numerous attempts to investigate these questions [2]) ††.

One of the simplest approximations to describe the self-consistent behaviour of a many-body system is provided by the Hartree-Fock equations. These

† Now at the Department of Applied Mathematics and Theoretical Physics, University of Cambridge.

†† Ref. [2]) can be consulted for further references.

equations can be generalised to include the effect of the pairing correlations [4,5]. The approximations describe a self-consistent independent particle motion and lead to simple semi-classical concepts. To obtain time-dependent, rotating solutions one has to consider the time-dependent Hartree-Fock equations. One of the aims of this work is to establish the existence of self-consistent rotating solutions of these equations, and to exhibit their properties and their relationship to other types of solutions. Features of this approximation which are simple to visualise contain some of the essential elements of nuclear rotation which should be recognisable in any more elaborate theory of rotational states.

Solutions of the time-dependent Hartree Fock equations approximate time-dependent states which are linear combinations of stationary states. A combination of states with different energies exhibits time-dependent oscillations with the frequency of the energy differences, and other relative properties manifested in the interference effects of the superimposed wave functions. Small time-dependent oscillations about a stationary solution of the Hartree-Fock equations may contain the approximate energies of single particle excitations and those of collective vibrations, and have been studied in several works [6]. A stationary solution with a non-spherical equilibrium shape is degenerate because of the different possible orientations in space. As can be shown, this degeneracy leads to the existence of rotating time-dependent solutions. A free rotation cannot be represented by a small change in the equilibrium solution. Infinitesimal rotations, however, manifest themselves in relation to zero frequency solutions of the equations for small oscillations. A study of these solutions brings to light the relative roles of vibrational and rotational degrees of freedom and leads to a simple approximate separation of the rotational energy.

The translational degeneracy due to the arbitrary position in space of a self-consistent potential leads similarly to solutions of the time-dependent Hartree-Fock equations which represent the motion of the nucleus with a uniform velocity †. An explicit construction of the rotational solutions is more involved because of the effect of inertial forces, but the effect of the rotational and translational degeneracies manifests itself in a very similar way in many respects. Because of this connection, the simpler translational case will be studied first in somewhat more detail than would be justified by the interest in a centre of gravity motion.

The approximations of the Hartree-Fock method destroy the translational and rotational symmetries of the exact wave functions and give a semi-classical description of the motions related to these degrees of freedom. In this way, they do not lead to a description of quantised rotational states. The time-dependent solutions of the Hartree-Fock equations represent, however, a two-parameter set of approximate time-independent solutions for each translational or rota-

† Time-dependent Slater determinant solutions of the Hartree-Fock equations which describe the translational motion of nuclei have been considered previously by C. van Winter [7].

tional degree of freedom, corresponding to an arbitrary initial position and initial velocity. This set of solutions should form a better starting point to obtain states with the right symmetry properties by forming linear combinations than the one-parameter set of states depending only on the initial positions †.

Most of the arguments will be presented on the simpler Hartree-Fock method. Extensions to the generalised Hartree-Fock method [4, 5]) which describes the pairing correlations are straightforward.

2. The Density Matrix Form of the Hartree-Fock Equations

The wave function of an N-particle system is approximated in the Hartree-Fock method by a Slater determinant formed with N single-particle wave functions $\varphi_\kappa(x)$. These determine an N-dimensional subspace of single-particle states, and unitary transformations which leave this subspace invariant lead to Slater determinants representing the same N-particle wave function. There is in this way an arbitrariness in choosing the single-particle states $\varphi_\kappa(x)$, and the Hartree-Fock equations determine only Dirac's density matrix

$$\varrho(x, x') = \sum_{\kappa=\kappa_1}^{\kappa_N} \varphi_\kappa(x)\varphi_\kappa^*(x'), \tag{1a}$$

in terms of which the equations obtain an especially simple form [9]). The variable x will stand here for the three space coordinates and for the spin and isobaric spin variables of a single particle, and integration signs will include the corresponding summations. If the functions form an orthonormal system, the equation

$$\varrho^2 = \varrho \tag{1b}$$

follows from the definition (1a). This expresses the fact that the density matrix represents the projection operator of the subspace formed by the N single particle states $\varphi_\kappa(x)$. The trace of the density matrix gives the number of dimensions, and one has accordingly from eq. (1a)

$$\text{tr}\,\varrho = N. \tag{1c}$$

By means of the density matrix, the time-dependent Hartree-Fock equations can be written in the form

$$i\frac{\partial \varrho}{\partial t} = [\nu, \varrho], \tag{2a}$$

where the self-consistent energy matrix

$$\nu(x, x') = \varepsilon(x, x') + u(x, x') \tag{2b}$$

† This is in agreement with a recent suggestion by Peierls to improve on the method of ref. [8]).

is the sum of the kinetic energy

$$\varepsilon(x, x') = -\frac{1}{2m} \nabla^2 \delta(x-x') \tag{2c}$$

and of the self-consistent potential u defined by

$$u(x_1, x'_1) = \iint dx_2 dx'_2 \mathscr{V}(x_1 x_2; x'_1 x'_2) \varrho(x'_2, x_2), \tag{2d}$$

with

$$\mathscr{V}(x_1 x_2; x'_1 x'_2) = V(x_1 x_2; x'_1 x'_2) - V(x_1 x_2; x'_2 x'_1). \tag{2e}$$

The two-particle interaction matrix elements $V(x_1 x_2; x'_1 x'_2)$ are written in a sufficiently general form to include the case of velocity dependent two-body forces. Units with $\hbar = 1$ are used. It will be found convenient to write the definition (2d) of the self-consistent potential in the more compact form

$$u_1 = \mathrm{tr}_2 \mathscr{V}_{12} \varrho_2. \tag{2f}$$

Time independent, stationary solutions of the Hartree-Fock equation (2a) satisfy the equation

$$[\nu, \varrho] = 0. \tag{2g}$$

3. Uniform Translation and Constants of Motion

In order to obtain solutions of the time-dependent Hartree-Fock equations which describe a motion with uniform velocity, one can transform the equations to a reference system moving with velocity v and determine stationary solutions in the moving frame of reference. Through a coordinate transformation $x \to x+vt$, the derivative $i\,\partial\varrho/\partial t$ is transformed into $i\,\partial\hat{\varrho}/\partial t + [vp, \hat{\varrho}]$, and the equation (2a) takes the form

$$i \frac{\partial \hat{\varrho}}{\partial t} = [\hat{\nu} - vp, \hat{\varrho}]. \tag{3a}$$

The notation $\hat{\varrho}$, $\hat{\nu}$ indicates that the matrices are expressed in terms of the variables of the moving frame; p is the momentum operator component in the direction of the velocity v. Stationary solutions in the moving frame satisfy the equation

$$[\hat{\nu} - vp, \hat{\varrho}] = 0. \tag{3b}$$

These can be obtained from solutions of the equation with $v = 0$,

$$[\hat{\nu}^{(0)}, \hat{\varrho}^{(0)}] = 0, \tag{3c}$$

by means of the simple transformation

$$\hat{\varrho} = e^{imvx} \hat{\varrho}^{(0)} e^{-imvx}. \tag{4a}$$

Indeed, since $[p, x] = -i$, this transformation gives

$$e^{imvx} p\, e^{-imvx} = p - mv, \tag{4b}$$

and transforms the commutator of (3c) into that of (3b), as can be seen from $\hat{v} = p^2/2m + \hat{u}$ and

$$e^{imvx} \frac{p^2}{2m} e^{-imvx} = \frac{p^2}{2m} - vp + \tfrac{1}{2} mv^2, \tag{4c}$$

$$e^{imvx}\, \hat{u}^{(0)} e^{-imvx} = \hat{u}. \tag{4d}$$

The self-consistent potentials $\hat{u}$, $\hat{u}^{(0)}$ are obtained from the definition (2d) in replacing ϱ by $\hat{\varrho}$, $\hat{\varrho}^{(0)}$, and the last relationship assumes the Galilean invariance of the two-body interaction which implies a factor $\delta(x_1+x_2-x'_1-x'_2)$ in the matrix element $V(x_1x_2; x'_1x'_2)$.

The coordinate representations of the two reference systems can be related by the operator transformation

$$x + vt = \exp(ivtp) x \exp(-ivtp), \tag{5a}$$

so that a time dependent solution ϱ of equation (2a) is obtained from a stationary solution (4a) of the moving frame as

$$\varrho = \exp(-ivtp) \exp(imvx)\, \hat{\varrho}^{(0)} \exp(-imvx) \exp(ivtp). \tag{5b}$$

In the x representation this can be written as

$$\varrho(x, x', t) = \varrho^{(0)}(x-vt, x'-vt) \exp[imv(x-x')], \tag{5c}$$

where $\varrho^{(0)}(x, x')$ is the stationary solution for $v = 0$.

If $\hat{\varrho}^{(0)}$ represents a momentum distribution with zero average momentum, the average total momentum and kinetic energy of the moving system results from eqs. (4a, b, c) as

$$\langle p \rangle = \operatorname{tr} p\hat{\varrho} = \operatorname{tr} (p+mv)\hat{\varrho}^{(0)} = Nmv = Mv, \tag{6a}$$

$$\left\langle \frac{p^2}{2m} \right\rangle = \operatorname{tr} \frac{p^2}{2m} \hat{\varrho} = \left\langle \frac{p^2}{2m} \right\rangle_0 + \tfrac{1}{2} Mv^2. \tag{6b}$$

If one expands the density matrix (4a) in powers of v, the difference $\hat{\varrho} - \hat{\varrho}^{(0)}$ is determined for small values of v by the first order change

$$\hat{\varrho}^{(1)} = imv[x, \hat{\varrho}^{(0)}]. \tag{7a}$$

An expansion of equation (3b) gives for $\hat{\varrho}^{(1)}$

$$[\hat{v}^{(0)}, \hat{\varrho}^{(1)}] + [\hat{u}^{(1)}, \hat{\varrho}^{(0)}] = [vp, \hat{\varrho}^{(0)}]. \tag{7b}$$

It is instructive to see explicitly how the expression (7a) satisfies this equation. With $[\hat{\nu}^{(0)}, \hat{\varrho}^{(0)}] = 0$ and $\hat{\nu}^{(0)} = p^2/2m + \hat{u}^{(0)}$, one has for this expression

$$\begin{aligned}[\hat{\nu}^{(0)}, \hat{\varrho}^{(1)}] + [\hat{u}^{(1)}, \hat{\varrho}^{(0)}] &= imv[[\nu^{(0)}, x], \hat{\varrho}^{(0)}] + [\hat{u}^{(1)}, \hat{\varrho}^{(0)}] \\ &= [vp, \hat{\varrho}^{(0)}] + [imv[\hat{u}^{(0)}, x] + \hat{u}^{(1)}, \hat{\varrho}^{(0)}]. \end{aligned} \quad (8a)$$

The definition (2f) of the self-consistent potential and a permutation of factors inside the trace gives

$$[\hat{u}^{(0)}, x] = [\mathrm{tr}_2\, \mathscr{V}_{12} \hat{\varrho}_2^{(0)}, x_1] = \mathrm{tr}_2\, [\mathscr{V}_{12}, x_1] \hat{\varrho}_2^{(0)}, \quad (8b)$$

$$\hat{u}_1^{(1)} = \mathrm{tr}_2\, \mathscr{V}_{12} \hat{\varrho}_2^{(1)} = imv\, \mathrm{tr}_2\, [\mathscr{V}_{12}, x_2] \hat{\varrho}_2^{(0)}, \quad (8c)$$

and leads equation (8a) into (7b) through

$$imv[\hat{u}^{(0)}, x]_1 + \hat{u}_1^{(1)} = imv\, \mathrm{tr}_2\, [\mathscr{V}_{12}, x_1 + x_2] \hat{\varrho}_2^{(0)} = 0. \quad (8d)$$

The last equality follows from $[\mathscr{V}_{12}, x_1 + x_2] = 0$ which expresses the Galilean invariance of the two-body interaction.

Replacing in this argument mvx by p, the same reasoning leads with $[\mathscr{V}_{12}, p_1 + p_2] = 0$ to the homogeneous equation

$$[\hat{\nu}^{(0)}, \tilde{\varrho}^{(1)}] + [\tilde{u}^{(1)}, \hat{\varrho}^{(0)}] = 0 \quad (9a)$$

for

$$\tilde{\varrho}^{(1)} = i[p, \hat{\varrho}^{(0)}]. \quad (9b)$$

Adding this with an arbitrary coefficient x_0 to (7a) the sum still satisfies the inhomogeneous equation (7b). With small values of v and x_0 these linear combinations represent a two-parameter set of small changes in the density matrix corresponding to different translational velocities and initial displacements. For small values of v and $vt = x_0$ they describe at different times $t = x_0/v$ the first order change

$$\varrho^{(1)} = \hat{\varrho}^{(1)} + vt\tilde{\varrho}^{(1)} \quad (9c)$$

of the time-dependent density matrix (5b). With $t = x_0/v$ the expression (5b) itself describes a two-parameter set of density matrices and Slater determinants which approximate the same intrinsic state.

A reasoning very similar to that used in the equations (8a-d) shows immediately that the average total momentum and angular momentum components in a laboratory system are constants of motion of the time-dependent Hartree-Fock equation $i\,\partial\varrho/\partial t = [\nu, \varrho]$. Indeed, with $\nu = \varepsilon + u$, one has for instance

$$\begin{aligned} i\frac{\mathrm{d}}{\mathrm{d}t}\langle p \rangle = \mathrm{tr}\, p i \frac{\partial \varrho}{\partial t} &= \mathrm{tr}\, p[\nu, \varrho] \\ &= \mathrm{tr}\, [p, \varepsilon]\varrho + \mathrm{tr}_1\, \mathrm{tr}_2\, [p_1, \mathscr{V}_{12}]\varrho_1\varrho_2 = 0. \end{aligned} \quad (10)$$

The last two terms vanish since the double trace can be symmetrised and $[p, \varepsilon] = 0$, $[p_1+p_2, \mathscr{V}_{12}] = 0$. With l instead of p, the same argument gives the constancy of the average total angular momentum components for a system with a rotation invariant Hamiltonian. This will play an important role in determining the possible rotational solutions. That the energy expectation value $W_0 = \text{tr}\,(\varepsilon+\frac{1}{2}u)\varrho$ of the Hartree-Fock approximation is a constant of motion of the time-dependent equation has been shown in Dirac's old paper [9]).

4. Rotating Solutions

If the density matrix $\varrho^{(0)}$ of the stationary equation $[\nu^{(0)}, \varrho^{(0)}] = 0$ has no spherical symmetry, the degeneracy due to the arbitrary orientation of the solution in space leads to the existence of rotating solutions. In order to find such solutions it is convenient to transform the equations to a reference system rotating at time t with angular velocity Ω about an axis through the origin. The time dependent equation $i\,\partial\varrho/\partial t = [\nu, \varrho]$ attains the form

$$i\,\frac{\partial\hat{\varrho}}{\partial t} = [\hat{\nu}-\Omega l, \hat{\varrho}] \tag{11a}$$

in such a system, where l is the angular momentum operator (the sum of orbital and spin angular momentum operators) in the direction of the angular velocity vector.

A general connection between solutions of the equation

$$[\hat{\nu}-\Omega l, \hat{\varrho}] = 0 \tag{11b}$$

and of the equation $[\hat{\nu}^{(0)}, \hat{\varrho}^{(0)}] = 0$ valid for $\Omega = 0$ cannot be given explicitly as in the translational case. The equation (11b) describes dynamical coupling effects related to the presence of inertial forces in the rotating system and includes higher order corrections to the inertial parameters which are functions of the angular velocity. For small values of Ω, however, with a given solution $\hat{\varrho}^{(0)}$ of the stationary problem for $\Omega = 0$, the equation leads for the first order changes $\hat{\varrho}^{(1)}$ to

$$[\hat{\nu}^{(0)}, \hat{\varrho}^{(1)}]+[\hat{u}^{(1)}, \hat{\varrho}^{(0)}] = [\Omega l, \hat{\varrho}^{(0)}], \tag{11c}$$

which is a linear equation in $\hat{\varrho}^{(1)}$. Higher order corrections can be obtained from higher order expansions in the perturbation approach.

The same argument as in the translational case gives for

$$\tilde{\varrho}^{(1)} = i[l, \hat{\varrho}^{(0)}] \tag{12a}$$

the homogeneous equation

$$[\hat{\nu}^{(0)}, \tilde{\varrho}^{(1)}]+[\tilde{u}^{(1)}, \hat{\varrho}^{(0)}] = 0. \tag{12b}$$

Adding a multiple of $\varrho^{(1)}$ to a solution of equation (11c) one obtains another solution, and these are determined only up to a small angular displacement. This reflects the degeneracy of the solution $\hat{\varrho}^{(0)}$ for $\Omega = 0$, and any angular displacement can actually be included in the initial choice of $\hat{\varrho}^{(0)}$. If $\hat{\varrho}^{(0)}$ has an axial symmetry and the rotation is chosen about the symmetry axis, the commutator (12a) and the right hand side of (11c) vanish. This shows explicitly that such rotations do not define a change in the density matrix.

With an angular velocity perpendicular to the symmetry axis, the moment of inertia $\mathscr{I}$ can be defined by means of a solution $\hat{\varrho}^{(1)}$ of equation (11c) by

$$\langle l \rangle^{(1)} = \operatorname{tr} l\hat{\varrho}^{(1)} = \mathscr{I}\Omega. \tag{13a}$$

With $\langle l \rangle^{(0)} = 0$, one has, to first order in Ω, $\langle l \rangle = \langle l \rangle^{(1)}$. The addition of a term proportional to (12a) to $\hat{\varrho}^{(1)}$ does not change the trace in (13a).

If there is no symmetry axis and the angular velocity vector is chosen in an arbitrary direction, the average angular momentum components along coordinate axes attached to the nucleus are still related to the angular velocity components by means of a linear relation of the form (13a) which is then a vector equation. The moment of inertia tensor $\mathscr{I}$ defines the principal axes along which the components of the equation obtain the form

$$\langle l_i \rangle = \mathscr{I}_i \Omega_i, \qquad i = 1, 2, 3, \tag{13b}$$

where $\mathscr{I}_1$, $\mathscr{I}_2$, $\mathscr{I}_3$ are the principal moments of inertia.

Choosing the angular velocity vector along one of the principal axes, solutions $\hat{\varrho}^{(1)}$ of equation (11c) define uniformly rotating solutions in the laboratory system. These are related to $\hat{\varrho} \approx \hat{\varrho}^{(0)} + \hat{\varrho}^{(1)}$ by means of the transformation

$$\varrho = \exp\,[-i\Omega t l]\hat{\varrho}\,\exp\,[i\Omega t l] \tag{14}$$

and satisfy the equation $i\,\partial\varrho/\partial t = [\nu, \varrho]$. At different time points $t = \varphi_0/\Omega$, this expression describes a two parameter set of density matrices corresponding to different values of the angular velocity Ω and the initial angular displacement φ_0.

According to (14), the change in the density matrix ϱ with respect to the initial $\hat{\varrho}$ is for an infinitesimal time interval $\mathrm{d}t$ given by $-i\,\mathrm{d}t[\Omega l, \hat{\varrho}]$. The equation (11c) has solutions for an arbitrary angular velocity $(\Omega_1, \Omega_2, \Omega_3)$ and one can enquire about the more general solutions of the time-dependent Hartree-Fock equation $i\,\partial\varrho/\partial t = [\nu, \varrho]$ which reduce for $t = 0$ to a given $\hat{\varrho}$ corresponding to a definite angular velocity and initial position. Since the infinitesimal changes are additive, the change in ϱ in the infinitesimal time interval $\mathrm{d}t$ is still $-i\,\mathrm{d}t[\Omega_1 l_1 + \Omega_2 l_2 + \Omega_3 l_3, \hat{\varrho}]$, but the angular velocity cannot remain constant in general. The change in the average angular momentum components $\langle l_i \rangle = \operatorname{tr} l_i \hat{\varrho}$, divided by d$t$, is given by

$$\begin{aligned}\frac{\mathrm{d}\langle l_1 \rangle}{\mathrm{d}t} &= -\operatorname{tr} i l_1 [\Omega_1 l_1 + \Omega_2 l_2 + \Omega_3 l_3, \hat{\varrho}] \\ &= -\operatorname{tr} i (\Omega_2 [l_1, l_2] + \Omega_3 [l_1, l_3]) \hat{\varrho} = \Omega_3 \langle l_2 \rangle - \Omega_2 \langle l_3 \rangle,\end{aligned} \tag{15a}$$

and by two similar equations. These equations for the change in the average angular momentum components in the system attached to the nucleus express the fact that the components in the laboratory system are constants of motion. The consistency of these equations with the relationship (13b) between angular momentum and angular velocity components requires a change in the angular velocity and leads to the equations

$$\begin{gathered}\mathscr{I}_1 \dot{\Omega}_1 = (\mathscr{I}_2 - \mathscr{I}_3) \Omega_2 \Omega_3, \quad \mathscr{I}_2 \dot{\Omega}_2 = (\mathscr{I}_3 - \mathscr{I}_1) \Omega_3 \Omega_1, \\ \mathscr{I}_3 \dot{\Omega}_3 = (\mathscr{I}_1 - \mathscr{I}_2) \Omega_1 \Omega_2,\end{gathered} \tag{15b}$$

which are Euler's equations for a classical top. They determine the time dependence of the angular velocity for given initial conditions.

In the case of an axial symmetry, one has $\mathscr{I}_1 = \mathscr{I}_2$, and since a rotation of the coordinate system about the symmetry axis with constant Ω_3 does not lead to any new time-dependent solution ϱ, the only relevant solutions of (15b) are those with $\Omega_3 = 0$, $\Omega_1 = \text{const.}$, $\Omega_2 = \text{const.}$, which represent uniform rotations about an axis perpendicular to the symmetry axis.

An expansion of the condition $\hat{\varrho} = \hat{\varrho}^2$ leads to the equations

$$\hat{\varrho}^{(0)} = \hat{\varrho}^{(0)2}, \tag{16a}$$

$$\hat{\varrho}^{(1)} = \hat{\varrho}^{(1)} \hat{\varrho}^{(0)} + \hat{\varrho}^{(0)} \hat{\varrho}^{(1)}. \tag{16b}$$

Multiplying the last equation by $\hat{\varrho}^{(0)}$ one obtains $\hat{\varrho}^{(0)} \hat{\varrho}^{(1)} \hat{\varrho}^{(0)} = 0$. The same equation can, therefore, be written in the form

$$\hat{\varrho}^{(1)} = (1 - \hat{\varrho}^{(0)}) \hat{\varrho}^{(1)} \hat{\varrho}^{(0)} + \hat{\varrho}^{(0)} \hat{\varrho}^{(1)} (1 - \hat{\varrho}^{(0)}), \tag{16c}$$

which shows explicitly that in a representation in which $\hat{\varrho}^{(0)}$ is diagonal, with eigenvalues 1 and 0, the only non-vanishing matrix elements of $\hat{\varrho}^{(1)}$ are those which connect states with different eigenvalues of $\hat{\varrho}^{(0)}$, that is an occupied and an unoccupied state. The solutions of equation (11c) have to satisfy this supplementary condition.

In a matrix representation in which $\hat{\varrho}^{(0)}$ and $\hat{v}^{(0)}$ are diagonal, and the first N states with labels i, j are eigenstates of $\hat{\varrho}^{(0)}$ with eigenvalue 1, and states with eigenvalue 0 are labelled by indices m, n, the only non-vanishing matrix elements of $\hat{\varrho}^{(1)}$ are of the form $\hat{\varrho}^{(1)}_{mi}$, $\hat{\varrho}^{(1)}_{im}$. The matrix elements of equation (11c) read in this representation

$$(\nu_m{}^{(0)}-\nu_i{}^{(0)})\hat{\varrho}^{(1)}_{mi}+\sum_{j=1}^{N}\sum_{n=N+1}^{\infty}\{\mathscr{V}_{mj,\,in}\hat{\varrho}^{(1)}_{nj}+\mathscr{V}_{mn,\,ij}\hat{\varrho}^{(1)}_{jn}\}=\Omega l_{mi},$$

$$-\sum_{j=1}^{N}\sum_{n=N+1}^{\infty}\{\mathscr{V}_{ij,\,mn}\hat{\varrho}^{(1)}_{nj}+\mathscr{V}_{in,\,mj}\hat{\varrho}^{(1)}_{jn}\}-(\nu_m{}^{(0)}-\nu_i{}^{(0)})\hat{\varrho}^{(1)}_{im}=-\Omega l_{im}, \tag{17a}$$

where

$$\mathscr{V}_{mj,\,in}=V_{mj,\,in}-V_{mj,\,ni} \tag{17b}$$

is the antisymmetrised two-body interaction matrix element. Only interaction matrix elements with two occupied and two unoccupied states appear in the equations.

With $\hat{\varrho}^{(1)}_{mi}=C_{mi}$ and some other slight changes in notation, the equations (17a) are identical with equations (23) of a previous paper [10]), in which they were derived for the coefficients C_{mi} which determine the change in the Slater determinant trial wave function of the time-independent Hartree-Fock method in minimising the energy under the supplementary condition of a fixed average value of a total angular momentum component. This relationship is not surprising since the Hamiltonian plus a Lagrangian multiplier times an angular momentum operator has formally the same expression as the Hamiltonian in a rotating reference system, and equation (11b) for the density matrix can be obtained by minimising the expectation value of the Hamiltonian in the rotating frame.

If one neglects the interaction terms in the equations (17a) one obtains

$$\hat{\varrho}^{(1)}_{mi}=\Omega\,\frac{l_{mi}}{\nu_m{}^{(0)}-\nu_i{}^{(0)}} \tag{17c}$$

and a similar expression for $\hat{\varrho}^{(1)}_{im}$. With (13a), this gives for the moment of inertia the expression calculated from a shell model cranking model formula in which the shell model energies have been replaced by the self-consistent energies $\nu_m{}^{(0)}$ of the Hartree-Fock method.

The commutator containing $\hat{u}^{(1)}$ in equation (11c) gives a correction term to this form of $\hat{\varrho}^{(1)}$ which represents the effect of the change in the self-consistent potential due to the transformation to the rotating reference system. The analogous term in the equation (7b) of the translational problem is reponsible for the fact that the solution of this equation leads to the exact value of the mass in forming the expectation value of the momentum.

In the case of a velocity-independent two-body interaction, the change $\hat{u}^{(1)}$ in the self-consistent potential, and this correction to the cranking model formula, comes entirely from the exchange part of the interaction. With

$$V(x_1x_2,\,x'_1x'_2)=V(x_1-x_2)\delta(x_1-x'_1)\delta(x_2-x'_2), \tag{18a}$$

one has from (2d, e)

$$\hat{u}^{(1)}(x_1, x'_1) = \delta(x_1-x'_1)\int \mathrm{d}x_2 V(x_1-x_2)\hat{\varrho}^{(1)}(x_2, x_2) - V(x_1-x'_1)\hat{\varrho}^{(1)}(x_1, x'_1), \tag{18b}$$

where the second term represents the effect of the exchange interaction. The first term, however, vanishes, since there is no first order correction $\hat{\varrho}^{(1)}(x, x)$ to the density because this would be proportional to Ω and has to be the same for Ω and $-\Omega$. A consideration of the time-reversal symmetry of equation (11c) leads of course to the same conclusion †.

5. Generalised Hartree-Fock Method

The equations of the generalised Hartree-Fock method which takes into account pairing effects can be cast in a form [5]) which shows a close analogy with the density matrix equations here discussed, and the previous considerations can be immediately extended to this case. The single-particle density matrix

$$\varrho(x, x') = \sum_{\kappa} h_\kappa \varphi_\kappa(x)\varphi_\kappa{}^*(x') \tag{19a}$$

of the generalised method does not satisfy the equation $\varrho^2 = \varrho$ but corresponds to a more general number distribution h_κ. The form (1a) of $\varrho(x, x')$ is included as the special case in which the occupation numbers h_κ take only values 1 or 0.

The density matrix $\varrho(x, x')$ is supplemented by the pair field

$$\chi(x, x') = \sum_{\kappa} \chi_\kappa \varphi_\kappa(x)\varphi_{-\kappa}(x) \tag{19b}$$

which is obtained as an expectation value of a pair of field operators. This form of χ exhibits a definite pairing of single particle states κ and $-\kappa$, and the coefficients χ_κ are related to h_κ by the definition

$$\chi_\kappa = +\sqrt{h_\kappa(1-h_\kappa)}, \qquad \text{for } \kappa > 0, \tag{19c}$$

$$\chi_{-\kappa} = -\chi_\kappa.$$

The self-consistent energy matrix $\nu(x, x')$ is defined apart from an additive constant representing the chemical potential, by the same equation (2b, c, d) but with the more general expression (19a) of the density matrix. It is supplemented by the pairing potential μ defined as

$$\mu(x, x') = \int \mathrm{d}x_1 \mathrm{d}x'_1 V(xx'; x_1 x'_1)\chi(x_1, x'_1). \tag{19d}$$

† In a paper by Shono and Tanaka which has been recently brought to the authors' attention [11]), the rotational problem is considered in connection with the Hartree equations without exchange. The claim of the paper that there are (strong) departures in this case from the cranking model formula conflicts with the present conclusions.

The equations which generalise the equations $i\,\partial\varrho/\partial t = [\nu, \varrho]$ and $[\nu, \varrho] = 0$ of the Hartree-Fock method are obtained by introducing matrices in a space with twice as many dimensions, defined as

$$\mathscr{K} = \begin{pmatrix} \varrho & \chi \\ -\chi^* & 1-\varrho^* \end{pmatrix}, \quad \mathscr{M} = \begin{pmatrix} \nu & \mu \\ -\mu^* & -\nu^* \end{pmatrix}, \tag{20a}$$

in which the star stands for the complex conjugate. The time-dependent equations of the generalised Hartree-Fock method are then given by

$$i\frac{\partial \mathscr{K}}{\partial t} = [\mathscr{M}, \mathscr{K}], \tag{20b}$$

the time-independent stationary equations by

$$[\mathscr{M}, \mathscr{K}] = 0. \tag{20c}$$

The relationship contained in the definitions (19a, b, c) takes the form

$$\mathscr{K}^2 = \mathscr{K}. \tag{20d}$$

The effect of a transformation to a reference system moving with velocity v is to replace ν by $\hat{\nu} - vp$ in the equations. Solutions of eq. (20b) which represent a uniform translational motion can still be given explicitly. The form of the relationship (5c) remains unchanged, and with the definition (20a) of $\mathscr{K}$, these solutions can be expressed as

$$\begin{aligned} \varrho(x, x', t) &= \varrho^{(0)}(x-vt, x'-vt) \exp\big(imv(x-x')\big), \\ \chi(x, x', t) &= \chi^{(0)}(x-vt, x'-vt) \exp\big(imv(x+x')\big), \end{aligned} \tag{21}$$

in terms of the stationary solution for $v = 0$ given by $\varrho^{(0)}$, $\chi^{(0)}$. All the previous conclusions concerning the translational motion can be adapted to apply to these solutions of the generalised equations.

The transformation to a rotating reference system replaces ν by $\hat{\nu} - \Omega l$. Stationary solutions in the rotating system satisfy accordingly the equation

$$[\hat{\mathscr{M}} - \Omega \mathscr{L}, \hat{\mathscr{K}}] = 0, \tag{22a}$$

with

$$\mathscr{L} = \begin{pmatrix} l & 0 \\ 0 & -l^* \end{pmatrix}, \tag{22b}$$

and first order changes in Ω are described by the equation

$$[\hat{\mathscr{M}}^{(0)}, \hat{\mathscr{K}}^{(1)}] + [\hat{\mathscr{M}}^{(1)}, \mathscr{K}^{(0)}] = [\Omega \mathscr{L}, \hat{\mathscr{K}}^{(0)}], \tag{22c}$$

which is a linear equation in $\mathscr{K}^{(1)}$. An analysis of the types of rotating solutions follows a similar line to that in the simpler case and the conclusions of the previous section can be accordingly extended.

The moment of inertia is defined as before by the relationship

$$\langle l \rangle^{(1)} = \text{tr}\, l\hat{\varrho}^{(1)} = \tfrac{1}{2}\text{Tr}\, \mathscr{L}\hat{\mathscr{K}}^{(1)} = \mathscr{I}\Omega. \tag{22d}$$

Neglecting the second commutator in (22c), this gives for the moment of inertia the generalised cranking model formula in which the energy denominators contain the quasi-particle energy eigenvalues of $\hat{\mathscr{M}}^{(0)}$ and which leads to an accordingly reduced value of the moment of inertia. The correction term with $\hat{\mathscr{M}}^{(1)}$ is determined by $\hat{u}^{(1)}$ and a first order correction $\hat{\mu}^{(1)}$ to the pairing potential. Both have the same origin, and they express the effect of the rotating reference system on the two self-consitent potentials. In the equivalent Green's function approximation, the correction term due to $\hat{\mu}^{(1)}$ has been first noticed by Migdal [3]), who has pointed out that the inclusion of this term is necessary to obtain the irrotational limit in the case of a large system.

With the help of an argument similar to one by Gross [12]) one can actually show in the present method that the moment of inertia defined by the irrotational motion of a liquid drop with the density distribution of the nucleus gives a lower bound for the moment of inertia. Eq. (22a) can be obtained by minimising the expectation value of the Hamiltonian in a rotating reference system with respect to trial state-vectors of the Bardeen-Cooper-Schrieffer type [5]). This expectation value is

$$W_0 = \text{tr}\,(\varepsilon - \Omega l)\hat{\varrho} + \tfrac{1}{2}\,\text{tr}\,(\hat{u}\hat{\varrho} - \hat{\chi}^*\hat{\mu}) \tag{23a}$$

and contains the rotational energy with a negative sign †. Any trial solution which reduces to the actual solution $\hat{\varrho}^{(0)}$, $\hat{\chi}^{(0)}$ for $\Omega = 0$ gives, therefore, through this expression a lower bound for the rotational energy $\frac{1}{2}\mathscr{I}\Omega^2$. With

$$\begin{aligned} \hat{\varrho}(x, x') &= \hat{\varrho}^{(0)}(x, x') \exp\,[im(S(x) - S(x'))], \\ \hat{\chi}(x, x') &= \hat{\chi}^{(0)}(x, x') \exp\,[im(S(x) + S(x'))], \end{aligned} \tag{23b}$$

the second term in (23a) is unchanged with respect to the case $S = 0$, and the change in W_0 is given by

$$\text{tr}\, m\hat{\varrho}^{(0)} \left\{ \tfrac{1}{2}\,(\text{grad}\, S)^2 - \Omega \frac{\partial S}{\partial \varphi} \right\}, \tag{23c}$$

where φ is an angle about the axis of rotation. This is minimised if S satisfies the equation

$$\text{div}\,(\hat{\varrho}_0\, \text{grad}\, S) = \Omega \frac{\partial \hat{\varrho}_0}{\partial \varphi}, \tag{23d}$$

† See for instance the last paper of ref. [1]).

where $\hat{\varrho}_0 = \hat{\varrho}^{(0)}(x, x)$ is the equilibrium density distribution of the nucleus. In the laboratory system, this equation is the continuity equation for an irrotational fluid motion of a liquid drop with a velocity potential S and a rotation of the boundaries with an angular velocity Ω. With S satisfying this equation, the second term in (23c) is equal to twice the first term with an opposite sign, and (23c) gives, with a minus sign, the rotational energy of the liquid drop motion.

6. Vibrations and Rotation. Separation of the Rotational Energy

Small oscillations about an equilibrium solution of the time-dependent equation $i\,\partial\varrho/\partial t = [\nu, \varrho]$ are described by the equation

$$i\,\frac{\partial\varrho^{(1)}}{\partial t} = [\nu^{(0)}, \varrho^{(1)}] + [u^{(1)}, \varrho^{(0)}]. \tag{24a}$$

A similar equation holds for small changes with respect to a solution of the equation $i\,\partial\mathscr{K}/\partial t = [\mathscr{M}, \mathscr{K}]$ and the conclusions that follow can be extended without difficulty to the generalised Hartree-Fock method.

Eq. (24a) has solutions of the form

$$\varrho^{(1)}(t) = \varrho^{(1)}(0)e^{-i\omega t} \tag{24b}$$

and Hermitian solutions can be obtained by adding to this its adjoint. These contain a positive and a negative frequency part and the non-zero frequencies ω of these solutions are related to the energies of single particle excitations and of collective vibrations. Since the translational and rotational degeneracies of a stationary density matrix mean in the Hartree-Fock approximation the existence of other stationary solutions with zero excitation energy, they lead to solutions of eq. (24a) which are of the form (9c) in the translational case and of the form $\varrho^{(1)} = \hat{\varrho}^{(1)} + \Omega t \tilde{\varrho}^{(1)}$ for small rotations with angular velocity Ω. This corresponds to the fact that solutions of the type $z = a \exp(-i\omega t) + b \exp(i\omega t)$ of the equation $\ddot{z} + \omega^2 z = 0$ of harmonic oscillations are replaced for $\omega = 0$ by solutions $z = \alpha + \beta t$ of the equation $\ddot{z} = 0$.

For an equilibrium shape with only axial symmetry there are two zero frequencies related to the rotating solutions of the equation $i\,\partial\varrho/\partial t = [\nu, \varrho]$. At the same time, there are two independent infinitesimal changes in the nuclear shape which represent free angular displacements and which are not connected with restoring forces. Two degrees of freedom in the oscillations of the nuclear surface for spherical shape have been transformed into rotational degrees of freedom.

Starting from a spherical equilibrium shape, the collective type solutions of eq. (24a) describe nuclear vibrations which can be visualized by the oscillating shape of the self-consistent potentials. If with a change of the relevant parameters the restoring forces to the equilibrium shape become weaker and weaker, this corresponds to a decrease in the vibrational frequencies, and when the deformed shape takes over as the equilibrium shape the two lost vibrational degrees of freedom reappear in the zero frequency solutions related to the rotational motion. A predominantly quadrupole deformation of the new equilibrium shape is related to the disappearance of the two quadrupole vibrations. The time-dependent Hartree-Fock equations give a qualitative understanding of the gradual decrease in the energies of collective excitations of spherical nuclei and the disappearance of two of these excitations with the appearance of the rotational structure, which is observed empirically in following the nuclear energy levels as a function of the atomic number between a closed shell and a deformed region †. Since the pairing forces play an important part in this transition, a more quantitative discussion should refer rather to the equations of the generalised Hartree-Fock method.

Solutions $\varrho^{(1)}$ of eq. (24a) which have the time-dependence (24b) satisfy a time independent equation. Writing ϱ_α instead of $\varrho^{(1)}$ in this section, by omitting the superfix which indicates a restriction to small first order changes and distinguishing different solutions through the index α, one obtains the equation

$$[v^{(0)}, \varrho_\alpha]+[u_\alpha, \varrho^{(0)}] = \omega_\alpha \varrho_\alpha. \tag{25a}$$

As in eqs. (16a, b, c), one has through the supplementary condition

$$\varrho_\alpha = (1-\varrho^{(0)})\varrho_\alpha\varrho^{(0)}+\varrho^{(0)}\varrho_\alpha(1-\varrho^{(0)}). \tag{25b}$$

The commutator $[\varrho_\alpha, \varrho^{(0)}]$ differs from ϱ_α by a minus sign in the second term of (25b), and $[[\varrho_\alpha, \varrho^{(0)}], \varrho^{(0)}] = \varrho_\alpha$.

The equations for small oscillations were studied in previous papers [10,13] in the form

$$\begin{pmatrix} A & B \\ -B^* & -A^* \end{pmatrix} \begin{pmatrix} X_\alpha \\ Y_\alpha \end{pmatrix} = \omega_\alpha \begin{pmatrix} X_\alpha \\ Y_\alpha \end{pmatrix}, \tag{25c}$$

which can be obtained from (25a) by writing

$$\varrho_{mi} = X_{mi}, \qquad \varrho_{im} = Y_{mi} \tag{25d}$$

for the matrix elements of the two terms in the decomposition (25b). The notation for the indices is as in eq. (17a), and the matrix elements of the non-Hermitian matrix

$$\mathscr{H} = \begin{pmatrix} A & B \\ -B^* & -A^* \end{pmatrix} \tag{25e}$$

can be read off explicitly from the left-hand side of that equation. The trans-

† The authors are indebted to Professor G. E. Brown for his part in elucidating this point.

pose of a Hermitian interaction matrix element in (17a) is equal to its conjugate complex.

With a more compact notation, eq. (25a) which is linear in ϱ_α can be written in the form

$$\mathscr{H}\{\varrho_\alpha\} = \omega_\alpha \varrho_\alpha. \tag{26a}$$

Forming the adjoint of this equation, taking into account (25b) and that $\varrho^{(0)}$ and $\nu^{(0)}$ are self-adjoint, one finds with a real ω_α

$$\mathscr{H}\{\varrho_\alpha{}^\dagger\} = -\omega_\alpha \varrho_\alpha{}^\dagger. \tag{26b}$$

This shows that real non-zero eigenvalues ω_α of (26a) appear in pairs of opposite sign. The indefinite metric introduced previously [13]) in connection with eq. (25c) appears in an equally simple form in this density matrix notation. Multiplying eq. (26b) by $[\varrho_{\alpha'}, \varrho^{(0)}]$, eq. (26a) for α' by $[\varrho_\alpha{}^\dagger, \varrho^{(0)}]$, subtracting and forming the trace one obtains

$$(\omega_\alpha - \omega_{\alpha'}) \operatorname{tr} [\varrho_\alpha{}^\dagger, \varrho^{(0)}]\varrho_{\alpha'} = 0. \tag{26c}$$

This means

$$\operatorname{tr} [\varrho_\alpha{}^\dagger, \varrho^{(0)}]\varrho_{\alpha'} = 0 \qquad \text{for } \omega_\alpha \neq \omega_{\alpha'}, \tag{26d}$$

and the eigensolutions ϱ_α of (26a) can be chosen to satisfy the normalisation condition

$$\operatorname{tr} [\varrho_\alpha{}^\dagger, \varrho^{(0)}]\varrho_\alpha = \begin{cases} \pm 1 & \text{for} \quad \omega_\alpha \neq 0, \\ \;\; 0 & \text{for} \quad \omega_\alpha = 0. \end{cases} \tag{26e}$$

The zero-frequency solutions have a vanishing norm because they can be chosen to be self-adjoint. To each zero-frequency solution there corresponds a conjugate degree of freedom [13]) which is to be included to obtain a complete set of small variations to describe all changes in the density matrix. By means of this metric one can separate into independent subspaces the intrinsic changes corresponding to $\omega_\alpha \neq 0$, and the changes due to the rotational and translational degrees of freedom.

The unit operator of this space of small variations can be decomposed accordingly into a sum of non-Hermitian projection operators

$$1 = \sum_\alpha \mathscr{P}_\alpha + \mathscr{P}_{\text{rot}} + \mathscr{P}_{\text{transl}}. \tag{27}$$

The first sum is extended over all non-zero frequencies. In the notation of eq. (25c), one has

$$\mathscr{P}_\alpha = \pm \begin{pmatrix} X_\alpha \\ Y_\alpha \end{pmatrix} (X_\alpha{}^\dagger, -Y_\alpha{}^\dagger) \quad \text{for} \quad \omega_\alpha \neq 0. \tag{28a}$$

In the notation of density matrices one can write

$$\mathscr{P}_\alpha = \pm\, \varrho_\alpha \cdot [\varrho_\alpha{}^\dagger, \varrho^{(0)}] \quad \text{for} \quad \omega_\alpha \gtrless 0, \tag{28b}$$

with the convention that the product operation $\mathscr{A} = a \cdot b$ means $\mathscr{A}\{\varrho\} = a \operatorname{tr} b\varrho$. With (26d, e) this gives

$$\begin{aligned} &\mathscr{P}_\alpha\{\varrho_{\alpha'}\} = \delta_{\alpha\alpha'}\varrho_\alpha, \\ &\mathscr{P}_\alpha^{\,2} = \mathscr{P}_\alpha, \qquad \mathscr{P}_\alpha\mathscr{P}_{\alpha'} = 0 \quad \text{for} \quad \alpha \neq \alpha'. \end{aligned} \tag{28c}$$

The infinitesimal changes related to the translational degeneracy in a given direction can be expanded by means of the matrices

$$\varrho_p = [p, \varrho^{(0)}], \qquad \varrho_x = im[x, \varrho^{(0)}]. \tag{29a}$$

According to (7a, b), (9a, b) they satisfy the equations

$$\mathscr{H}\{\varrho_p\} = 0, \qquad \mathscr{H}\{\varrho_x\} = \varrho_p. \tag{29b}$$

They both have a zero norm, as seen with $\varrho_p{}^\dagger = -\varrho_p$, $\varrho_x{}^\dagger = \varrho_x$ from the identities

$$\operatorname{tr}\,[\varrho_p, \varrho^{(0)}]\varrho_p = 0, \qquad \operatorname{tr}\,[\varrho_x, \varrho^{(0)}]\varrho_x = 0. \tag{29c}$$

On the other hand, one has

$$\operatorname{tr}\,[\varrho_p, \varrho^{(0)}]\varrho_x = -\operatorname{tr}\,[\varrho_x, \varrho^{(0)}]\varrho_p = \operatorname{tr} p\varrho_x = Nm = M. \tag{29d}$$

This gives for the projection operator of the translational degrees of freedom

$$\mathscr{P}_{\text{transl.}} = \frac{1}{M}\sum_1^3 \{\varrho_x \cdot [\varrho_p, \varrho^{(0)}] - \varrho_p \cdot [\varrho_x, \varrho^{(0)}]\}, \tag{30a}$$

where the summation is over three perpendicular space directions. One has

$$\begin{aligned} &\mathscr{P}_{\text{transl.}}\{\varrho_p\} = \varrho_p, \qquad \mathscr{P}_{\text{transl.}}\{\varrho_x\} = \varrho_x, \\ &\mathscr{P}^2_{\text{transl.}} = \mathscr{P}_{\text{transl.}}, \qquad \mathscr{P}_{\text{transl.}}\mathscr{P}_\alpha = \mathscr{P}_\alpha\mathscr{P}_{\text{transl.}} = 0. \end{aligned} \tag{30b}$$

In a similar way, if $\varrho^{(0)}$ has only cylindrical symmetry, infinitesimal changes in the density matrix related to a rotation about an axis perpendicular to the symmetry axis can be expanded by ϱ_l and ϱ_φ, where

$$\varrho_l = [l, \varrho^{(0)}] \tag{31a}$$

satisfies the equation

$$\mathscr{H}\{\varrho_l\} = 0, \tag{31b}$$

and ϱ_φ can be defined as a Hermitian solution of the equation

$$\mathscr{H}\{\varrho_\varphi\} = \varrho_l. \tag{31c}$$

Both have a zero norm, and one has

$$\mathrm{tr}\,[\varrho_l, \varrho^{(0)}]\varrho_\varphi = -\mathrm{tr}\,[\varrho_\varphi, \varrho^{(0)}]\varrho_l = \mathrm{tr}\,l\varrho_\varphi = \mathscr{I} \tag{31d}$$

with the definition (13a) of the moment of inertia. This leads to

$$\mathscr{P}_{\mathrm{rot.}} = \frac{1}{\mathscr{I}} \sum_1^2 \{\varrho_\varphi \cdot [\varrho_l, \varrho^{(0)}] - \varrho_l \cdot [\varrho_\varphi, \varrho^{(0)}]\} \tag{32}$$

as the projection operator of the rotational degrees of freedom in the decomposition (27). The summation is over two directions perpendicular to the symmetry axis.

This decomposition into independent subspaces leads to a separation of the operator $\mathscr{H}$ itself in the form

$$\mathscr{H} = \sum_\alpha \omega_\alpha \mathscr{P}_\alpha + \mathscr{H}_{\mathrm{rot.}} + \mathscr{H}_{\mathrm{transl.}}. \tag{33a}$$

The first "intrinsic" part is summed over all positive and negative frequencies ω_α, the rotational and translational parts are given by

$$\mathscr{H}_{\mathrm{rot.}} = \frac{1}{\mathscr{I}} \sum_1^2 \varrho_l \cdot [\varrho_l, \varrho^{(0)}], \tag{33b}$$

$$\mathscr{H}_{\mathrm{transl.}} = \frac{1}{M} \sum_1^3 \varrho_p \cdot [\varrho_p, \varrho^{(0)}]. \tag{33c}$$

This form of $\mathscr{H}$ gives immediately the equations (25a), (29b), (31b, c).

Second quantised operators of the many body system can be expressed by means of the quantised density matrix operator

$$R(x, x') = \psi^*(x')\psi(x). \tag{37a}$$

The part of R which contains only creation and annihilation operators of particle and hole pairs with respect to a Slater determinant ground state defined by $\varrho^{(0)}$ can be written as

$$R_0 = [[R, \varrho^{(0)}], \varrho^{(0)}], \tag{34b}$$

in which the matrix operations are taken only with respect to the single particle variables x, x'.

The many-body operator

$$\tfrac{1}{2}\,\mathrm{tr}\,[\varrho^{(0)}, R_0]\mathscr{H}\{R_0\} \tag{34c}$$

gives then the approximate Hamiltonian considered by Sawada [14]) in discussing a dense electron gas, apart from self-energy terms which can be discarded without influencing the argument. The decomposition (33a, b, c) of $\mathscr{H}$ leads to a decomposition of this approximate Hamiltonian and to an explicit separation of the rotational and translational energies.

The total momentum operator P of the nucleus is in this notation

$$P = \operatorname{tr} pR, \tag{35a}$$

and the kinetic energy of a translational motion is

$$\frac{1}{2M}(P_{x'}^2 + P_{y'}^2 + P_{z'}^2). \tag{35b}$$

With a coordinate system x, y, z fixed to the nucleus, the total angular momentum operator L_z has zero eigenvalue for states which have a symmetry axis along the z direction, and the rotational energy of states with a moment of inertia $\mathscr{I}$ is given by

$$\frac{1}{2\mathscr{I}}(L_x{}^2 + L_y{}^2). \tag{35c}$$

The contribution of the translational and rotational parts (33b, c) of $\mathscr{H}$ to the Hamiltonian (34c) of the random phase approximation is of the form (35b, c) with P replaced by $P_0 = \operatorname{tr} pR_0$, and L by $L_0 = \operatorname{tr} lR_0$.

If one subtracts the operators (35b, c) from the exact Hamiltonian, one obtains a degenerate eigenvalue problem. The multiplicity of the degenerate eigenstates obtained in this way is however smaller, even for the translational states, then that of the set of Slater determinants which appear in the present considerations and which depend on two free parameters for each degree of freedom. This larger multiplicity of the Slater determinant states affords the possibility of eliminating the spurious motion of the centre of gravity and of the principal axes which is inherent in the approximation.

Part of this work has been done during the authors' stay at the Institute for Theoretical Physics of the University of Copenhagen in the summer of 1960, and they would like to express their thanks to Professor Niels Bohr and to Professor Aage Bohr for the hospitality extended to them at the Institute.

References

1) D. R. Inglis, Phys. Rev. **96** (1954) 1059; **97** (1955) 701;
A. Bohr and B. Mottelson, Mat. Fys. Medd. Dan. Vid. Selsk. **30**, No. 1 (1955);
J. G. Valatin, Proc. Roy. Soc. A **238** (1956) 132
2) A. Bohr and B. Mottelson, Forh. Norske Vidensk. Selsk. **31**, No. 12 (1958)
3) S. T. Belyaev, Mat. Fys. Medd. Dan. Vid. Selsk. **31**, No. 11 (1959);
A. B. Migdal, Nuclear Physics **13** (1959) 655;
J. J. Griffin and M. Rich. Phys. Rev. **118** (1960) 850;
S. G. Nilsson and O. Prior, Mat. Fys. Medd. Dan. Vid. Selsk. **32**, No. 16 (1960)

4) J. Bardeen, L. N. Cooper and J. R. Schrieffer, Phys. Rev. **108** (1957) 1175;
J. G. Valatin, Nuovo Cim. **7** (1958) 843;
N. N. Bogolubov, Nuovo Cim. **7** (1958) 794; Uspekhi fiz. Nauk. **67** (1959) 549 [translation in Uspekhi (Soviet Phys.) **67** (1959) 236]
5) J. G. Valatin, Phys. Rev. **122** (1961) 1012
6) P. S. Zyrianov and V. M. Eleonoskii, JETP (USSR) **30** (1956) 592 [translation in JETP (Soviet Phys.) **3** (1956) 620];
R. A. Ferrell, Phys. Rev. **107** (1957) 1631;
J. Goldstone and K. Gottfried, Nuovo Cim. **13** (1959) 849;
H. Ehrenreich and M. H. Cohen, Phys. Rev. **115** (1959) 786
7) C. van Winter, unpublished
8) R. E. Peierls and J. Yoccoz, Proc. Phys. Soc. **70** (1957) 381;
J. J. Griffin and J. A. Wheeler, Phys. Rev. **108** (1957) 311
9) P. A. M. Dirac, Proc. Camb. Phil. Soc. **26** (1930) 376
10) D. J. Thouless, Nuclear Physics **21** (1960) 225
11) Y. Shono and H. Tanaka, Progr. Theor. Phys. **22** (1959) 177
12) E. P. Gross, Nuclear Physics **14** (1960) 389
13) D. J. Thouless, Nuclear Physics **22** (1961) 78
14) K. Sawada, Phys. Rev. **106** (1957) 372

1.D.1 *Nuclear Physics* **35** (1962) 544—556; © *North-Holland Publishing Co., Amsterdam*

ON THE COLLECTIVE QUADRUPOLE STATE OF C^{12}

A. GOSWAMI
Saha Institute of Nuclear Physics, Calcutta
and
M. K. PAL †
Atomic Energy Research Establishment, Harwell, Berkshire

Received 5 March 1962

Abstract: A configuration-mixing calculation has been carried out for the 4.43 MeV, 2^+ state of C^{12}. The hole-particle pairing interaction has been treated on a model where the matrix elements consist of two factorable terms, one of them representing no spin flip, and the other spin flip. The quadrupole transition probability has been calculated with and without ground state correlations. It is concluded that ground state correlations are important in C^{12} and responsible for the observed enhancement of the transition rate of the quadrupole level.

1. Introduction

The collective character of the 2^+ ($T = 0$), 4.43 MeV state of C^{12} is well-known from the results of inelastic electron scattering experiments and from the short gamma lifetime †† for E2 transition to the ground state. The experimental value of the E2 transition probability is about 8 times larger than the single-particle value. Morpurgo [3]) gives the value of this quantity on the *LS*- and *jj*-coupling models and finds that the former gives a value lower by a factor of 2.5 and the latter lower by a factor of 6. That intermediate-coupling calculations make the situation worse than the *LS*-limit has been shown by Pal and Nagarajan [4]). Banerjee and Levinson [5]), however, have shown from the analysis of the (p, p'γ) angular correlation data that the wave function for this state must be very nearly the *jj*-coupled function. But, as noted above, the pure *jj*-coupling model gives a very poor agreement with the experimentally observed E2 transition probability. We are thus led to consider some sort of configuration mixing between the different *jj*-coupling configurations.

On the *jj*-coupling model, the C^{12} ground state has a closed $1s_{\frac{1}{2}}$ and closed $1p_{\frac{3}{2}}$ shells. The first excited state, according to the work of ref. [5]), is obtained primarily by promoting a $1p_{\frac{3}{2}}$ nucleon to the $1p_{\frac{1}{2}}$ level. We consider the effect of mixing of other configurations obtained by exciting a $1s_{\frac{1}{2}}$ nucleon or a $1p_{\frac{3}{2}}$ nucleon through 2 major shells. From energetic considerations alone the

† Permanent address: Saha Institute of Nuclear Physics, Calcutta.
†† For references to all the electron scattering data and the gamma-decay data, see ref. [1]).

configurations, where two nucleons from the $1p_{\frac{3}{2}}$ level have been excited through 1 major shell, will be equally favourable. These two-particle excited configurations do not contribute directly to the quadrupole transition matrix element. They have been omitted in the present work.

The type of configuration mixing that we consider here, is produced by the interaction between the excited particle, and the hole left behind by it in the closed shell. It is well-known [6–8]) that in doubly closed shell nuclei the hole-particle interaction can build up correlation effects which act coherently to produce collective states like the giant-dipole state or the octupole state of vibration. Ferrell and Visscher [9]) and Fallieros and Ferrell [10]) had considered much earlier the role of such coherent configuration mixing effects in producing collective states of monopole and quadrupole oscillations. The importance of the presence of correlation effects in the ground state in causing enhancement of the transition rate was stressed in the work of ref. [10]). Later treatments of the ground state correlation are available in the work of Kobayasi and Marumori [11]), Baranger [12]) and Brown, Evans and Thouless [13]).

The numerical calculation with a finite-range interaction between the particle and the hole, for the configuration-mixing problem we are here concerned with is quite an elaborate job. In the work of ref. [6]), however, a schematic model has been set up for this interaction, which not only simplifies enormously the problem of finding the eigenvalues and eigenfunctions, but provides at the same time the key to the understanding of the collective nature of one of the eigenfunctions. The quantitative agreement of this schematic model with the results of elaborate calculations for a zero-range interaction is also highly satisfactory [7]). In this note, therefore, we have avoided entering into such elaborate calculations, and have used a *jj*-coupling schematic model, where each hole-particle matrix element is a sum of one 'non-spin-flip' and one 'spin-flip' term.

In the work of Fallieros, Ferrell and Pal [14]) and Pal and Lee [15]) it was proposed and shown from exact calculations with a finite range interaction that there is one non-spin-flip and one spin-flip dipole state, which are mixed via the spin-orbit coupling to produce the splitting of the giant-dipole resonance observed in O^{16}. The decomposition of this schematic model *jj*-coupling matrix elements into the spin-flip and non-spin-flip contributions essentially ties down with the above idea, and has been proposed and discussed in that context by H. Banerjee and M. K Banerjee [16]). In the simple model of ref. [6]) spin was not considered and, therefore, nothing analogous to the spin-flip term of ref. [16]) and the present work did enter there.

The Hamiltonian matrix for this schematic model can be diagonalized and its eigenfunctions found in a very simple and elegant way. The slightly altered formulae after the introduction of the ground-state correlation can also be worked out easily.

Within the limits of the schematic model, and the simplifying assumption of omitting the two-particle excited configurations, the present work makes the following major conclusion: the ground state correlations are important in C^{12} and must be considered to explain the large enhancement of the E2 transition probability of the 2^+, 4.43 MeV state.

The general method of solving the schematic model Hamiltonian matrix in the absence and presence of ground-state correlations has been indicated in sect. 2. Sect. 3 contains the results of numerical calculations for the 2^+ level and a discussion of these results. In order to show the consistency of the schematic model interaction the giant-dipole states of C^{12} have also been calculated with the same Hamiltonian and fairly good agreement obtained with experiment. These results are presented in sect. 4. Sect. 5 summarizes the main conclusion and discusses how far it would be affected if one removes the simpliyfing features of the present work and does a more exact calculation.

2. Theoretical Method

2.1. THE SCHEMATIC MODEL

The jj-coupled states, we shall consider, are of the type $|\bar{j}j'\,JM\rangle$ where $\bar{j}$ denotes the hole (we are using $\bar{j}$ instead of the usual symbol j^{-1}), j' denotes the particle, and J is the total angular momentum with projection M. The unperturbed energy of such a configuration is $\varepsilon_{\bar{j}}+\varepsilon_{j'}$ where $\varepsilon_{\bar{j}}$ and $\varepsilon_{j'}$ are the energy of the hole and the particle, respectively. The two-body interaction will have diagonal matrix elements consisting of three kinds of contributions: (i) Particle-shell interaction (the interaction of particle j' with the closed shell), (ii) hole-shell interaction (the interaction of the hole $\bar{j}$ with the closed shell, and (iii) the hole-particle interaction between $\bar{j}$ and j'. The non-diagonal matrix elements will have the third contribution alone. The experimentally determined single particle and single hole energies already contain in them the particle-shell and the hole-shell interaction, respectively. The sum of these two experimentally determined quantities will be denoted by $\lambda_{\bar{j}j'\,J}$, and will be referred to, from now on, as the unperturbed energies of the configurations. The task that finally remains is to compute the matrix elements of the hole-particle interaction, add these unperturbed energies to the diagonal elements, and then find the eigenvalues and eigenfunctions of the matrix.

To abbreviate notation, from now on, we shall use the symbols $|K\rangle$, $|L\rangle$ etc., to denote the jj-coupled hole-particle states $|\bar{j}j'JM\rangle$. The labels on the unperturbed energies are also correspondingly shortened. In the schematic model of ref. [6]) the matrix elements of the hole-particle interaction are given in the following factored form:

$$V_{K,L} = \langle K|V|L\rangle = \pm D_K D_L, \tag{1}$$

where the + and − signs refer to the repulsive and attractive nature of the interaction and correspond to the isobaric spin 1 and 0 states, respectively. One gets this factored form provided it is assumed that all the radial integrals appearing in the matrix elements are equal. The explicit form for D_K used in ref. [6]) corresponds to particles and holes of no spin.

It has been emphasized in the introductory section that the schematic model Hamiltonian should include a spin-flip term over and above the non-spin-flip term in order that the model can explain the splitting of giant dipole resonance in a natural way. In fact, if one uses a δ-function interaction and properly antisymmetrized jj-coupled states to calculate matrix elements (thereby obtaining both the direct and exchange terms), and finally puts all the radial integrals equal following ref. [6]), one automatically obtains the following extended schematic model Hamiltonian:

$$V_{K,L} = -a_K a_L + b_K b_L, \qquad T = 0, \tag{2a}$$

$$V_{K,L} = a'_K a'_L + b'_K b'_L, \qquad T = 1. \tag{2b}$$

The first and second terms in each of these expressions represent the non-spin-flip and the spin-flip contributions, respectively. The explicit expressions for a_K and b_K are as follows:

$$a_K \equiv a_{\bar{j}j'J} = \sqrt{3(V_s+V_t)\mathscr{I}}(-)^{l+l'+j-\frac{1}{2}} \frac{\{[j][j']\}^{\frac{1}{2}}}{2[J]^{\frac{1}{2}}} \begin{bmatrix} j & j' & J \\ \frac{1}{2} & -\frac{1}{2} & 0 \end{bmatrix}, \tag{3a}$$

$$b_K \equiv b_{\bar{j}j'J} = \sqrt{(3V_s-V_t)\mathscr{I}}(-)^{l+j+j'} \frac{\{[j][j']\}^{\frac{1}{2}}}{2[J]^{\frac{1}{2}}} \begin{bmatrix} j & j' & J \\ \frac{1}{2} & \frac{1}{2} & 1 \end{bmatrix}. \tag{3b}$$

The corresponding expressions for the primed quantities of (2b) are obtained by replacing $3(V_s+V_t)$ in a_K by $(3V_t-V_s)$ and $(3V_s-V_t)$ in b_K by (V_t+V_s). Here V_s and V_t denote the strengths (strength = |depth|) of the singlet and triplet potentials, respectively. The notation

$$\begin{bmatrix} j & j' & J \\ m & m' & M \end{bmatrix}$$

stands for a Clebsch-Gordan coefficient, and the symbol $[j]$ is an abbreviation for $(2j+1)$. The quantity $\mathscr{I}$ denotes the average value of the radial integrals that occur in the matrix (this is where the schematic model assumption enters into the results). The quantities l and l' are the orbital angular momenta corresponding to j and j', respectively.

From now on the form (2a) of $V_{K,L}$ for the case of zero isobaric spin will be used in the derivation. It would be apparent that the same steps could be followed for the case $T = 1$ as well.

Write the wave function as

$$\Psi = \sum_K X_K|K\rangle. \tag{4}$$

If Ψ is an eigenfunction with eigenvalue ε then one must have

$$\sum_L (\lambda_K \delta_{K,L} + V_{K,L}) X_L = \varepsilon X_K$$

or

$$\sum_L (-a_K a_L + b_K b_L) X_L = (\varepsilon - \lambda_K) X_K. \tag{5}$$

Obviously the X_K have the form:

$$X_K = \frac{\alpha a_K + \beta b_K}{\varepsilon - \lambda_K}, \tag{6}$$

where

$$\alpha = -\sum_L a_L X_L \quad \text{and} \quad \beta = \sum_L b_L X_L. \tag{7}$$

Putting (6) back in (7) one gets

$$-\left(\sum_L \frac{a_L{}^2}{\varepsilon - \lambda_L} + 1\right)\alpha - \sum_L \frac{a_L b_L}{\varepsilon - \lambda_L}\beta = 0, \qquad \sum_L \frac{a_L b_L}{\varepsilon - \lambda_L}\alpha + \left(\sum_L \frac{b_L{}^2}{\varepsilon - \lambda_L} - 1\right)\beta = 0. \tag{8}$$

The condition that the determinant of the coefficients of α and β in (8) should vanish gives the equation for the eigenvalues ε:

$$1 = \sum_K \frac{-a_K{}^2 + b_K{}^2 + F_K}{\varepsilon - \lambda_K}, \tag{9}$$

where

$$F_K = \sum_{L \neq K} \frac{(a_K b_L - a_L b_K)^2}{\lambda_K - \lambda_L}. \tag{10}$$

For a particular eigenvalue ε, the corresponding amplitudes of the wave functions are given by (6), where

$$\beta/\alpha = -\sum_L a_L b_L \Big/ \left(\sum_L \frac{b_L{}^2}{\varepsilon - \lambda_L} - 1\right). \tag{11}$$

The constant α is fixed by the normalization requirement

$$\sum_K X_K{}^2 = 1. \tag{12}$$

2.2 GROUND-STATE CORRELATION

In order to take into account the effect of correlations in the ground state the standard procedure is the method of Sawada [17]), developed for the treatment of plasma oscillations in the electron gas. As has been mentioned in the introductory section, this method has been applied to the nuclear collective oscillations in refs. [10–12]. In the following derivation the work of ref. [12] will be followed very closely.

Denote by $A_K{}^\dagger$ the creation operator for the angular momentum coupled hole-particle state $|K\rangle(\equiv|\bar{j}j'JM\rangle)$ where A_K is the corresponding destruction operator. By $|\bar{K}\rangle$ we shall mean the state $|\bar{j}j'J-M\rangle$, while Ψ_0 is the actual correlated ground state and Ψ the excited collective vibrational state. The following two amplitudes are defined:

$$\langle\Psi_0|A_K|\Psi\rangle = X_K, \qquad \langle\Psi_0|A_{\bar{K}}{}^\dagger|\Psi\rangle S_K = \bar{X}_K, \tag{13}$$

where S_K is a phase-factor equal to $(-1)^{J-M}$. If the ground state is uncorrelated, obviously $\bar{X}_K = 0$, and the amplitude X_K becomes the same as introduced in subsect. 2.1. In the presence of correlations in Ψ_0 both types of amplitudes are non-vanishing. To obtain the equations satisfied by these amplitudes, one starts from the following identities:

$$\langle\Psi_0|[A_K, H]|\Psi\rangle = (E-E_0)\langle\Psi_0|A_K|\Psi\rangle = \varepsilon X_K, \tag{14a}$$

$$S_K\langle\Psi_0|[A_{\bar{K}}{}^\dagger, H]|\Psi\rangle = \varepsilon\bar{X}_K, \tag{14b}$$

where E and E_0 are the eigenvalues of H for states Ψ and Ψ_0, respectively. Next one uses the second-quantised form of H and evaluates the commutators directly. All terms in the commutator which are non-linear in A_K and $A_{\bar{K}}{}^\dagger$ are thrown away (the Sawada approximation) and one ends up finally with two coupled linear equations for X_K and $\bar{X}_K$. Before writing down these equations we would indicate the arguments that show the collective vibrational nature of Ψ.

Denote by $Q^\dagger$ the following linear combination of $A_K{}^\dagger$ and $A_{\bar{K}}$:

$$Q^\dagger = \sum_K (Y_K A_K{}^\dagger - S_K \bar{Y}_K A_{\bar{K}}), \tag{15}$$

and require that Q and $Q^\dagger$ satisfy the harmonic oscillator equations:

$$[Q, H] = \varepsilon Q, \qquad [Q^\dagger, H] = -\varepsilon Q^\dagger. \tag{16}$$

Under the same approximation of retaining only the terms linear in A_K and $A_{\bar{K}}{}^\dagger$ out of the commutators, one obtains from (16) two coupled linear equations for Y_K and $\bar{Y}_K$, which are found to be identical with the equations satisfied by X_K and $\bar{X}_K$. Hence one can replace the Y in (15) by the X, and the $Q^\dagger$ obtained in such a way, by virtue of eqs. (16), creates an oscillator quantum of energy ε, the corresponding state of one vibrational quantum being

$$|\Psi\rangle = Q^\dagger|\Psi_0\rangle. \tag{17}$$

The normalization requirement is

$$1 = \langle\Psi|\Psi\rangle = \langle\Psi_0|Q|\Psi\rangle = \sum_K (X_K\langle\Psi_0|A_K|\Psi\rangle - S_K\bar{X}_K\langle\Psi_0|A_{\bar{K}}^\dagger|\Psi\rangle)$$
$$= \sum_K (X_K{}^2 - \bar{X}_K{}^2) = \sum_K f_K g_K, \tag{18}$$

where

$$f_K = X_K + \bar{X}_K, \qquad g_K = X_K - \bar{X}_K. \tag{19}$$

We shall now write down the coupled equations, already mentioned, in terms of the new amplitudes f_K and g_K. For our schematic model Hamiltonian, in the case of $T = 0$ and even J, we obtain

$$\varepsilon f_K = \lambda_K g_K + 2b_K \sum_L b_L g_L, \qquad \varepsilon g_K = \lambda_K f_K - 2a_K \sum_L a_L f_L. \tag{20}$$

Substituting for g_K from the second equation into the first, and for f_K from the first equation into the second, one gets

$$f_K = \frac{-\lambda_K a_K \alpha + \varepsilon b_K \beta}{\varepsilon^2 - \lambda_K{}^2}, \qquad g_K = \frac{\lambda_K b_K \beta - \varepsilon a_K \alpha}{\varepsilon^2 - \lambda_K{}^2}, \tag{21}$$

where

$$\alpha = 2\sum_K a_K f_K, \quad \beta = 2\sum_K b_K g_K. \tag{22}$$

Putting (21) back in (22) one obtains two linear homogeneous equations for α and β; the determinant of the coefficients, equated to zero, yields the equation for ε:

$$1 = \sum_K \frac{2\lambda_K(-a_K{}^2 + b_K{}^2 + F_K - G_K)}{\varepsilon^2 - \lambda_K{}^2}, \tag{23}$$

where F_K is the same as in subsect. 2.1 and G_K is given by

$$G_K = \sum_{L \neq K} \frac{(a_K b_L + a_L b_K)^2}{\lambda_K + \lambda_L}. \tag{24}$$

For a particular eigenvalue ε the linear equations for α and β determine the ratio β/α as

$$\frac{\beta}{\alpha} = \left\{\sum_K \frac{2\lambda_K a_K{}^2}{\varepsilon^2 - \lambda_K{}^2} + 1\right\}\left\{\sum_K \frac{2a_K b_K}{\varepsilon^2 - \lambda_K{}^2}\right\}^{-1}. \tag{25}$$

The constant α is determined from the normalization requirement (18).

2.3. E2 TRANSITION PROBABILITY

The second-quantized form for the E2 transition operator, connecting to $T = 0$ states, is given by

$$Q_M = \tfrac{1}{2} e \sum_{\alpha,\beta} a_\alpha{}^\dagger a_\beta \langle\alpha|r^2 Y_M{}^2|\beta\rangle, \tag{26}$$

where α, β stand for the jj-coupling single particle states.

The relevant part of this operator connecting the quadrupole state $\Psi(J = 2)$ with the ground state $\Psi_0(J = 0)$ can be written as

$$Q_M^{\text{eff}} = \tfrac{1}{2}e \sum_{j'}^{\text{particles}} \sum_{j}^{\text{holes}} \langle j'||r^2 Y^2||j\rangle(-)^{j'-j}\sqrt{\frac{[j']}{[2]}}\,\{A^\dagger_{jj'2M}+A_{jj'2-M}(-)^M\}. \quad (27)$$

The operators A and $A^\dagger$ are the same as before, only the labels K and $\bar{K}$ on them have been explicitly written in (27). The summation of j' runs only over particles, i.e. states beyond the closed shell, and that of j over the holes i.e. states occupied in the closed shell. The double-barred matrix element of r^2Y^2 is given by

$$\langle j'||r^2 Y^2||j\rangle = \sqrt{\frac{5}{4\pi}}\begin{bmatrix} j' & 2 & j \\ \frac{1}{2} & 0 & \frac{1}{2}\end{bmatrix}\int_0^\infty R_l R_{l'} r^4 \mathrm{d}r, \quad (28)$$

where R_l and $R_{l'}$ denote the radial wave functions of particles j and j', respectively. On taking the matrix element of (27) between $\langle\Psi_0|$ and $|\Psi\rangle$, and squaring we obtain the reduced transition probability $B(\text{E2})$. The final result after using (28) is given by

$$B(\text{E2}) = \frac{e^2}{16\pi}\left|\sum_{j'}^{\text{particles}} \sum_{j}^{\text{holes}} f_{jj'2}(-)^{j'-j}[j']^{\frac{1}{2}}\begin{bmatrix} j' & 2 & j \\ \frac{1}{2} & 0 & \frac{1}{2}\end{bmatrix}\mathscr{R}\right|^2, \quad (29)$$

where $\mathscr{R}$ is the radial integral contained in (28). Note that the averaging and summation over the initial and final state magnetic quantum numbers do not give rise to any extra factor in this case.

3. Results for C^{12} 4.43 MeV State

3.1. THE UNPERTURBED ENERGIES

In this case we have one $0-\hbar\omega$ transition, $1p_{\frac{3}{2}} \rightarrow 1p_{\frac{1}{2}}$ and six $2-\hbar\omega$ transitions corresponding to $1p_{\frac{3}{2}} \rightarrow 2p_{\frac{1}{2}}$ and $2p_{\frac{3}{2}}$, $1p_{\frac{3}{2}} \rightarrow 1f_{\frac{5}{2}}$ and $1f_{\frac{7}{2}}$ and $1s_{\frac{1}{2}} \rightarrow 1d_{\frac{3}{2}}$ and $1d_{\frac{5}{2}}$. The jj-coupled configurations and their unperturbed energies λ_K are shown in table 1. The unperturbed energies for the configurations $(1\bar{p}_{\frac{3}{2}}, 1p_{\frac{1}{2}})$

TABLE 1

Energies of one-particle, one-hole configurations

Configuration	Energy λ (MeV)
[1] $(1\bar{s}_{\frac{1}{2}}, 1d_{\frac{3}{2}})$	33.63
[2] $(1\bar{s}_{\frac{1}{2}}, 1d_{\frac{5}{2}})$	29.80
[3] $(1\bar{p}_{\frac{3}{2}}, 2p_{\frac{1}{2}})$	29.84
[4] $(1\bar{p}_{\frac{3}{2}}, 2p_{\frac{3}{2}})$	27.64
[5] $(1\bar{p}_{\frac{3}{2}}, 1f_{\frac{5}{2}})$	32.14
[6] $(1\bar{p}_{\frac{3}{2}}, 1f_{\frac{7}{2}})$	25.74
[7] $(1\bar{p}_{\frac{3}{2}}, 1p_{\frac{1}{2}})$	13.77

The hole state has been denoted by a bar overhead. The energies of the first two configurations have been calculated from the value of $2\hbar\omega$ derived from 1p-1f oscillator level difference.

and ($1\bar{p}_{\frac{3}{2}}$, $1f_{\frac{7}{2}}$) have been determined fairly reliably from the experimental level spectra. The energies of the other configurations shown in the table are not so reliable as these two values, the reason being the lack of adequate experimental data on them. To compute the energies of configurations [3]-[5] we have made use of the energy of [6], together with the experimental values of the splittings between the different levels of 1f-2p shell observed in Sc^{41} by Class, Davis and Johnson [18]). The assumption here is that the relative splittings of the 1f-2p shell levels are the same so long as these levels do not start filling up. (It is well-known that the process of filling up changes the relative level positions appreciably.) The energies for the configurations [1] and [2] have been determined from the observed oscillator energy difference $2\hbar\omega$ between the 1p and 1f shells and assuming that this is identical with the same between 1s and 1d shells.

3.2. THE SCHEMATIC MODEL APPROXIMATION

As already noted the main approximation involved in the schematic model is the treating of all the radial integrals as equal. Table 2 shows the radial integrals that appear in the matrix elements of the interaction. It is seen that the majority of them are nearly equal, although two of them show large deviations from the average.

TABLE 2

Radial integrals appearing in the matrix elements of the interaction

$$\mathscr{I}(n_1 l_1, n_2 l_2; n_3 l_3, n_4 l_4) = \frac{1}{4\pi}\int_0^\infty R(n_1 l_1) R(n_2 l_2) R(n_3 l_3) R(n_4 l_4) r^2 \, dr$$

	Radial integrals	Value in $b^{-3}/4\pi\ \sqrt{\pi}$
[1]	$\mathscr{I}$(1s, 1d; 1s, 1d)	0.353
[2]	$\mathscr{I}$(1s, 1d; 1p, 2p)	0.216
[3]	$\mathscr{I}$(1p, 2p: 1p, 2p)	0.338
[4]	$\mathscr{I}$(1s, 1d; 1p, 1f)	0.270
[5]	$\mathscr{I}$(1p, 1f; 1p, 1f)	0.265
[6]	$\mathscr{I}$(1p, 2p; 1p, 1f)	0.055
[7]	$\mathscr{I}$(1p, 1p: 1p, 2p)	0.279
[8]	$\mathscr{I}$(1p, 1p; 1s, 1d)	0.456
[9]	$\mathscr{I}$(1p, 1p; 1p, 1f)	0.348
[10]	$\mathscr{I}$(1p, 1p; 1p, 1p)	0.589

$R(nl)$ is the radial wave function. Oscillator wave functions with oscillator parameter b have been used.

For the singlet spin potential V_s we have used a value 0.6 V_t, V_t being the triplet depth. The matrix elements are then given in units of $V_t\mathscr{I}$, which is treated as a parameter. Since only one radial integral enters in the case of the 6.14 MeV octupole (3^-) state of O^{16}, the value of V_t is uniquely fixed from these. The value of the parameter $V_t\mathscr{I}$ that is necessary to reproduce the C^{12} 2^+ state at 4.43 MeV, taken together with the average value of $\mathscr{I}$ in table 2, is fairly consistent with the value of V_t determined from O^{16}, 3^- state. The same consistency has been checked for the dipole states of O^{16} and C^{12}. The results for O^{16} octupole and dipole states are contained in ref. [16]) and the same for C^{12} dipole states are presented in a later section of this paper.

3.3. RESULTS FOR THE 2^+ STATE OF C^{12}

When we do not include ground state correlations, the normalized wave function for the 2^+ state is given by

$$\Psi = 0.234|1\bar{s}_{\frac{1}{2}}, 1d_{\frac{3}{2}}\rangle + 0.304|1\bar{s}_{\frac{1}{2}}, 1d_{\frac{5}{2}}\rangle - 0.243|1\bar{p}_{\frac{3}{2}}, 2p_{\frac{1}{2}}\rangle$$
$$-0.280|1\bar{p}_{\frac{3}{2}}, 2p_{\frac{3}{2}}\rangle + 0.141|1\bar{p}_{\frac{3}{2}}, 1f_{\frac{5}{2}}\rangle + 0.506|1\bar{p}_{\frac{3}{2}}, 1f_{\frac{7}{2}}\rangle - 0.662|1\bar{p}_{\frac{3}{2}}, 1p_{\frac{1}{2}}\rangle.$$

The ratio of the experimental value of the quadrupole transition probability to the theoretical value calculated with the above wave function is given by

$$\frac{B_{\text{exp}}(\text{E2})}{B_{\text{theor}}(\text{E2})} = 3.86.$$

The amplitudes f_K, for the case of ground state correlations, are given in the first column of table 3. The theoretical result for the quadrupole transition probability now improves to the extent, $B_{\text{exp}}^{(\text{E2})}/B_{\text{theor}}^{(\text{E2})} = 0.85$.

TABLE 3

Amplitudes f_K when ground state correlations are present

Configurations	f_K (subsect. 3.3)	f_K (subsect. 3.4)
[1] $(1\bar{s}_{\frac{1}{2}}, 1d_{\frac{3}{2}})$	0.508	0.488
[2] $(1\bar{s}_{\frac{1}{2}}, 1d_{\frac{5}{2}})$	0.703	0.670
[3] $(1\bar{p}_{\frac{3}{2}}, 2p_{\frac{1}{2}})$	−0.573	−0.546
[4] $(1\bar{p}_{\frac{3}{2}}, 2p_{\frac{3}{2}})$	−0.622	−0.593
[5] $(1\bar{p}_{\frac{3}{2}}, 1f_{\frac{5}{2}})$	0.347	0.330
[6] $(1\bar{p}_{\frac{3}{2}}, 1f_{\frac{7}{2}})$	1.078	0.995
[7] $(1\bar{p}_{\frac{3}{2}}, 1p_{\frac{1}{2}})$	−1.352	−1.379

3.4. DISCUSSION OF THE RESULTS

We have thus found that the inclusion of ground-state correlations produces very satisfactorily the collective enhancement of the quadrupole transition probability of the 4.43 MeV 2^+ state of C^{12}. The amount of enhancement obtained from our schematic model is in very good quantitative agreement with the experimental data. The fact that the ordinary *jj*-coupling component $|1\bar{p}_{\frac{3}{2}}\, 1p_{\frac{1}{2}}\rangle$ is still the dominant component of this excited state would help one in reproducing the (p, p′γ) angular correlation results for this level. However, this point needs detailed quantitative checking in view of the presence of the excited configurations in the wave function.

The amount of admixture of one of the excited configurations, namely $|1\bar{p}_{\frac{3}{2}}, 1f_{\frac{7}{2}}\rangle$, seems to be a little too high. This is, to some extent, an outcome of our use of the schematic model. If one looks at table 2 of the radial integrals, one finds that the radial integral which appears in the diagonal elements of $|1\bar{p}_{\frac{3}{2}}, 1f_{\frac{7}{2}}\rangle$ state is only about $\frac{1}{2}$ of that for $|1\bar{p}_{\frac{3}{2}}, 1p_{\frac{1}{2}}\rangle$. Since the schematic model amounts to putting all the radial integrals equal to an average value, the direct consequence of this fact would be to enhance ($|1\bar{p}_{\frac{3}{2}}, 1f_{\frac{7}{2}}\rangle$ in relation to $|1\bar{p}_{\frac{3}{2}}, 1p_{\frac{1}{2}}\rangle$.

In order to see this more clearly let us modify the schematic model to the extent that the radial integrals appearing in the non-diagonal matrix elements are still treated as equal, while those in the diagonal elements are evaluated exactly, and the difference between the exact diagonal elements and the schematic model values are absorbed in the configuration energies. Then the entire set of formulae derived for the schematic model can be applied once again with the new altered values of λ_K. The amplitudes f_K, in the case of ground state correlation obtained in this way, are given in the second column for these quantities in table 3. It is seen that the amplitude for the $|1\bar{p}_{\frac{3}{2}}, 1f_{\frac{7}{2}}\rangle$ state has now decreased, while that for $|1\bar{p}_{\frac{3}{2}}, 1p_{\frac{1}{2}}\rangle$ has increased. The new value of the quadrupole transition probability is expressed by $B^{(E2)}_{\text{exp}}/B^{(E2)}_{\text{theor}} = 0.91$.

An exact diagonalization with a realistic finite-range force, we believe, would make the $|1\bar{p}_{\frac{3}{2}}, 1p_{\frac{1}{2}}\rangle$ state more predominant over the other components.

4. Results for the Dipole State of C^{12}

In this case there are four configurations to be mixed corresponding to the transitions, $1s_{\frac{1}{2}} \rightarrow 1p_{\frac{1}{2}}$, $1p_{\frac{3}{2}} \rightarrow 2s_{\frac{1}{2}}$, $1p_{\frac{3}{2}} \rightarrow 1d_{\frac{3}{2}}$ and $1d_{\frac{5}{2}}$. Table 4 gives the

TABLE 4

Energies of configurations appearing in the dipole state of C^{12}

Configurations		Energy λ (MeV)
[1]	$(1\bar{p}_{\frac{3}{2}}, 2s_{\frac{1}{2}})$	16.38
[2]	$(1\bar{p}_{\frac{3}{2}}, 1d_{\frac{5}{2}})$	20.92
[3]	$(1\bar{p}_{\frac{3}{2}}, 1d_{\frac{3}{2}})$	17.57
[4]	$(1\bar{s}_{\frac{1}{2}}, 1p_{\frac{1}{2}})$	18.39

unperturbed energies of these configurations. The resulting 4×4 energy matrix, without ground-state correlation, was solved by the iteration method. The energies, together with the percentage dipole strengths, are given in table 5. It is seen from the table that the dipole strength is concentrated in the two uppermost states, and so there should be a splitting of the giant-dipole resonance. This splitting, as was mentioned in the introduction, is due to the presence of a spin-flip-dipole state, which mixes through our schematic model Hamiltonian with the ordinary non-spin-flip dipole state. The omission of the spin-flip term in the Hamiltonian would take away this effect.

TABLE 5

Calculated energies and dipole strengths of 1^- states of C^{12}

	Energy (MeV)	Dipole strength (%)
[1]	24.26	25
[2]	22.48	54
[3]	18.70	9
[4]	17.09	12

In the case of C^{12} giant dipole resonance the experimental data reported by various authors are not very much in mutual agreement, and the whole situation is in a confused state. A review of the experimental results can be found in a report by Katz [19]). At the present moment the experimental situation is not clear as to the existence of the splitting of giant dipole resonance in C^{12}. The theory, however, predicts a splitting similar to that in the case of O^{16}. The mean of the two topmost calculated levels agrees fairly well with the present experimental situation.

5. Summary and Conclusions

We have shown that the hole-particle pairing correlations can indeed produce the 4.43 MeV, 2^+ state of C^{12}. In order to get the correct result for the E2 transition probability of this level one has got to include the effects of ground-state correlation.

Admittedly our method has several limitations: (i) the unperturbed energies of the configurations used in the calculations are not all very reliable. However, the energy of $|1\bar{p}_{\frac{3}{2}}, 1p_{\frac{1}{2}}\rangle$ is determined beyond doubt; to see that the uncertainty in the energies of the other configurations does not change our conclusion, we have done a calculation assuming these others to form a degenerate bunch, and found that the numerical results are not every much changed. (ii) We have used a schematic model Hamiltonian. We believe, however, that an exact calculation, with a realistic finite-range force, also will reveal the same importance of the ground-state correlations. (iii) We have considered only one-particle excitations through two shells and have ignored the effect of two-particle excitations through one shell.

After the completion of the present work we came across a report by Gillet and Vinh Mau [2]), who have done the exact calculations with a finite range force and have failed to push down the collective quadrupole state of C^{12} below

12.14 MeV. It is not clear to us whether these authors omitted the $(1\bar{p}_{\frac{3}{2}}, 1p_{\frac{1}{2}})$ configuration, which was stressed by the Levinson and Banerjee [5]) work.

It is a pleasure to acknowledge the valuable discussions we had with Professor M. K. Banerjee and Mr. H. Banerjee. Our thanks are due to Dr. A. M. Lane for helpful discussions and a critical reading of the manuscript.

Note added in proof: In table 4 we have taken the energy of $(1\bar{s}_{\frac{1}{2}}, 1p_{\frac{1}{2}})$ configuration as calculated from the value of $\hbar\omega$ derived from the 1p-(2s-1d) oscillator level difference. It has subsequently come to our notice [13]) that the binding energy of the 1s-nucleon, determined from (p, 2p) experiments, is 35 MeV, which gives an energy for the above configuration equal to 30 MeV. This correction will change our results for the dipole states of C^{12} presented in table 5.

References

1) D. Ajzenberg-Selove and T. Lauritsen, Nuclear Physics **11** (1959)
2) V. Gillet and N. Vinh Mau, in Proc. Rutherford Jubilee Int. Conf. (Heywood and Co. Ltd., London 1961) p. 315
3) G. Morpurgo, Nuovo Cim. **3** (1956) 430
4) M. K. Pal and M. A. Nagarajan, Phys. Rev. **108** (1957) 1577
5) M. K. Banerjee and C. A. Levinson, Ann. Phys. **2** (1957) 499
6) G. E. Brown and M. Bolsterli, Phys. Rev. Lett. **3** (1955) 472
7) G. E. Brown, L. Castillejo and J. A. Evans, Nuclear Physics **22** (1960) 1
8) G. E. Brown, J. A. Evans and D. J. Thouless, Nuclear Physics **24** (1961) 1
9) R. A. Ferrell and W. M. Visscher, Phys. Rev. **102** (1956) 450
10) S. Fallieros and R. A. Ferrell, Phys. Rev. **116** (1959) 660;
S. Fallieros, Ph. D. thesis, University of Maryland Physics Department, technical report No. **128** (1959) unpublished
11) M. Kobayasi and T. Marumori, Progr. Theor. Phys. **23** (1960) 387
12) M. Baranger, Phys. Rev. **120** (1960) 957
13) N. Vinh-Mau and G. E. Brown, Nuclear Physics **29** (1962) 89
14) S. Fallieros, R. A. Ferrell and M. K. Pal, Nuclear Physics **15** (1960) 363
15) M. K. Pal and Y. C. Lee, Bull. Am. Phys. Soc. **4** (1959) 406
16) H. Banerjee and M. K. Banerjee, in Proc. Summer School on Theoretical Physics held at Dalhousie, India (1961), to be published
17) K. Sawada, Phys. Rev. **106** (1957) 372
18) C. M. Class, R. H. David and J. H. Johnson, Phys. Rev. Lett. **3** (1959) 41
19) L. Katz, in Proc. Int. Conf. on Nuclear Structure Kingston, ed. by D. A. Bromley and E. W. Vogt (North Holland Publ. Co., Amsterdam 1960) p. 710.

(see next page for errata)

ERRATA

Ref.	*Instead of*	*Read*
p. 548, Eq. (11)	$\sum_L a_L b_L$	$\sum_L \frac{a_L b_L}{\varepsilon - \lambda_L}$
p. 550, Eq. (24)	$\sum_{L \neq K}$	$\sum_L$
p. 550, denominator of Eq. (25)	$2a_K b_K$	$2\varepsilon a_K b_K$
p. 551, Eq. (27)	$\frac{1}{2}$	$\frac{1}{\sqrt{2}}$
p. 551, Eq. (29)	$\frac{e^2}{16\pi}$	$\frac{2e^2}{16\pi}$

INDEX†

PART I: PAIRING FORCE THEORY

† Parts I and II are indexed separately.

PART II: COLLECTIVE MOTIONS